Les Routiers
in Britain Guide
Eat, drink and sleep

2007

Les Routiers is an association of mainly owner-managed establishments. However, membership is not automatic. Many applications are refused because every establishment displaying Les Routiers' symbol must satisfy our rigorous quality criteria. All opinions included in the Guide entries are based upon the findings of external assessors.

Published in 2006 by:
Routiers Limited
Oak House
39-41 The Parade
Claygate
Surrey KT10 0PD
Tel: 0845 050 1189
Fax: 01372 466062
Email: info@routiers.co.uk

Book-trade distribution:
Portfolio Books Ltd
Unit 5, Perivale Industrial Park
Horsenden Lane South
Greenford, Middlesex
UB6 7RL

ISBN 0-900057-24-6
Copyright © 2006 Routiers Limited

Maps © Routiers Limited 2006
Maps designed and produced by Cosmographics
www.cosmographics.co.uk
Great Britain Digital Database © Cosmographics
Reproduced by kind permission of Ordnance Survey
Crown Copyright NC/01/365"
Including mapping content © Automobile Association Developments
Limited 2001 and © Bartholomew Digital Database
London Digital Data © Cosmographics
Central London Map is based on information derived from aerial
photography and an original field survey conducted by Cosmographics
Greater London Map based on information derived from satellite
imagery and an original ground survey by Cosmographics.
Satellite data provided by USGS and Infoterra Ltd

British Library Cataloguing in Publication Data.
A catalogue record for this book is available from the British Library.

Editor:
David Hancock

Production and Design Editor:
Alexis Bailey

Design:
Oliver Carter
info@ographics.co.uk

Sub-editor:
Gill Wing

Editorial Contributor:
Melanie Leyshon

Location Photographers:
britainonview.com
Oliver Carter
Annie Hanson
Rebecca Harris

Pub Walks:
Chris Bagshaw
Nick Channer
Neil Coates
David Hancock

Cover Photography:
iStockphoto®

Printed by:
London Print and Design plc

www.routiers.co.uk

Les Routiers Guide – De bons restaurants pas chers et pour tous was originally written for truck drivers who were looking for fairly priced hotels and restaurants. It soon became popular with travelling salesmen, and French and foreign tourists.

Today, the red-and-blue Les Routiers sign has become a cult symbol, standing alongside the Gitanes pack and the Ricard logo as the essence of French style, and the Routiers' original concept of a warm homely welcome and affordable good value is as strong today as when it was first conceived in the 1930s.

Les Routiers Guide – De bons restaurants pas chers et pour tous is still a boon for travellers in France, listing simple, inexpensive roadside restaurants and hotels for both truck drivers and motorists.

To obtain a copy visit:

www.routiers.com

Contents

🛏 Accommodation	🌶 Food shop
◉ Residents only	▯ Set menu
🍺 Pub or bar	★ Award winner 2005
🫖 Teashop or café	★ Award winner 2006

ABOUT THIS GUIDE

Individual, friendly, welcoming and value for money – you'll find all these attributes at Les Routiers' select collection of owner-managed hotels, restaurants, pubs and cafés around Britain. On their search of the regions, Les Routiers' inspectors look out for the most special places. Those that combine character and quality, and have that special British quirkiness, be it a B&B in the far-flung Highlands of Scotland, a historic country-house hotel in the Cotswolds, or an Indian restaurant serving curry made with locally caught fish or haggis.

Les Routiers' approach and philosophy is very much in tune with the discerning traveller, who wants style but informality, without the anonymous atmosphere and impersonal service of some of the larger chains. Our members champion regional foods and source most of their ingredients locally. This means you get to enjoy foods in season when they're at their most flavoursome, from regional cheeses and organic herbs and vegetables to game and speciality-breed meats. As well as offering good food, you will be assured warm and welcoming hospitality, comfortable, well-appointed bedrooms and excellent value for money.

How our members make the grade

Pubs, hotels and restaurants interested in applying for membership are fully inspected and have the marketing benefits of joining Les Routiers explained. Only after passing our rigorous criteria are new members accepted and invited to become part of our select group. There is a charge for inclusion in the guide, but this annual membership fee goes towards covering the inspections and producing the annual guide book.

Perfect pub walks

To the walker, beer and beautiful countryside go hand-in-hand, providing the essential ingredients for a great day's ramble. Having stimulated a healthy appetite and a parched throat, the sight of a welcoming country pub will quicken the step of even the weariest of legs.

Our Pub Walks pages feature 25 beautiful walks (3-8 miles) across the country, including seven new walks for 2007. All have been fully researched and provide detailed route directions, information on places of interest along the way, and essential notes on terrain and the Ordnance Survey map you should take with you. Many start from the front door of cosy inns with comfortable accommodation, so take your walking boots with you for the weekend and explore the surrounding countryside.

Food maps

Dotted throughout this guide you will find Food Maps that identify Les Routiers members who are champions of local foods. Each member shares his or her key local suppliers and some of the interesting food shops in the area, whether that's a farm growing asparagus or soft fruits, a smallholding that delivers organic vegetables or a local fishing boat that lands fresh fish and crab.

Just off the motorway

We've all been there: the motorway service station that short-changes you on food, but charges the earth. Check out the 12 maps to find your detour off the motorway to a Les Routiers' member. The members suggested are just a short drive from the main motorway junction, but miles ahead on food and accommodation.

Quick reference guide

Here you will find at a glance our selection of top places for alfresco eating or the best views, and waterside locations. We also list the best venues at which to eat seafood and game, and those offering private-dining facilities.

How to use this Guide

Finding an establishment

Les Routiers in Britain Guide 2007 is sectioned into England, the Channel Islands Scotland and Wales. The countries are listed alphabetically by county, listing town and establishment name. There are four ways to track down an establishment.

1. If you are seeking a place in a particular area, first turn to the maps at the back of the book. County boundaries are marked in lilac and each establishment has a numbered marker alongside its listing town. Once you know the member entry number, go to the relevant section in the book to find the entry. Entry numbers are in the bottom corner of each member page.

2. Each page is colour-coded at the side so you can flick through the guide and find what you are looking for with ease. Turn to the contents pages for the colour key.

3. Turn to the index on page 530, where both establishment names and listing towns appear in alphabetical order.

4. Turn to the quick-reference guide on page 538 to help you find a place that will suit you, whether it be somewhere with riverside seating or beautiful gardens.

How to read a guide entry

A sample entry is set out on the facing page. At the top of the entry you will find the establishment's name, address, telephone number and, if it has them, an email and website address. Also, any symbols that may apply to the establishment; an explanation of what these symbols stand for appears beside the sample entry. The review describes accommodation, atmosphere, food, wines and so on, while the final section gives additional information and a map number.

Listing town and county: Many of our establishments are in the countryside, so their listing town may be a location several miles away. If you are unsure of the county, look up the town in the index and it will refer you to the correct page.

Telephone: Numbers include the international code for dialling the UK from abroad. To dial from within the UK, start the number with the 0 in brackets; from outside the UK, dial all numbers except the 0 in brackets.

Last orders: Times by which to order drinks, lunch and dinner are given for the bar and restaurant where applicable. Where there is only an evening time given, the establishment serves food and drinks throughout the day.

Closed: Where 'Never' is stated, the establishment is open throughout the year. Where 'Rarely' is stated, the establishment is open throughout the year except on certain holidays (Christmas, New Year). Otherwise, dates and days closed are stated.

Directions: These have been supplied by the proprietor of the establishment. The map number at the end refers to the map section at the back of the guide.

Listing town

Name

Country pub

Address
Telephone: +44(0)870 000000
excellentpub@hotmail.com

A lovely cream-painted cottage tucked away in a tiny hamlet on the edge of Marlow Common…

Prices: **Restaurant main course from £10.25. House wine £11.50.**
Last orders: **Bar: 23.00. Food: lunch 14.30 (Sunday 16.00); dinner 22.00.**
Closed: **Rarely.**
Food: **Modern British.**
Real ale: **Fuller's London Pride, Brakspear Ales, Marlow Rebellion.**
Other points: **Smoking area. Children welcome. Dogs welcome in the bar. Garden. Car park. Wheelchair access.**
Directions: **Exit 9/M4 and 4/M40. In Marlow, take the A4155 towards Henley-on-Thames, and after 300 yards, turn right towards Bovingdon Green. (Map 8)**
See pub walk on page 452

Symbols:
🔶 Accommodation
🔵 Residents only
🅿 Pub or bar
🍵 Teashop or café
🥄 Food shop
🍽 Set menu
★ Award winner 2005
☆ Award winner 2006

All symbols are in their country's colour, apart from the award-winner stars. We do not have a good-food or good-wine symbol, as it is part of our requirements for membership that all Les Routiers establishments serve good food and wine at reasonable prices.

Rooms: For establishments offering overnight accommodation, the number of rooms is given, along with the lowest price for a double/twin and single room. Where this price is per person, it is indicated. Prices usually include breakfast. Where the price includes bed, breakfast and dinner, it is indicated.

Prices: Set meals usually consist of three courses but can include more. If a set meal has fewer or more than three courses, this is stated. Where no set meal is offered, we give the price of the cheapest main course on the menu. House wine prices are by the bottle, unless otherwise stated.

Other points:

Smoking – The majority of establishments are either totally no-smoking or have a smoking area. A total ban on smoking inside pubs and restaurants throughout England will come into force in June 2007.

Credit cards – Very few places don't take credit cards; those that don't are stated here.

Children – Although we indicate whether children are welcome in the establishment, we do not list facilities for guests with babies; we advise telephoning beforehand to sort out any particular requirements.

Dogs – We indicate whether dogs are allowed in the public bar and/or overnight accommodation of the establishment. However, please mention this when booking.

Disabled – We indicate whether an establishment does have wheelchair access. If this does not apply to the WC, this is also stated. However, we recommend telephoning the hotel or restaurant of your choice to discuss your needs with the manager or proprietor directly.

Les Routiers
Awards 2007

Our annual awards recognise members that excel at meeting the standards required for Les Routiers' membership. There are ten categories and, as always, it was a tough call to decide, as overall standards of accommodation, food and drink are excellent. Congratulations to our winners, who just had the edge, and will attend the Les Routiers' awards dinner.

Hospitality and Service Award

The award for hospitality and service is sponsored by American Express. American Express consistently delivers new business and high-spending Card members to its merchants, and works to support independent establishments across Britain. Good service deserves recognition. Offering customers their preferred payment methods contributes to good service, in both city centres and the countryside. Friendly, efficient staff and a slick front-of-house, all make for a pleasant, stress-free stay or dining-out experience. We believe the winners of this award ensure customers feel at ease and are well looked-after, from initial booking through to paying the bill.

Local Food Supporters of the Year

Pubs winning this award are true champions of local produce, run by food-loving chefs or landlords who go out of their way to source, use and promote first-class food and drink from select suppliers in their immediate area.

Hotel of the Year

All our hotels are independently run, and this is evident from their friendly, personal service, individually designed interiors and comfortable accommodation. Our winners successfully combine warm hospitality with a high standard of décor, and often provide the extras that you would expect of deluxe hotels.

Restaurant of the Year

Les Routiers' restaurants are champions of fresh, local seasonal produce. This means we have a network of restaurants around the country that serve good food at its flavoursome best. Our winners source ingredients from specialist local suppliers, which they use imaginatively in their unpretentious, and often regional, dishes. Their appreciation of regional produce is what underpins Les Routiers' philosophy.

Café of the Year

Les Routiers' cafés are a rare and varied bunch, ranging from traditional tearooms and cafés to contemporary conservatories serving all-day homemade snacks. The emphasis is on quality food and friendly service, and all our winners are shining examples of this combination.

Bed & Breakfast of the Year

Gone are the days when bed and breakfast was considered second best. Our members offer first-class accommodation with a friendly, although not obtrusive, service. The bedrooms and public areas combine a comfortable home-from-home feel with stylish interiors. Our winners surpass in all these elements, and many offer good food options.

Wine List of the Year

This award recognises a passion and enthusiasm for choosing quality wines at value-for-money prices. We have chosen members who put as much effort into their house selection as they do into choosing their fine-wine collection.

Inn of the Year

Here we highlight some of Britain's great inns – the new breed of country hotels and restaurants. Our winners successfully combine a relaxed, informal atmosphere with superlative food, genuine warm hospitality, individuality and comfortable accommodation.

Dining Pub of the Year

Innovation, imagination and use of local, regional and fresh produce are the key ingredients in judging this award. All our winners offer first-class cooking.

Real Ale Pub of the Year

This award applauds those enthusiastic, even fanatical, landlords whose passion extends beyond their quest to offer a tip-top pint at every pull to only featuring local micro- and regional-brewery beers.

Local Food Supporter

WINNERS

Central & East Anglia – Holly Bush, Salt, Staffordshire
'Landlord Geoff Holland is passionate about using local produce, and his interesting menus list local butcher meats, venison from Cannock Chase and homegrown vegetables – he even smokes his own meat and fish.'

London & South East – Compasses at Pattiswick, Pattiswick, Essex
'Jono and Jane Clarke's exciting new pub venture brings the same philosophy, a passion for real hospitality and great care in sourcing local foods, which extends to listing individual suppliers on their imaginative menus.'

The North – Winder Hall Country House, Cockermouth, Cumbria
'The menu choice at this historic manor house may be limited but it incorporates local ingredients, organic meats and homegrown free-range eggs and pork.'

Wales & The Marches – Jabajak Restaurant & Country Retreat, Whitland, Carmarthenshire
'The cooking at Amanda and Julian Stuart-Robson's hugely individual rural retreat makes good use of high-quality local and fully traceable ingredients. Vegetables are homegrown and the Welsh Celtic Pride steaks are exceptional.'

South West – California Country Inn, Modbury, Devon
'The Bell family's popular South Hams dining venue offers menus that focus on quality produce sourced within 25 miles of the pub, including Devon cheeses and farm-reared meats.'

Scotland – Craigadam, Castle Douglas, Dumfries & Galloway
'Locally smoked salmon, estate game, home-reared lamb, homegrown vegetables, home-baked bread and regional cheeses make a fine meal at Celia and Richard Pickup's charming farmhouse.'

Hotel of the Year

NATIONAL WINNER
South West – St Vincent House Hotel & Restaurant, Lynton, Devon
'You'll find is easy to feel at home at this understated stylish hotel. The comfort of guests is paramount, especially in the elegantly furnished bedrooms, and the Belgian owner is passionate about serving good, seasonal food.'

REGIONAL WINNERS
Central & East Anglia – The Crown, Southwold, Suffolk
'Beautifully refurbished and maintained bedrooms, imaginative wines and impeccable service simply underline the thread of quality that runs throughout Adnams flagship inn.'

London & South East – Wellington Hotel, Ventnor, Isle of Wight
'Lovingly restored to its Victorian splendour, this beautifully upgraded hotel brings a stylish new look to this traditional resort town. Bedrooms are fresh and contemporary, and sea-facing rooms boast private balconies.'

The North – Raffles Hotel and Tea Rooms, Blackpool, Lancashire
'Owners Graham Poole and Ian Balmforth have a real passion for their exceptional small hotel. Housekeeping is exemplary in meticulously decorated rooms and the atmosphere is relaxed from the moment you arrive.'

Wales & The Marches – Bae Abermaw, Barmouth, Gwynedd
'The contemporary jewel in traditional Barmouth, this imposing Victorian building hides a smart, modern interior, which combines old and new to great effect. Well-presented bedrooms have fabulous sea views and the food is excellent.'

Scotland – Royal Hotel, Comrie, Perth & Kinross
'The Milsom family's beautifully appointed town-centre hotel has a country-house ambience, where stylish furnishings and fixed-price dinners are complemented by high standards of hospitality.'

Restaurant of the Year

NATIONAL WINNER

Wales & The Marches – The Crown at Whitebrook, Whitebrook, Monmouthshire

'New and exciting interpretations of modern British and French dishes are really tickling the taste buds of diners at this famous restaurant-with-rooms close to the Wye. Dishes are elegantly presented, big on flavour and draw on first-class local ingredients.'

REGIONAL WINNERS

Central & East Anglia – The Bridge, Bidford-on-Avon, Warwickshire

'Opened in 2005, this relaxing and stylish brasserie on the banks on the River Avon goes from strength to strength. Expect classic, well-executed brasserie dishes that draw on sound Mediterranean traditions.'

London & South East – Gallops Restaurant, Henfield, West Sussex

'Transformed under the stewardship of Richard Holmes and Cara Bexton, this sophisticated and modern restaurant offers a tantalising parade of Modern European dishes made using well-sourced ingredients.'

The North – Weezos@The Old Tollhouse, Clitheroe, Lancashire

'Exceptional style, service, wine and, above all, an innovative kitchen with a real understanding of quality ingredients and how to use them lift this charming restaurant into a class of its own.'

South West – The Orange Tree Restaurant, Torquay, Devon

'Its reputation for quality food in classy surroundings continues to grow in Torquay, thanks to the skilful cooking of Tony Fagan, who sources only the best Devon produce for his imaginative seasonal menus.'

Scotland – La Garrigue, Edinburgh, City of Edinburgh

'Chef-proprietor Jean Michel Gauffre pays homage to his culinary roots at this exquisite bistro. Authentically good and gutsy cooking draws on the Languedoc's fine food and wine, offering a quality dining experience from start to finish.'

Café of the Year

NATIONAL WINNER
Wales & The Marches – Oriel-y-Felin Gallery & Tea Room, Trefin, Pembrokeshire
'It's the quality of the ingredients that turn the ordinary light dishes at this spick-and-span and welcoming tea room-cum-gallery into the extraordinary. Everything is freshly prepared from locally sourced ingredients, right down to the organic bread from an artisan baker.'

REGIONAL WINNERS
Central & East Anglia – The Kitchen, Lincoln, Lincolnshire
'A unique roadside diner housed in a former RAF mess hall beside the A15, now a prime pit-stop for traditional and hearty meals prepared from fresh local produce.'

London & South East – Le Truc Vert, London
'A quality deli and restaurant that's a feast for the senses and a haven of civility. Come for breakfast, to buy wonderful fresh produce, or experience its slick transformation into a smart evening restaurant.'

The North – Alan's Café Restaurant, Penrith, Cumbria
'A café on weekdays and a sophisticated restaurant on Friday and Saturday evenings, and the chef-owner pulls off both with aplomb. Expect fresh baked-cakes, delicious light lunches and imaginative dinners.'

Scotland – Coach House Coffee Shop, Luss, Argyll & Bute
'This shop and coffee shop may draw the crowds all day, but Rowena Ferguson and her excellent staff manage the high demand efficiently. The attraction is the impressive line-up of home-baked cakes and first-class light lunches.'

Bed & Breakfast of the Year
Sponsored by Lurpak

NATIONAL WINNER
Scotland – Trafford Bank Guesthouse, Inverness
'A modern, brighter and smaller version of a traditional Scottish country house – this fine Victorian house is the place to stay in town. The whole place is immaculately presented, cosy bedrooms offer every conceivable extra, and breakfast presents the best locally sourced produce. Magnificent.'

REGIONAL WINNERS
Central & East Anglia – The Limes, Catfield, Norfolk
'A most welcoming and wonderfully positioned B&B, run by charming hosts Simon and Jean Partridge. Bedrooms are comfortable and spacious and the atmosphere immediately relaxing. Excellent set dinners are great value.'

London & South East – Jeake's Hotel, Rye, East Sussex
'Fresh flowers and deft personal touches create an opulent feel at Jenny Hadfield's exemplary small hotel. Add a 17th-century setting, striking rooms and legendary breakfasts and you won't want to leave.'

The North – 1 Park Road, Windermere, Cumbria
'Mark and Alexandra Soden's stylish Victorian villa is a cut above the norm in Windermere. Expect elegantly restored period rooms, stylish bedrooms that ooze comfort and cosseting extras, and don't miss Mark's candlelit dinners.'

Wales & The Marches – Penmachno Hall, Betws-y-Coed, Conwy
'This stylishly updated Victorian house, set in a wonderfully rural setting in Snowdonia, is perfect for those in search of views, peace and quiet and hearty, freshly prepared food. A relaxing Welsh gem.'

South West – Highland Court Lodge, St Austell, Cornwall
'Meticulous attention to detail and a passion for the business combine with luxury, style and good taste to create this hugely individual B&B. Elegant, well-equipped bedrooms and splendid set dinners add to the appeal.'

LURPAK®
perfect
BREAKFASTS

Enjoy a perfect breakfast with Lurpak,®
proud sponsors of the Les Routiers
Bed and Breakfast of The Year 2006.

Wine List of the Year

NATIONAL WINNER

The North – Freemasons Arms, Clitheroe, Lancashire

'Chef-proprietor Ian Martin has an intimate knowledge of wine, and his global list of 500 bins is just fantastic. The depth of quality and range of vintages is outstanding, and mark-ups are minimal.'

REGIONAL WINNERS

Central & East Anglia – Olive Branch, Clipsham, Rutland

'Wine is a real passion at this famous foodie hang-out. Beyond a quality list with excellent tasting notes, there are chalkboards highlighting keenly priced bin-end specials, classics and up-and-coming producers, and there's a wholesale list of wines at competitive, take-out prices.'

London & South East – Froggie's at the Timber Batts, Bodsham, Kent

'Like the style of cooking and the cheeses at Joel Gross's remote 15th-century pub, the wine list is totally French, with some classy clarets and a very drinkable house wine grown by Joel's cousin in the Loire Valley.'

Wales & The Marches – The Bell at Skenfrith, Skenfrith, Monmouthshire

'William's wine list is superb and reflects his passions for rare and unusual champagnes, rarified clarets and fine cognac. The globetrotting list screams quality and value wherever you look, and there's a fine range of half bottles, a raft of exemplary pudding wines and 13 wines by the glass. Excellent tasting notes and fascinating potted history's make good reading.'

South West – White Horse, Frampton Mansell, Gloucestershire

'The global wine list at Shaun and Emma Davies's dining pub may only list 60 bins, but it offers great value and focuses on respected smaller growers.'

Scotland – La Parmigiana, Glasgow

'Great Italian food is matched by a wine list that offers good Italian favourites, from a prosecco aperitivo to serious Tuscan reds such as Roccato Vino Da Tavola 'Rocca Delle Macie', with plenty to tempt in between.'

Inn of the Year

NATIONAL WINNER
London & South East – Carnarvon Arms, Newbury, Berkshire
'Classy bedrooms and a mix of classic bar food and innovative modern dishes draw the discerning to this revamped old coaching inn, which successfully bridges the gap between restaurant and gastropub.'

REGIONAL WINNERS
Central & East Anglia – The Red House, Nether Broughton, Leicestershire
'A stylish, contemporary and highly individual pub-restaurant with rooms that combines modern luxury with a relaxed atmosphere.'

The North – Anglers Arms, Longframlington, Northumberland
'Refurbished bedrooms, handsome bars and lounges, and soothing rural views make this 18th-century coaching inn a splendid base for exploring Northumberland's coast and castles.'

Wales & The Marches – The Inn at Grinshill, Shrewsbury, Shropshire
'Kevin and Victoria Brazier have transformed this country inn into a classy pub-restaurant with rooms. Fabulous bedrooms are furnished with style and panache, and contemporary pub food showcases local produce.'

South West – Sandy Park Inn, Chagford, Devon
'This thatched 17th-century inn is the perfect Dartmoor hideaway. Recently refurbished, it provides cosy and stylish bedrooms and short, creative menus that reflect the seasons.'

Scotland – Famous Bein Inn, Perth, Perth & Kinross
'This remote drovers' inn may be an institution and local landmark, famous for its basement Rock Bar, but it also provides travellers with honest, home-cooked food and good accommodation in unpretentious rooms.'

Dining Pub of the Year

NATIONAL WINNER
Wales & The Marches – Lough Pool Inn at Sellack, Ross-on-Wye, Herefordshire
'The key appeal of David and Janice Birch's 16th-century timbered pub, other than its olde-worlde charm and rural seclusion, are the innovative daily menus that showcase the first-class local produce available.'

REGIONAL WINNERS
Central & East Anglia – The Chequers Inn, Belvoir, Lincolnshire
'Food is taken very serious at Justin and Jo Chad's stylishly refurbished inn. The freshest local ingredients are used to create modern, simple dishes with exciting taste and texture.'

London & South East – The Bugle, Hamble, Hampshire
'Beautifully remodelled by the team behind the hugely successful White Star Tavern in Southampton, this famous 16th-century pub now delivers first-class classic pubs meals and inventive evening dishes.'

The North – The Old Bore, Rishworth, West Yorkshire
'Scott Hessel's revamped dining pub is far from boring. He cooks with flair and imagination and has been wowing local foodies with ambitious modern dishes that utilise the finest local produce available.'

South West – The Rose & Crown and Seafood Restaurant, Yealmpton, Devon
'The Wykeham Inns group has done it again, transforming a sleepy local into a modern, food-driven pub. Already thriving, this South Hams pub draws diners in for the freshest fish and seafood delivered from local markets and fishermen.'

Scotland – Four Seasons Country Pub & Restaurant, Fort William, Highland
'This unique pub, set in a chalet-and-hostel complex near Glencoe, is the place to come for Highland ales and some robust Scottish cooking prepared from locally sourced produce.'

Real Ale Pub of the Year

NATIONAL WINNER
The North – Tempest Arms, Skipton, North Yorkshire
'New bedrooms may have elevated the Tempest to hotel status, but it retains the character and atmosphere of a country pub, which extends to offering four tip-top Yorkshire ales. Stay the night and quaff ales from Theakston, Wharfedale, Copper Dragon and Black Sheep.'

REGIONAL WINNERS
Central & East Anglia – Queen's Head, Bulwick, Northamptonshire
'Top-notch local Rockingham or Newby Wyke micro-brewery ales accompany hand-pumped Shepherd Neame Spitfire on the bar at this historic village pub, which is also worth seeking out for its quality pub food.'

London & South East – The Ship Inn, Chichester, West Sussex
'Walkers and yachting types fill this nautically themed pub just 150 yards from Chichester Harbour, the draw being fresh fish and four hand-pumps dispensing cracking local beers from Horsham, Ballards and Itchen Valley breweries.'

Wales & The Marches – Cottage of Content, Hereford, Herefordshire
'A treasure of a pub set in remote countryside, offering carefully prepared food based on locally sourced produce. You can wash it all down with an exceptional pint of Wye Valley Butty Bach.'

South West – Wild Duck Inn, Cirencester, Gloucestershire
'Well worth seeking out for its classic bar, which brims with character and atmosphere, providing the perfect setting in which to quaff one of the five well-kept ales on tap.'

Scotland – Clachaig Inn, Glencoe, Highland
'A beacon for weary walkers and climbers in Glencoe, the stone-flagged Boots Bar at this 300-year-old inn is their favoured refuelling stop. Why? A well-stocked bar dispensing eight splendid real ales from Highland micro-breweries, perhaps from Cairngorm, Caledonian and Skye.'

Hospitality and Service Award

Sponsored by American Express

NATIONAL WINNER
The Royal Oak, Chicester, West Sussex

'Entrepreneur landlord Nick Sutherland and his designer wife Lisa have combined their respective talents to create two classy pubs-with-rooms. Rooms have been stylishly refurbished with great attention to detail, food, wine and ales are excellent, and the welcome and service at both is first-class.'

The world has much to offer.
It's just knowing where to find it.

If you're an American Express Cardmember, simply visit
americanexpress.co.uk/selects or visit your local homepage, and click on
'offers'. You'll find great offers wherever you are today, all in one place.

selects. AMERICAN EXPRESS

THE WORLD OFFERS. WE SELECT. YOU ENJOY.

What's the catch?

A new wave of enthusiasm for different seafood varieties means there is a wider choice of exciting dishes on restaurant menus. We net a rich source of species from our coastline, and our chefs have devised fabulous ways of serving them.

It is not only delicious and versatile, but seafood is low in calories, high in protein and rich in vitamins, minerals and natural oils – in fact, it is one of the most nutritious foods we can eat.

Seafood features in many different guises on menus around the world, and in the UK it has become the star feature on many of Les Routiers members' menus. More restaurants than ever are creating superb dishes from a variety of seafood caught off the British coast.

Apart from the national favourite – battered and fried fish served with chips – seafood offers plenty of cooking possibilities. You can oven roast it whole, stuffed with aromatic herbs, a simple and fuss-free option, or lightly pan-fry fillets and serve with a butter or caper sauce. White fish is a brilliant canvas for absorbing a range of spicy and citrussy marinades, and once flavoured, takes no time to cook on the barbecue or griddle, or under the grill.

The cooking possibilities are endless, especially as we are widening our choices and buying alternatives to the ever-popular cod and haddock. Sea bass, sea bream, halibut and monkfish are among the top choices. But that's not all. There are more than 21,000 species of fish in the world, and more than 100 varieties widely available to try in the UK.

Many of the fish varieties caught off our coastline are served at Les Routiers' establishments. In winter, try line-caught sea bass, coley, red gurnard and brill; in summer, flounder, hake, sardines, megrim, lemon or Dover sole. All year round, we can tuck into marvellous monkfish, John Dory, redfish and mackerel – just a few to look out for on menus or at fishmongers around the country.

Seafish was set up in 1981 and works to help consumers find out more about the wide variety of seafood available and the many benefits that it offers, as well as to help all sectors of the seafood industry raise standards, improve efficiency and develop environmentally responsible practices.

A key date in the Seafish calendar is the annual **Seafood Week**, which is held every October. And the date is no coincidence, for it is at this time of year when the best stocks of many different types of seafood are available to buy.

During Seafood Week, Seafish will be advising on buying and cooking seafood. It will be running special promotions with many restaurants and retailers. For information about the week, and events at other times of the year, check out its website at **www.seafish.org/2aweek.** It offers a wealth of information, and a wide database of restaurants, pubs and fish-and-chip shops, and even recipes to try for yourself. The new '2 a week' campaign aims to raise awareness of the wide variety of delicious seafood available in the UK, and the many health benefits of eating it.

England

Bath

Eastern Eye

Indian restaurant

8a Quite Street, Bath BA1 2JS
Telephone: +44(0)1225 422323
info@easterneye.com
www.easterneye.com

'A setting that's as majestic as the Taj Mahal.'

Prices: Main course from £7.50. House wine £11.95.
Last orders: **Food: lunch 14.30; dinner 23.30.**
Closed: **Rarely.**
Food: **Indian.**
Other points: **Smoking area. Children welcome.**
Directions: **Exit 18/M4. (Map 4)**

Fancy eating Indian food in a setting that's as majestic as the Taj Mahal? Then head to the Eastern Eye, where you can enjoy spicy specialities in Georgian splendour. The large, open-plan room has three glass ceiling domes, large windows, stunning ceilings, columns and fanlights, which turn dining into quite an occasion. The menu specialises in northern Indian and Bengali cooking.

There's much to tempt you away from the usual selection of jalfrezis or dansaks. If you're not sure where to head, check out the chef's recommendations first, which include splendid seafood and vegetarian dishes. The butty kebabs from Bengal, small slices of delicately spiced and tender lamb cooked in a tandoori oven, are a perfect partner to another Bengali dish of channa bhaji – fried chickpeas in a spicy sauce. Main courses such as Karali lamb and garlic chilli masala chicken are produced with panache, and the pilau rice is fresh and fluffy. The combination of freshly cooked food, reasonable prices and swift, friendly service means the Eastern Eye is always busy and we recommend that you book.

MEMBER
1
ENTRY

Country inn

*'Kids can make use of the
miniature railway in the garden.'*

The Hunters Rest Inn

King Lane, Clutton Hill, Bath BS39 5QL
Telephone: +44(0)1761 452303
paul@huntersrest.co.uk
www.huntersrest.co.uk

Built in 1755 as a hunting lodge for the Earl of Warwick, this small rural inn is difficult to find, as it's at the end of a winding country lane, with views over the Cam Valley towards the Mendip Hills. Inside, a stone bar is surrounded by a number of interconnecting rooms; all are traditionally furnished and one leads into the bright conservatory. Old farm paraphernalia hangs from walls, and dried hops adorn the beamed ceilings, along with brass plates, hunting pictures and brass horns. Ale drinkers will find local Butcombe and Bath Gem on tap.

The food is traditional, the specials locally sourced, and runs from hearty ploughman's lunches with locally produced cheddar, and giant pastry 'oggies' filled with beef and stilton to lamb with red wine, garlic and herbs. Tuna steak with lime, chilli and coriander butter may appear on the specials menu. Wednesday night is family night, and kids can make use of the miniature railway in the garden. All four bedrooms are individually decorated; each comes with bags of character, rich fabrics, great views and a smart bathroom.

Rooms: 5. Double room from £87.50, single from £62.50, family from £125.
Prices: Set lunch £12.50 and dinner £18.50. Restaurant main course from £10. Bar main course from £7. House wine £9.25.
Last orders: Bar: afternoon 15.00; evening 23.00. Food: lunch 14.00; dinner 21.30 (Friday and Saturday 22.15).
Closed: Never.
Food: Traditional English.
Real ale: Bass, Butcombe Bitter, Otter Ale, Bath Gem Bitter.
Other points: Smoking area. Children welcome. Dogs welcome in the bar. Garden. Car park. Wheelchair access to the restaurant/pub.
Directions: Clutton Hill lies between the A39 and A37 south of Bristol, near Chelwood and Farmborough. (Map 4)
See pub walk on page 450

...for special offers

Bath

Rajpoot

Rajpoot House, 4 Argyle Street,
Bath BA2 4BA
Telephone: +44(0)1225 466833/464758
www.rajpoot.com

'Everything is done with style at this popular Indian restaurant.'

Prices: **Set lunch £7.95 and dinner £25. House wine £12.50.**
Last orders: **Food: lunch 14.30; dinner 23.00 (Friday and Saturday 23.30).**
Closed: **Rarely.**
Food: **Indian.**
Other points: **No smoking. Children welcome. Wheelchair access by arrangement.**
Directions: **Exit 18/M4. In the city centre, off Pulteney Bridge. (Map 4)**

Everything is done with style at this popular Indian restaurant close to Pulteney Bridge, from the smartly turbaned waiters to the vibrant décor and menu. A smell of spices greets you as you descend the stairs to the basement, which is divided into three snug, but cool, air-conditioned rooms, each individually themed along the lines of Old India, Indian Cottage and Kamra. The authentic feel is further enhanced by the richly coloured ceilings, while crisp white tableclothes provide contemporary touches.

The menu brings together a comprehensive selection of tandoori, vegetarian, biryani and curry specialities such as massala, punjabi and charga dishes, the latter featuring chicken cooked with almonds and sultanas. Fish is also a star feature, from the unusual Rajpoot salmon to the fish Himshore – cod chunks cooked in coconut milk garnished with prawns and green pepper. For those who would rather not agonise over the extensive list, there are two very appealing set menus. The wine cellar covers a wide spectrum and includes two Indian varieties worth trying.

Tilley's Bistro

City-centre bistro

'It has bags of character, thanks to its many cosy nooks and crannies.'

3 North Parade Passage,
Bath BA1 1NX
Telephone: +44(0)1225 484200
dmott@tilleysbistro.co.uk
www.tilleysbistro.co.uk

Tilley's occupies one of the oldest houses in Bath – it used to be the refectory for the Abbey. Set over three floors, it has bags of character, thanks to its many cosy nooks and crannies. The main, beamed dining room, with an original stone fireplace at either end, has a wine-bar atmosphere. Up winding stairs are a comfortable lounge, small bar and private dining room. Good food at good prices means that David and Dawn Mott's bistro remains popular, so it's always best to book.

The set lunches are freshly flavoursome, with chicken liver and bacon salad, or cream of watercress soup to start. Second courses of roast duck leg with Puy lentils cooked with pancetta, onions and tomatoes or fish of the day come with a choice of accompaniments. In the evening, the carte and separate vegetarian menu offer a wide choice. The carte ranges from fresh asparagus and parmesan tart and Toulouse sausages with Dijon mustard, brandy and cream sauce through to lamb with port and redcurrant jus. The fabulous pudding menu includes baked clotted-cream cheesecake. There's a global selection of wines, nearly all at under £20.

Prices: Set lunch £13.50 and dinner £20 and £25. Main course from £10. Pre-theatre menu 18.00-19.00 (2 courses) £10. House wine £14.
Last orders: Food: lunch 14.30; dinner 23.00.
Closed: Sunday.
Food: French/English.
Other points: No smoking. Children welcome. Wheelchair access.
Directions: Exit 18/M4. In the centre of Bath near to the Abbey. (Map 4)

...for the latest news

MEMBER 4 ENTRY

Bed and breakfast

'All the downstairs rooms have wonderful views over the grounds.'

Harptree Court

East Harptree, near Bristol,
Bath and NE Somerset BS40 6AA
Telephone: +44(0)1761 221729
linda.hill@harptreecourt.co.uk
www.harptreecourt.co.uk

Built in 1796 by the city architect of Bath, this handsome Georgian country house stands in 17 acres of landscaped gardens. You will feel as if you are deep in the countryside, but Harptree is conveniently near Bristol, Bristol Airport and Bath. Despite the grandness of its long drive that takes you past water features and ornate bridges, this grand B&B retains the warmth and friendliness of a family home. Tea on arrival makes you feel immediately welcome.

Guests have a choice of sitting rooms: a smaller upstairs room with log fire or, downstairs, a larger room attired in period style. All the downstairs rooms have wonderful views over the grounds. Breakfast is light and healthy continental or the full-on English, and can be taken in the dining room or in the hall in front of a roaring fire. Dinner prepared by Linda Hill needs to be pre-booked, or you can walk to the village pub. The bedrooms are large and furnished with antiques and Persian rugs, with stunning garden views. In-room entertainment runs to DVD players, tea/coffee-making facilities, books, magazines, chocolates, fresh fruit and flowers.

Rooms: **3, 2 en-suite. Double/twin room from £80, single from £60.**
Prices: **Set dinner £22.50.**
Closed: **25 December.**
Food: **Traditional British.**
Other points: **No smoking. Garden. Car park.**
Directions: **Exit 18/M4 and Exit 18/M5. Turn off the A368 onto the B3114 for Chewton Mendip. After approximately half a mile, turn right into the drive just after the crossroads. (Map 4)**

MEMBER ENTRY
5

Harrold

The Muntjac

Country inn

71 High Street, Harrold,
Bedfordshire MK43 7BJ
Telephone: +44(0)1234 721500
russell@themuntjac.co.uk
www.themuntjac.co.uk

'North Bedfordshire now has a gastropub-with-rooms to be proud of.'

Rooms: 4. Double/twin room from £48, single from £35.
Prices: Restaurant main course from £9.95. Bar main course from £3.75. House wine £10.95.
Last orders: Bar: afternoon 14.15 (Sunday 15.00); evening 21.00 (Friday and Saturday 21.30). Food: lunch 14.30 (Sunday 15.00); dinner 21.15 (Friday and Saturday 22.00). No food Sunday evening and all day Monday.
Closed: Monday lunch (closed all day for food).
Food: European.
Real ale: Timothy Taylor Landlord, Caledonian Deuchars IPA, Shepherd Neame, Spitfire, Bateman's XB Bitter, Fuller's London Pride. Three guest beers.
Other points: Smoking area. Garden. Car park.
Directions: Exit 14/M1. Follow signs to Newport Pagnell, Olney to Lavendon, then Harrold. (Map 8)

North Bedfordshire now has a gastropub-with-rooms to be proud of in the form of the recently spruced-up Muntjac in the pretty village of Harrold. Wendy and Russell Martin acquired the 400-year-old coaching inn early in 2004 and set about the huge refurbishment task with enthusiasm, passion and vision. The rewards are clear to see: a smart bar area boasting oak beams and big open fireplaces, and equally convivial dining areas. Serious thought has also been given to the four en-suite bedrooms. Stripped out and revamped in contemporary style, each has a large TV, CD/DVD player, internet access, modern furnishings and a cosy bathroom.

Using local, seasonal and organic produce where possible, innovative menus successfully blend traditional and modern pub dishes. At lunch, tuck into homemade burgers or steak-and-ale pie with a pint of locally brewed Potton Ale. Cooking moves up a gear in the evenings – a typical meal may take in warm salad of scallops, black pudding and smoked bacon, followed by rack of Welsh lamb with mint-and-caper jus, and baked dark-chocolate cheesecake. There is a good list of wines.

MEMBER
6
ENTRY

Barkham

The Bull at Barkham

Pub

'A traditional village pub that oozes history and character.'

Barkham Road, Barkham, Wokingham,
Berkshire RG41 4TL
Telephone: +44(0)1189 760324
barkhambull@barbox.net
www.thebullatbarkham.com

Just south of the M4 (J10) and close to the California Country Park, the Bull is a traditional village pub that oozes history and character. At one time it also doubled as the village blacksmith. The original forge still stands in the centre of restaurant and scorch marks are visible on the adjacent beams. The main building was originally a brewhouse and the restaurant extension was the working blacksmith's forge from 1728 until it closed in 1982. You can eat informally in the bar or in the large, attractive garden. In the restaurant, linen-clothed tables create a more formal setting for chef-proprietor Adrian Brunswick's traditional country cooking.

Expect a modern twist to familiar dishes, perhaps rack of lamb with mustard glaze and port-wine jus. As well as the hearty pies – try the steak-and-ale with shortcrust pastry – fillet steak with all the trimmings, and beer-battered haddock, lighter dishes are available at lunchtime, as is an excellent-value two-course lunch menu. Wife Susie oversees the attractively refurbished bar, dispensing Adnams ales and well-chosen wines to locals and intending diners.

Prices: **Main course from £7. House wine £10.95.**
Last orders: **Lunch 14.15; dinner 21.30.**
Closed: **Rarely.**
Food: **Modern/traditional British and European.**
Real ale: **Adnams Broadside, Courage Best Bitter, Adnams Best, Theakston Old Peculier. One guest beer.**
Other points: **Smoking area. Dogs welcome in the bar. Garden. Car park.**
Directions: **Exit 10/M4. Head towards Wokingham and follow signposts to Barkham. The Bull Inn is in the centre of Barkham. (Map 5)**

...for recipe ideas

MEMBER
7
ENTRY

Newbury

Carnarvon Arms

Country inn

Winchester Road, Whitway, Burghclere,
Newbury, Berkshire RG20 9LE
Telephone: +44(0)1635 278222
info@carnarvonarms.com
www.carnarvonarms.com

'Classic bar food alongside more innovative modern dishes.'

Rooms: 12. Double/twin room from £79.95, single from £59.95.
Prices: Set lunch £14.95. Restaurant main course from £7.95. Bar main course from £7.95. House wine £12.95.
Last orders: Bar: 23.00. Food: lunch 14.30; dinner 21.30 (Friday and Saturday 22.00). Bar food served all day.
Closed: Never.
Food: Modern British.
Real ale: Three guest beers.
Other points: Smoking area. Children welcome. Dogs welcome in the bar. Garden. Car park. Wheelchair access.
Directions: Exit 13/M4. Take the A34 south and exit at Highclere Castle and Tothill services. Follow signs to the castle. Carnarvon Arms is on the right-hand side. (Map 5)

The Carnarvon Arms is a rambling old coaching inn built in the mid-1800s to serve travellers to nearby Highclere Castle. Reopened in November 2005 as a 'fine dining, traditional country inn', following extensive refurbishment by Merchant Inns, it successfully bridges the gap between restaurant and gastropub, offering a relaxed, informal atmosphere, classic bar food alongside more innovative modern dishes, and 12 classy bedrooms. Today's incarnation has bare boards, subtle lighting, deep sofas in a stylish lounge and bar area, and a high-vaulted dining room.

Quality food comes courtesy of Robert Clayton, whose skilled cooking, based on modern British cuisine, has seen him head up several Michelin-star kitchens. With the help of head chef Simon Pitney-Baxter, his carte could feature Cornish crab soup, smoked haddock and thyme risotto, rump of lamb with olive-and-thyme sauce, and vanilla-bean panna cotta. Despite such accomplished cooking, the Carnarvon is still a pub, with three ales on tap, a raft of wines by the glass, and a bar menu listing traditional pub dishes.

London Street Brasserie

Town-centre restaurant

'Puddings are indulgent, none more so than white chocolate and raspberry cheesecake.'

2-4 London Street, Riverside, Reading, Berkshire RG1 4SE
Telephone: +44(0)1189 505036
www.londonstbrasserie.co.uk

Once the tollgate on Duke Street bridge, this contemporary brasserie is housed in one of Reading's oldest buildings. Interiors have been stylishly refurbished and there's an appealing modern menu to match. Eat in the bright restaurant, with its white walls, polished wooden floors and tables, scanning the art for sale, or in fine weather, dine alfresco on the attractive decked area.

The modern British carte also takes in the flavours of the Mediterranean, the Orient and Asia. Start with scallops, black pudding, apple compote and red-wine jus, or the duck liver and foie gras parfait. Mains include an exotically assembled Moroccan meze board, classic brasserie dishes made from local meat and game such as pan-fried calves' liver and saddleback bacon, or more modern teamings of rump of lamb with Tuscan vegetables, broad beans, fennel and a red wine and rosemary sauce. Puddings are indulgent, none more so than white-chocolate and raspberry cheesecake. The 40-bin globetrotting wine list offers much by the glass. The brasserie is under the same ownership as the Crooked Billet, Stoke Row.

Prices: Set lunch £13.50 (two courses, 12.00-19.00 daily). Main course from £11. House wine £13.50.
Last orders: Food: 22.30 (Friday and Saturday 23.00).
Closed: Rarely.
Food: Modern British and global.
Other points: Smoking area. Riverside terrace (heated). Car park. Wheelchair access.
Directions: Exit 10 or 11/M4. Follow the signs to 'Oracle' park in 'Oracle' multi-storey car park. (Map 5)

...for events

MEMBER
9
ENTRY

Bristol

The Ganges

Indian restaurant

368 Gloucester Road, Bristol BS7 8TP
Telephone: +44(0)117 924 5234

'Vegetarian dishes are a high point, as the vegetables are always fresh, never frozen.'

Prices: **Set lunch and dinner from £14.50. House wine £8.95.**
Last orders: **Food: lunch 14.30; dinner 23.30.**
Closed: **Rarely.**
Food: **Indian/Bangladeshi.**
Other points: **Smoking area. Children welcome.**
Directions: **On the A38 Gloucester Road.**
(Map 4)

The long-established Ganges consistently serves authentic Indian food in glitzy surroundings. The restaurant is vividly decorated with large, glittering chandeliers, giving it the edge in the glamour stakes. The menu is just as vibrant, focusing on the three main regions through which the River Ganges flows: it rises in Tibet, flows through India and reaches the sea at Bangladesh. The major influence, though, comes from north India and so you'll find the most popular curries – from mild lamb pasanda to a fiery vindaloo king prawn – alongside biryanis on the menu.

If you tend to stick to your favourite dish, this is the place to branch out, as the chef has half a dozen well-thought-out and well-priced set menus, plus there's an all-encompassing thali of tandoori murg, lamb tikka, shish kebab, naan, pilau rice, and chicken tikka. Vegetarian dishes, including a vegetarian thali, are a high point, as the vegetables are always fresh, never frozen. The wine list is a cut above, too, and includes classics such as Sancerre and Barolo. There's a refreshing selection of bottled and draught beers, including Cobra, Kingfisher and Lal Toofan.

San Carlo Restaurant

Italian restaurant

44 Corn Street, Bristol BS1 1HQ
Telephone: +44(0)117 922 6586
www.sancarlo.co.uk

*'San Carlo's buzzy atmosphere
and friendly service are bound to
raise your spirits.'*

Authentic Italian cooking and a city-centre
location mean this restaurant is always busy,
but plenty of seating means you should get
a table without having to book. The tall
Victorian building stands in an attractive
pedestrianised area. Inside, clever décor
means the long, narrow room is light, bright
and airy. The atmosphere is unmistakeably
Mediterranean with a contemporary theme:
mirrored walls, white-tiled floor and colour
in the form of potted plants and trees of
different shapes and sizes.

It serves all the popular favourites at
reasonable prices, and the cooking is a cut
above the norm for a city-centre eaterie
majoring in pizzas and pastas. The menu lists
familiar trattoria dishes: fritto misto; buffalo
mozzarella with tomato, basil and avocado;
saltimboca alla Romana; piccata al limone;
and suprema di pollo Genovese. Chalkboard
specials extend the choice with a range of
seafood that could include taglioni lobster,
Dover sole and mixed grilled fish. There's
a good selection of wines by the glass.
San Carlo's buzzy atmosphere and friendly
service are bound to raise your spirits.

Prices: **Main course from £11. House wine
£12.95.**
Last orders: **Food: 23.00.**
Closed: **Rarely.**
Food: **Italian.**
Other points: **Smoking throughout. Children
welcome. Wheelchair access.**
Directions: **In Bristol city centre. (Map 4)**

...for competitions

MEMBER
11
ENTRY

Bristol

Westfield House

Bed and breakfast

37 Stoke Hill, Stoke Bishop,
Bristol BS9 1LQ
Telephone: +44(0)117 962 6119
guest@westfieldhouse.net
www.westfieldhouse.net

'The perfect retreat for those who want to be within easy reach of Bristol city centre.'

Rooms: **3. Double/twin room from £85, single from £55.**
Prices: **Set lunch £15 and dinner £20. Restaurant main course from £10. Room-service sandwiches/snacks from £7.**
Food: **Traditional British.**
Other points: **No smoking. Garden. Children over 12 welcome. Dogs welcome (not in bedrooms). Car park.**
Directions: **Exit 17/M5. Follow the A4018 to Durdham Downs. At Blackboy Hill roundabout turn right, crossing the Downs. On Stoke Road go through the traffic lights into Stoke Hill. Westfield House is the fourth entrance on the left after Church Avenue. (Map 4)**

Neo-Georgian in style, Westfield House stands in two and a half acres of wildlife-rich gardens within the prosperous area of Stoke Hill in Sneyd Park. It is a friendly, family-run guesthouse and provides the perfect retreat for those who want to be within easy reach of Bristol city centre, but prefer calmer surroundings. The ground-floor rooms are well proportioned and decorated in pleasant pastel shades. There's a comfortable living room with seating around the fireplace and large french windows that lead on to the garden terrace. Upstairs, the bedrooms are beautifully appointed, en suite, and have TV and coffee-making facilities.

Ann Jell cooks more or less to order, be that a simple breakfast or a full-cooked meal. Whichever you choose, you'll find all ingredients are from local and organic suppliers or Bristol's farmers' market. Typical evening meals might include carrot, orange and coriander soup, followed by duck marinated in honey and cider, and lime-and-lemon tart. Attention to detail is evident, from the homemade jams and butter pats to the excellent coffee.

MEMBER ENTRY

Dinton Hermit

Country inn

'After dinner, there's the option of a Cuban cigar and a brandy from the cellar collection.'

Water Lane, Ford, Aylesbury,
Buckinghamshire HP17 8XH
Telephone: +44(0)1296 747473
colinswooddeb@aol.com
www.dinton-hermit.com

This splendid stone-built hostelry dating back to the 17th-century is a quintessential historic English country pub. It's named after John Bigg, who lost the plot after signing the death warrant of Charles I. Today, its convivial and appealing look is thanks to a sympathetic, stylish restoration – bare brick and white walls, exposed beams and beautifully restored terracotta tiles. Ceilings are cosily low and a roaring fireplace makes an excellent focal point of a chilly evening.

Each of the 13 bedrooms is individually styled, modern or traditional, and all are en suite and come with broadband internet access. There's a strong commitment to British cooking and the best-in-season local fish and meat feature on the menus and specials board, perhaps including guinea fowl with black-pudding mousse and honey jus, and chargrilled tuna with crab-and-lemon risotto. Sandwiches, salads and pasta meals feature at lunch. The wine list majors in French and Spanish classics. After dinner, there's also the option of a Cuban cigar and a brandy from the cellar collection. At the time of going to press, this establishment was for sale.

Rooms: 13. Double/twin room from £80.
Prices: Restaurant main course from £11.95. Bar main course from £6.95. House wine £14.50.
Last orders: Food: lunch 14.00 (Sunday 15.30); dinner: 21.00, (no food Sunday evening).
Closed: Rarely.
Food: Traditional British.
Real ale: Adnams, Brakspear Ales, Wadworth 6X.
Other points: Smoking area. Children over 10 welcome. Garden. Car park. Licence for civil weddings. Wheelchair access.
Directions: Exit 6/M40. Follow signs to Chinnor and then for Princes Risborough. Head straight across Longwich roundabout and take the second left, signposted to Ford. (Map 8)

...for special offers

Chalfont St Giles

The Ivy House

Country inn

London Road, Chalfont St Giles,
Buckinghamshire HP8 4RS
Telephone: +44(0)1494 872184
enquiries@theivyhouse-bucks.co.uk
www.theivyhouse-bucks.co.uk

'Beautiful arched windows frame the lovely views.'

Rooms: **5. Double room from £75, single occupancy £60.**
Prices: **Main course from £9.50. House wine £11.95.**
Last orders: Bar: afternoon 15.00; evening 23.00 (open all day at the weekend). Food: lunch 14.30; dinner 21.30 (all day at the weekend).
Closed: **Never.**
Food: **Modern British.**
Real ale: **Fuller's London Pride, Wadworth 6X, Brakspear Bitter. Three guest beers.**
Other points: **Smoking area. Children welcome. Dogs welcome in the bar. Garden and courtyard. Car park. Wheelchair access to the restaurant/pub.**
Directions: **Exit 18/M25 and 2/M40. Situated directly between Amersham and Gerrards Cross on the A413. (Map 8)**

This much-loved 17th-century brick-and-flint free house is set in the heart of the Chiltern Hills, with beautiful arched windows framing the lovely views across the Misbourne Valley. Formerly Ivy House Farm, and a pub since 1797, it oozes history and charm, from tales of a ghost to the welcoming atmosphere in the traditional wood and slate-floored bar, with its old beams, cosy armchairs and wood-burning fires. There's also a dining room, a smart patio for alfresco eating and five en-suite rooms.

Chef-proprietor Jane Mears offers a menu of modern British dishes that reveals a happiness to experiment with top-notch local ingredients to produce unusual dishes – look to the chalkboard for the day's creations. Starter choices include homemade soups and mussels with chilli, coriander and lemongrass butter. Main courses extend to wild boar with a cream-and-paprika sauce, and roast salmon with pesto, plus winter casseroles, summer salads, pasta meals and homemade puddings, perhaps bread-and-butter pudding. Retire to one of the individually furnished bedrooms and wake up to a hearty breakfast.

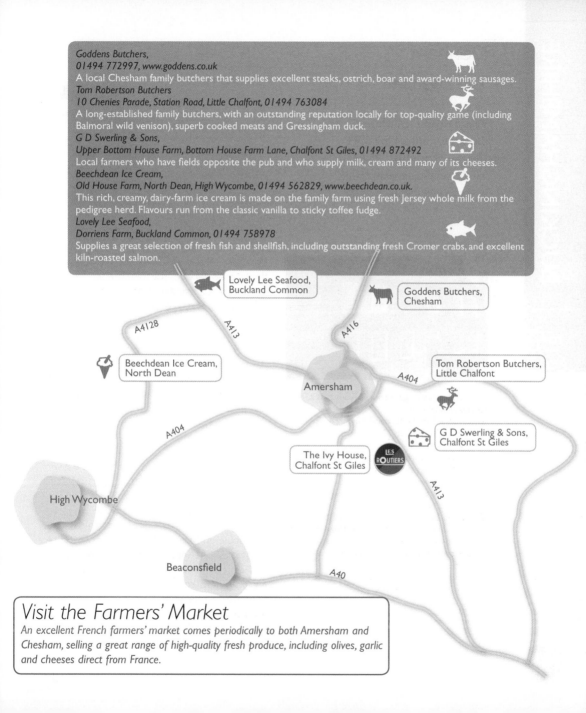

Goddens Butchers,
01494 772997, www.goddens.co.uk
A local Chesham family butchers that supplies excellent steaks, ostrich, boar and award-winning sausages.

Tom Robertson Butchers
10 Chenies Parade, Station Road, Little Chalfont, 01494 763084
A long-established family butchers, with an outstanding reputation locally for top-quality game (including Balmoral wild venison), superb cooked meats and Gressingham duck.

G D Swerling & Sons,
Upper Bottom House Farm, Bottom House Farm Lane, Chalfont St Giles, 01494 872492
Local farmers who have fields opposite the pub and who supply milk, cream and many of its cheeses.

Beechdean Ice Cream,
Old House Farm, North Dean, High Wycombe, 01494 562829, www.beechdean.co.uk.
This rich, creamy, dairy-farm ice cream is made on the family farm using fresh Jersey whole milk from the pedigree herd. Flavours run from the classic vanilla to sticky toffee fudge.

Lovely Lee Seafood,
Dorriens Farm, Buckland Common, 01494 758978
Supplies a great selection of fresh fish and shellfish, including outstanding fresh Cromer crabs, and excellent kiln-roasted salmon.

Lovely Lee Seafood,
Buckland Common

Goddens Butchers,
Chesham

A4128

A413

A416

Beechdean Ice Cream,
North Dean

Tom Robertson Butchers,
Little Chalfont

A404

Amersham

A404

G D Swerling & Sons,
Chalfont St Giles

The Ivy House,
Chalfont St Giles

LES
ROUTIERS

A413

High Wycombe

Beaconsfield

A40

Visit the Farmers' Market

An excellent French farmers' market comes periodically to both Amersham and Chesham, selling a great range of high-quality fresh produce, including olives, garlic and cheeses direct from France.

Denham

The Swan Inn

Country pub

Village Road, Denham,
Buckinghamshire UB9 5BH
Telephone: +44(0)1895 832085
info@swaninndenham.co.uk
www.swaninndenham.co.uk

'The best motorway pitstop for miles.'

Prices: **Restaurant main course from £10.25. House wine £11.50.**
Last orders: **Bar: 23.00. Food: lunch 14.30 (Sunday 15.00); dinner 22.00.**
Closed: **Rarely.**
Food: **Modern British.**
Real ale: **Courage Best Bitter, Wadworth 6X, Marlow Rebellion IPA.**
Other points: **Smoking area. Children welcome. Dogs welcome in the bar. Garden. Car park.**
Directions: **Exit 1/M40 and exit 17/M25. From the M40 take the A412 Uxbridge to Rickmansworth Road. After 200 yards, turn left for Denham. (Map 8)**

Weary M25 and M40 travellers should shun the faceless services for this creeper-clad pub in upmarket Denham. With fine houses and brick-and-timber cottages for neighbours, and a magnificent rear terrace and garden, the Swan must be the best motorway pitstop for miles. Like its stylish siblings (The Alford Arms, Frithsden; The Royal Oak, Marlow; Old Queens Head, Penn – see entries), the Swan's single bar and informal dining area has been refurbished with style, with a rug-strewn floor, sturdy tables, cushioned settles and a splendid log fire.

A chalkboard menu and printed carte deliver modern pub food at its best. 'Small plates' range from rustic breads with roast garlic, balsamic and olive oil for an appetiser, to starters/light meals such as oak-smoked bacon on bubble-and-squeak with hollandaise. More substantial offerings include roast salt cod on chorizo, bean and herb broth and confit duck leg on potato rösti with beetroot and apple compote. Puddings include spiced pear-and-frangipane tart. Top-notch wines include 18 by the glass.

Marlow

The Royal Oak

Country pub

'Menus promise food that reveals a lot of imagination at work in the kitchen.'

Frieth Road, Bovingdon Green, Marlow,
Buckinghamshire SL7 2JF
Telephone: +44(0)1628 488611
info@royaloakmarlow.co.uk
www.royaloakmarlow.co.uk

A lovely cream-painted cottage tucked away in a tiny hamlet on the edge of Marlow Common, a mile north of Marlow. Beyond the front gravel terrace, edged with rosemary and with bay trees in pots either side of the door, you will find a stylish refurbished interior. There's a cosy snug (open fire, rug-strewn boards, an array of scrubbed oak tables), while piped jazz, and a buzzy atmosphere characterise the beamed bar and dining areas. Informality is the key here – eat anywhere, with the choice extending to the landscaped garden in summer.

Both chalkboards and printed menus promise food that reveals a lot of imagination at work in the kitchen. 'Small plates' take in smoked haddock fishcake with blackened lime mayonnaise, while mains range from slow-roast belly pork with red cabbage and port-wine sauce to wild mushroom, courgette and parmesan risotto. Try the rustic breads with roast garlic and olive oil; there are excellent lunchtime sandwiches and good puddings. Sister pub-restaurant to The Alford Arms, Frithsden; The Swan at Denham; and the Old Queens Head, Penn (see entries).

Prices: **Restaurant main course from £10.25. House wine £11.50.**
Last orders: **Bar: 23.00. Food: lunch 14.30 (Sunday 16.00); dinner 22.00.**
Closed: **Rarely.**
Food: **Modern British.**
Real ale: **Fuller's London Pride, Brakspear Ales, Marlow Rebellion.**
Other points: **Smoking area. Children welcome. Dogs welcome in the bar. Garden. Car park. Wheelchair access.**
Directions: **Exit 9/M4 and 4/M40. In Marlow, take the A4155 towards Henley-on-Thames, and after 300 yards, turn right towards Bovingdon Green. (Map 8)**
See pub walk on page 452

...for the latest news

Mentmore

The Stag

The Green, Mentmore,
Buckinghamshire LU7 0QF
Telephone: +44(0)1296 668423
reservations@thestagmentmore.com
www.thestagmentmore.com

Country pub

'A passion for food, fresh local produce and unrushed dining draws folk from far and wide.'

Prices: **Restaurant set lunch £15 and dinner £30. Main course from £18. Bar lunch from £5.50 and dinner from £8.50.**
Last orders: **Food: lunch 14.00; dinner 21.00; Sunday 20.30.**
Closed: **Rarely.**
Food: **Modern British.**
Real ale: **Charles Wells Bombardier, Charles Wells Eagle. Occasional guest beers.**
Other points: **Smoking area. Children welcome. Dogs welcome in the bar. Sloping garden with seating. Limited car park. Wheelchair access (not WC).**
Directions: **Five miles north-east of Aylesbury off the A418 towards Leighton Buzzard.**
(Map 8)

Built in 1840 to serve the local estate workers, the Stag stands in a picture-postcard village with a lovely garden, overlooking Mentmore House, and is run by Mike and Jenny Tuckwood, whose fresh modern approach to running a traditional country pub has proved a great success. Mike's passion for food, fresh local produce and unrushed dining draws folk from far and wide. The classic bar is the place to sample Charles Wells ales and some good bar food: sandwiches – chicken and herb mayonnaise, for example – and one-dish meals of fishcakes with fries and tartare sauce, or spaghetti with fresh pesto.

Imaginative, seasonally changing evening menus are served in the stylish, two-tiered restaurant, which has direct access to the garden. A plate of tempura of zucchini on a spicy tomato sauce makes an unusual starter. Thoughtful attention to inherent flavours produces main courses such as crab ravioli with saffron broth, wilted spinach and sautéed tiger prawns, or braised lamb wrapped in Parma ham with pepper ragout and minted jus. An alternative to dessert is a plate of British cheeses.

Penn

The Old Queens Head

Country pub

'A glorious summer garden and terrace complete the inviting picture.'

Hammersley Lane, Penn,
Buckinghamshire HP10 8EY
Telephone: +44(0)1494 813371
info@oldqueensheadpenn.co.uk
www.oldqueensheadpenn.co.uk

David and Becky Salisbury's mini pub empire expanded to four in early 2006 with the inspired acquisition of this historic pub set by the green in the affluent village of Penn. Dating from 1666, it exudes charm and character, the old beams and timbers in the rambling bar and dining areas blending perfectly with the stylish interior décor – rug-strewn flagstones, warm, colour-washed walls, polished boards, classic fabrics, and lovely old oak furnishings sourced from local auctions.

Food follows the hugely successful formula found at The Alford Arms, The Swan and The Royal Oak (see entries), the innovative seasonal menu and chalkboard specials mixing pub classics with modern British flair. Choices range from 'small plates' of rustic breads and roast garlic and smoked haddock and salmon fishcake with sorrel hollandaise, to main dishes such as crispy roast belly pork on chive mash with Puy lentil and Madeira jus, and pan-fried sea bass with saffron potatoes and red-pepper confit. Great puddings, 17 wines by the glass and a glorious summer garden and terrace complete the inviting picture.

Prices: Restaurant and bar main course from £10.50. House wine £11.50.
Last orders: Bar: 23.00. Food: lunch 14.30 (Sunday 16.00); dinner 22.00.
Closed: Rarely.
Food: Modern British.
Real ale: Greene King IPA, Morland Original Ale.
Other points: Smoking area. Children welcome. Dogs welcome in the bar. Garden. Car park.
Directions: Exit 2,3,4/M40. From Beaconsfield Old Town, take B474 Penn Road. Carry on towards Penn. After three miles, turn left into School Road and left again into Hammersley Lane. The pub is on the corner opposite the church. (Map 8)

...for recipe ideas

MEMBER
18
ENTRY

Waddesdon

Five Arrows Hotel

Restaurant-with-rooms

High Street, Waddesdon, Aylesbury,
Buckinghamshire HP18 0JE
Telephone: +44(0)1296 651727
bookings@thefivearrows
hotel.fsnet.co.uk
www.waddesdon.org.uk

'An exceptional wine list and regular wine tastings.'

Rooms: 11. Double room from £75, single from £65.
Prices: Main course from £13.50. House wine £12.50.
Last orders: Bar: afternoon 15.00; evening 23.00. Food: lunch 14.30; dinner 21.00 (Sunday 19.00). All day high season.
Closed: Rarely.
Food: Modern British/European.
Real ale: Fuller's London Pride.
Other points: No smoking. Children welcome. Garden. Car park. Wheelchair access to the restaurant/pub.
Directions: Six miles north west of Aylesbury beside the A41 in Waddesdon. (Map 8)

Named after the Rothschild family coat of arms – the five arrows representing the five sons of Mayer Amschel Rothschild – this imposing Victorian building was built by the family in 1887 to house the architects and craftsmen who were building Waddesdon Manor. The Five Arrows is set in the village with the vast estate behind. Now a stylish small hotel-cum-inn, you enter straight into the bar, from which open several civilised dining rooms with antique tables, and pictures from Lord Rothschild's collection.

Locally sourced ingredients and homegrown herbs influence the menu. A typical starter of fricassée of lamb's kidneys and black pudding could be followed by fillet of Kirtlington beef with morel-cream sauce, homemade chips and watercress. To finish, choose between the cheese table or Black Forest mousse of dark chocolate and cherry compote. There are also chalkboard specials and lighter lunchtime meals. The exceptional wine list majors on the various Rothschild wine interests, with eight by the glass, and there are regular wine tastings. Eleven good-sized bedrooms boast all the modern comforts.

Truc Vert

Restaurant

'Top-quality dining in a relaxed and modern setting.'

21 High Street, Harston,
Cambridgeshire CB2 5PX
Telephone: +44(0)1223 873107
harston@trucvert.co.uk
www.trucvert.co.uk

The sister restaurant to London's eponymous café, deli and restaurant in the heart of Mayfair stands hard beside the A10, yet surrounded by green fields and gardens. Unlike its city sibling, it operates solely as a restaurant, offering top-quality dining in a relaxed and modern setting. It has proved a hit with the affluent local clientele since opening in April 2006. Inside, various hues of brown dominate the light and airy and tastefully minimalist décor. Expect chunky wooden tables set with smart crockery and glasses, subtle spotlighting and piped jazz.

Light lunch and fixed-price menus list an eclectic choice of modern European dishes. Cooking is skilled yet unpretentious in style, with the emphasis soundly on the best ingredients. Try Truc Vert's renowned charcuterie, cheese or pâté selections, or opt for a full-flavoured dish of roast corn-fed chicken with wilted spinach and a bacon-and-mushroom sauce. Alternatives include roast butternut-squash soup with truffle oil and roast duck with sautéed cabbage, chorizo and harissa dressing. A welcome addition to the Cambridge restaurant scene.

Prices: **Set lunch £15. Restaurant main course from £9.95. House wine £15.**
Last orders: **Food: lunch 15.00, dinner 22.00. Open all day for light snacks and coffee.**
Closed: **Rarely.**
Food: **Modern European.**
Other points: **No smoking. Children welcome. Car park.**
Directions: **Exit 11/M11. On the A10, follow signs for Royston. Truc Vert is located on the High Street in Harston. (Map 6)**

...for events

20
MEMBER ENTRY

Keyston

Pheasant Inn

Country pub

Keyston, Huntingdon,
Cambridgeshire PE18 0RE
Telephone: +44(0)1832 710241
pheasant.keyston@btopenworld.com

'Alfresco tables and chairs out front make you a temporary part of this picture-postcard scene.'

Prices: **Set lunch £14.95. House wine £12.50.**
Last orders: **Food: lunch 14.00; dinner 21.30 (Sunday 22.00).**
Closed: **Rarely.**
Food: **Modern British.**
Real ale: **Adnams. Two guest beers.**
Other points: **No smoking. Children welcome. Garden. Car park.**
Directions: **The village is signed off the A14, 12 miles west of Huntingdon. (Map 8)**

At the heart of sleepy Keyston, beneath a huge sycamore tree, sits the Pheasant, housed in a row of classic 16th-century English cottages, with dark thatch and a mass of floral planters adorning the façade. Alfresco tables and chairs out front make you a temporary part of this picture-postcard scene. Within, it is quintessentially 'olde England': leather upholstery, a mass of blackened beams, brick inglenooks, flagstone floor and stripped boards.

Jay Scrimshaw's cooking, however, is bang up-to-date. Whether you eat in the informal lounge or in the more formal dining room, the menu is the same, with no restrictions as to how much you eat. Sorrel-and-mascarpone soup, confit pork belly with parsnip purée and orange sauce, roast leg of lamb with mixed-bean cassoulet, and rice pudding with rhubarb purée is modern food cooked with skill and assurance, and based on prime raw materials, including Denham Estate venison, fruit from the village and herbs from the pub garden. The delights of the wine list are a joy to behold, with 18 of the 100 well-chosen wines available by the glass.

Madingley

Three Horseshoes

Country pub

'Stylish country chic and a lively, cosmopolitan atmosphere.'

High Street, Madingley, Cambridge,
Cambridgeshire CB3 8AB
Telephone: +44(0)1954 210221

The quintessential rural look of this very picturesque, thatched inn gives way to stylish country chic and a lively, cosmopolitan atmosphere as you step inside the early 1900s building. The Victorian orangery look does justice to the original architecture, mixing a light Mediterranean feel with period elegance through pastel-coloured, waxed wood and stripped boards. Moving through to the conservatory restaurant, although similar in design and with an identical menu to the bar area, white linen, wicker chairs and indoor plants create a relaxed mood.

Richard Stokes's confident Italian-style cooking is a sound interpretation of the Huntsbridge Group's policy of seasonal food on monthly changing menus and using prime raw materials. Thus, a typical meal could bring olive-braised salmon with peas, broad beans, baby spinach, mint and aïoli, chargrilled beef fillet with sweetbreads and truffle oil, followed by vanilla panna cotta with raspberries and grappa. As with all Huntsbridge places, there's a superb choice of wines, offering the great and godly, as well as the unusual, and 18 by the glass.

Prices: **Bar main course from £9.50. House wine £12.10.**
Last orders: **lunch 14.00 (Sunday 14.30); dinner 21.30.**
Closed: **Rarely.**
Food: **Italian.**
Real ale: **Adnams Southwold. One guest beer.**
Other points: **Smoking area. Children welcome. Garden. Car park.**
Directions: **Two miles west of Cambridge. From London, leave the M11 at the A1303 exit. From the north, take the A14 then the A1307. (Map 6)**

...for competitions

Chester

Aquavit

58 Watergate Street, Chester,
Cheshire CH1 2LA
Telephone: +44(0)1244 313721
www.aquavit.co.uk

City-centre restaurant

'A smorgasbord of good food and good service.'

Prices: **Set lunch £6.95 and dinner £18 (two courses £15). À la carte menu price from £15.25. House wine £10.95.**
Last orders: **Food: lunch 14.45; dinner 22.30.**
Closed: **Sunday.**
Food: **Swedish and French.**
Other points: **Smoking area. Children welcome.**
Directions: **Exit 12/M53. In the centre of Chester. (Map 9)**

Graham and Birgitta Burling offer a smorgasbord of good food and good service at their restaurant in one of Chester's ancient streets. The interiors are an oasis of calm – a mix of Scandinavian cool with a British emphasis on proper settings and fine glassware. The predominantly modern British menus have many pleasing Swedish accents, as Graham spent many years cooking in Sweden. He combines a Nordic simplicity with fabulous flavours and racy presentation through his set lunch, evening and carte menus.

As well as a fine lobster bisque, you will find dishes such as a starter of herring three ways (dill, sweet cure, and tomato and madeira) served with egg, new potatoes, chopped dill and sour cream. The accompanying aromatic liqueur Akvavit is de rigueur. Main courses might be a wonderful skewer of large prawns and monkfish and a single vast king scallop, all perfectly cooked and presented, braised oxtail or rib-eye, or pumpkin-and-fennel risotto, such is the wide choice of cooking on offer.

Tarporley

The Fox and Barrel

Country pub

Forest Road, Cotebrook, Tarporley,
Cheshire CW6 9DZ
Telephone: +44(0)1829 760529
info@thefoxandbarrel.com
www.thefoxandbarrel.com

'There's a secluded summer patio for alfresco eating, and live New Orleans jazz every Monday.'

Prices: Set Sunday lunch £14.50. Main course from £8.25. Bar snacks from £4.25. House wine £9.95.
Last orders: Bar: afternoon 15.00; evening 23.00 (Saturday and Sunday all day). Food: lunch 14.30; dinner 21.30 (Sunday 12.00 to 20.00).
Closed: Rarely.
Food: Modern pub food with Mediterranean influences.
Real ale: Jennings Cumberland Ale, Marston's Pedigree, John Smith's Cask. One guest beer.
Other points: Smoking area. Garden. Car park. Wheelchair access.
Directions: On the main A49, close to Oulton Park race circuit, on the Warrington side of Tarporley. (Map 9)

A genuine Cheshire welcome awaits visitors to this thriving food pub. Named The Fox and Barrel after a former landlord let a pursued fox escape to the cellar, it is worth seeking out this friendly pub for its interesting seasonal menus and a tip-top pint of Bass. Beyond the snug bar, with its huge log fire, china ornaments and jugs, the half-panelled dining area sports a rug-strewn wood floor and rustic farmhouse tables topped with church candles.

Interesting menus list bar meals such as homemade beef burgers with chunky chips, ploughman's with local cheese, or smoked salmon and mushroom pasta. More inventive restaurant meals take in a salad of fresh honeyed figs and Parma ham, Barbary duck breast with a sauce of apple, honey-grain mustard and cream, and homemade steak, ale and mushroom pie. Puddings include apple-and-rhubarb crumble or white-chocolate and strawberry terrine. There's a good choice of wines, with 15 by the glass, malt whiskies, a secluded summer patio for alfresco eating, and live New Orleans jazz every Monday.

Wine bar and brasserie

Mitchell's Wine Bar & Brasserie

'The fresh fish choice changes daily and is cooked with imagination.'

Lyndale House, High Street, Tattenhall,
Cheshire CH3 9PX
Telephone: +44(0)1829 771477
info@mitchellswinebar.co.uk
www.mitchellswinebar.co.uk

Set in the delightful village of Tattenhall in an early 19th-century building, this friendly, family-run wine bar and brasserie has become a firm favourite since proprietors Martin and Peterene Cocking and their staff moved en masse from The Fox and Barrel at nearby Tarporley. With attractive gardens to the front and hardwood floors, comfortable furniture and large windows inside, it all makes for a pleasurable experience.

Chef Kevin Morris's consistently good food is internationally influenced and the brasserie-style menu starts with his freshly baked breads, which come with butter and olives. Starters include warm black pudding and smoked-chicken salad, or toasted goat's cheese on olive ciabatta, and they could be followed by roast breast of Gressingham duck with sweet-chilli noodles and beansprouts, or gilt-head bream with prawns in garlic butter. Steaks come plain or with a classic sauce, and the fresh fish choice changes daily and is cooked with imagination. Mitchells' wine includes interesting choices among its mainstream collection, and they are all favourably priced.

Prices: Set lunch £15 and dinner £14.50.
Restaurant main course from £9.75. Bar main course from £4.50.
Last orders: Bar: afternoon 15.00; evening: 23.00.
Food: lunch 14.15 (Sunday 15.00); dinner: 21.00 (Friday and Saturday 21.30).
Closed: Monday.
Food: Global.
Real ale: One guest beer.
Other points: No smoking. Garden. Car park. Wheelchair access.
Directions: M53 Chester exit. Just off the A41, seven miles outside Chester on Tattenhall high street. (Map 9)

...for special offers

MEMBER
ENTRY
25

Warmingham

The Bear's Paw Hotel

Country inn

School Lane, Warmingham, Sandbach,
Cheshire CW11 3QN
Telephone: +44(0)1270 526317
enquiries@thebearspaw.co.uk
www.thebearspaw.co.uk

'Real-ale fans will be delighted to learn that there are micro-brewery guest ales on handpump.'

Rooms: 12. Double room from £70, single from £60, family from £80.
Prices: Restaurant main course from £11.95. Bar main course from £7.95. House wine £9.95.
Last orders: Bar: 01.00 (weekends). Food: dinner 21.00 (21.30 weekends).
Closed: From Monday to Friday daytime.
Food: Modern British.
Real ale: Tetley's Bitter. Two guest beers.
Other points: Smoking area. Children welcome. Garden. Car park. Wheelchair access to the restaurant/pub.
Directions: Exit 16, 17 or 18/M6, near Sandbach. (Map 9)

This late-Victorian brick-built hotel beside the River Weaver overlooks willow-dappled water meadows and Warmingham's pretty parish church. If you put a premium on spacious bedrooms and bathrooms, then you've come to the right place as there are twelve large en-suite bedrooms. Overall, the public-room décor leans towards the traditional, but this is part of its down-to-earth charm. The open-plan lounge surrounds a spacious central bar and there are log fires and plenty of traditional-style wood panelling and seating to make it feel cosy.

The bar menu offers light bites such as club sandwiches or a good-value, weekly changing set-lunch menu. Real-ale fans will be delighted to learn that there are micro-brewery guest ales on handpump, perhaps Slater's Premium or Khean's Fine Leg Bitter. In the restaurant, the carte menu offers a range of traditional fare and steaks as well as the more unusual. Start with chicken liver and wild-mushroom pâté before moving on to rack of lamb with honey-and-thyme sauce or duck breast with red-berry sauce. The short wine list travels far in terms of grapes and varieties.

www.routiers.co.uk

The Rose and Crown at Romaldkirk

Country inn

'A class act and the perfect Teesdale retreat.'

Romaldkirk, Barnard Castle,
Co Durham DL12 9EB
Telephone: +44(0)1833 650213
hotel@rose-and-crown.co.uk
www.rose-and-crown.co.uk

CO DURHAM

Over their 17-year tenancy at this exemplary, 18th-century coaching inn, Christopher and Alison Davy's tireless enthusiasm and dedication to providing high standards of hospitality, service and cooking has created one of the finest all-round inns in the country. It stands beside the Saxon church and one of the beautifully maintained greens in this most picturesque of Teesdale villages. Much of this success can be attributed to consistent cooking that is inspired by the seasons and backed by first-class local produce.

Lunchtime filled baps are well presented and traditional favourites, such as steak, kidney and mushroom pie, are always cooked with flair. Weekly changing menus may also list pigeon with onion confit and juniper sauce, chargrilled beef fillet with frites and parsley butter, sticky walnut tart, and perfectly selected local cheeses. Four-course dinners are served in the civilised, part-panelled restaurant. The spotlessly maintained en-suite bedrooms have wooden floorboards, beams, well-chosen antique furniture, stylish contemporary fabrics, and a host of extras. A class act and the perfect Teesdale retreat.

Rooms: 12. Double/twin room from £126.
Prices: Set lunch £17.25 and dinner £28. Bar main course from £7.95. House wine £13.95.
Last orders: Bar: afternoon 15.00; evening 23.00. Food: lunch 13.30; dinner 21.30 (Sunday 21.00).
Closed: Rarely.
Food: Modern British.
Real ale: Black Sheep Best, Theakston Best.
Other points: Smoking area. Children welcome. Car park.
Directions: Six miles north west of Barnard Castle on the B6277 towards Middleton-in-Teesdale. (Map 12)

See pub walk on page 454

...for the latest news

Indian Queens

Port & Starboard

Chapel Road, Indian Queens,
Cornwall TR9 6JZ
Telephone: +44(0)1726 860270
port.starboard@virgin.net
www.portandstarboard-cornwall.co.uk

Restaurant/takeaway

'A sublime fish-and-chips medley, namely cod, haddock, hake, skate and plaice with all the trimmings.'

Prices: **Restaurant main course from £4.50. House wine £9.50.**
Last orders: **Food: lunch 14.00 (closed Sunday lunch); dinner 21.00 (Sunday 20.00).**
Closed: **Rarely.**
Food: **Traditional British.**
Other points: **No smoking. Children welcome. Dogs welcome. Garden. Car park. Wheelchair access.**
Directions: **Follow the brown tourist-information signs from the A39 and A30. (Map 3)**

If the cuisine of Cornwall conjures up fish (and the ubiquitous chips), then there's no finer place to enjoy this catch than at this restaurant/takeaway. Winner of the Seafood Authority's Best Fish and Chip Shop for 2005/2006, it certainly shows off the local fish and potatoes to their optimum. The light and airy conservatory makes for a bright and cheerful setting, and the staff are equally upbeat and efficient.

If you don't opt for the sublime fish-and-chips medley, namely cod, haddock, hake, skate and plaice with all the trimmings, there are hearty pie, meat and burger meals among the extensive selection. Bargain hunters will appreciate the Captain's set menu, which comes with a main, sides and beverage, all for under £6. Naturally, the fish is from local ports and the potatoes and steaks are Cornish. Stronger stuff, such as Cornish wine and beers, both highly rated, are excellent accompaniments. The new owners have upgraded the facilities and extended, but lost none of the charm or friendliness of this 50-year-old establishment. You can dine alfresco and order to take away.

Liskeard

Webbs Inn & Restaurant

Town-centre pub

'A great ambience, which is complemented by the fabulous food.'

Pike Street, Liskeard,
Cornwall PL14 3HW
Telephone: +44(0)1579 343839
info@webbsinn.co.uk
www.webbsinn.co.uk

Another establishment from the expanding stable of John Stevens and his Wykeham Group, Webbs Inn follows in a similar vein from The Dartmoor Union in Holbeton and The Rose & Crown at Yealmpton (see entries), with rich-coloured walls, themed wall art, squashy sofas and dark leather chairs for diners. Away from the 30ft bar and eclectic tables for informal dining, the basement restaurant is open plan, with a suitably subterranean feel perpetuated by the rich, dark red colour of the walls and the subdued lighting.

It all adds up to a great ambience, which is complemented by the fabulous food from Graham Ledwith and his team. The menu changes daily and offers a good cross-section of seafood, meat and vegetarian dishes. Try the pan-seared scallops with crispy pancetta and champagne butter, or braised pork belly with apple-and-celeriac mash and Bordelaise sauce. Finish with one of the many delicious desserts: caramelised-apple tarte Tatin or homemade vanilla pancakes with chocolate sauce. The short, well-balanced global list of wines offers great value for money.

Prices: **Set lunch £12.95. Restaurant main course from £9.95. Bar main course from £4.25. House wine £9.95.**
Last orders: Bar: afternoon 15.00; evening 24.00. Food: lunch 14.00; dinner: 21.30.
Closed: Sunday.
Food: **Modern European.**
Real ale: St Austell Tribute.
Other points: No smoking. Wheelchair access.
Directions: A38. Exit A390 towards Liskeard town centre. Once in town, the large Webbs building can be seen on your left. Turn left into Pike Street. Public car park nearby. (Map 3)

...for recipe ideas

MEMBER
29
ENTRY

The Lizard

Cadgwith Cove Inn

Village Inn

Cadgwith, Ruan Minor, Helston,
Cornwall TR12 7JX
Telephone: +44(0)1326 290513
enquiries@cadgwithcoveinn.com
www.cadgwithcoveinn.com

'Fish fanciers should look no further than the chalkboard, which lists the daily catch.'

Rooms: 6, 3 en-suite. Rooms from £27.50 per person.
Prices: Set lunch from £10 and dinner from £13. Restaurant main course from £5.95. House wine £8.95.
Last orders: Bar: afternoon 15.00 (Thursday 17.00); evening 23.00 (all day weekends).
Food: lunch 15.00; dinner 21.30.
Closed: Check for seasonal variations.
Food: Seafood and traditional European.
Real ale: Guest beers change weekly.
Other points: Smoking area. Dogs welcome in the bar and overnight. Garden and patio.
Directions: The village is signposted off the A3083, nine miles south of Helston. (Map 3)

A fishing hamlet of thatched cottages on the rugged Lizard coastline is the appealing setting for this 300-year-old pub, formerly the haunt of smugglers and now popular with coastal-path walkers and local fishermen. In front of the whitewashed building, a sunny patio affords drinkers views across the old pilchard cellar to the peaceful cove. Down the lane are the shingle beach and the colourful fishing vessels that provide the inn with freshly caught fish and the best crab and lobster on the peninsula. Furnished simply and decked with seafaring mementoes, the two bars, both with open fires, serve five real ales, notably a cracking pint of Sharp's Doom Bar Bitter.

Expect traditional homemade pub food, but note the delicious white crab-meat sandwiches or the crab soup served with chunks of crusty bread. Fish fanciers should look no further than the chalkboard, which lists the daily catch, or plump for the beer-battered haddock. Alternatives include a real Cornish cheese lunch – perfect with a pint after a coastal walk. Bedrooms are homely and simply equipped; two are en-suite.

www.routiers.co.uk

Trewithen Restaurant

Restaurant

'A popular dining venue with a loyal clientele.'

3 Fore Street, Lostwithiel,
Cornwall PL22 0BP
Telephone: +44(0)1208 872373

This long-established restaurant, a popular dining venue with a loyal clientele, changed hands as we went to press in July 2006. New owners Paul and Claire Murray plan to run the place along similar lines, so expect the emphasis to be on homemade, from breads to the after-dinner chocolates, and West Country specialities. Locally reared meats, such as venison from the moors, pork from Tywardreath and lamb from Ladock, are perennial favourites.

The daily fish catch is used creatively in the Trewithen platter starter of prawns in sweet-and-sour sauce, melon, homemade pâté and Cornish smoked fish, or fresh South Coast scallops in a Pernod-and-cream sauce. Other notables include pears with St Endellion brie, trout terrine, lamb with minted yogurt and red-wine jus, and local venison served in a juniper sauce with smoked bacon and mushrooms. Puddings include chocolate-truffle terrine and bananas in butterscotch sauce. The restaurant's original walls date from the 16th-century when it was part of the Duchy Palace complex.

Prices: **Set dinner £26. Main course from £15. House wine £11.85.**
Last orders: **Food: dinner 21.30.**
Closed: **Sunday and Monday except for bank holiday weekends and Mondays during the summer.**
Food: **Modern British with international influences.**
Other points: **Smoking area. Children welcome. Garden/patio. Wheelchair access.**
Directions: **M5. Lostwithiel is on the A390, halfway between Liskeard and St Austell, five miles south of Bodmin (A30) and five miles east of the Eden Project. (Map 3)**

...for events

Newquay

Degembris Farmhouse

Bed and breakfast

St Newlyn East, Newquay,
Cornwall TR8 5HY
Telephone: +44(0)1872 510555
kathy@degembris.co.uk
www.degembris.co.uk

'A tranquil holiday haven a world away from the busy A30.'

Rooms: **5, 3 with private bathroom. Double/ twin room from £30, single from £28. Prices are per person.**
Closed: **Rarely.**
Food: **British.**
Other points: **No smoking. Garden. Children welcome. Car park.**
Directions: **A30. Exit at Summercourt and, in the village, turn right towards Newquay on the A3058. Take the third left turn and then the second lane left to Degembris. (Map 3)**

Roger and Kathy Woodley's slate-hung farmhouse dates from the 16th century and stands in 165 acres of rolling countryside close to Cornwall's rugged north coast. The Woodleys, whose family have resided at Degembris for over 100 years, offer a tranquil holiday haven a world away from the busy A30 and nearby Newquay's bustling beaches. Expect a warm welcome and tea on arrival, best enjoyed in summer in the flower-filled cottage garden with its serene country views.

Comfortable, pine-furnished bedrooms share the view, and all are prettily decorated and well equipped with TV, hairdryer and beverage-making facilities. Two share a spacious bathroom. There's a homely sitting room with plush sofas, books, magazines and games, and a cottagey, low-ceilinged dining area where Kathy serves her memorable breakfasts. Opt for her hearty full English and you will tuck into free-range eggs, quality sausages and bacon sourced from the local butcher. Work it off with a saunter around the waymarked farm trail or walk to historic Trerice Manor, a National Trust property.

Port Gaverne Hotel

Seaside inn

'You can eat on a balcony looking out to sea, or in the terraced garden.'

Port Gaverne, Port Isaac,
Cornwall PL29 3SQ
Telephone: +44(0)1208 880244
Freephone 0500 657867
www.portgavernehotel.co.uk

Graham and Annabelle Sylvester's charming 17th-century inn is peacefully situated in a sheltered cove just 50 yards from the beach. The ship-shape and characterful, pubby bar has a polished slate floor, a big log fire, low beams, Sharp's ales on tap, and first-rate traditional bar food in the form of ploughman's lunches and seafood pie. A tiny snug bar, the Captain's Cabin, has a genuine ship's table, and an equally pleasant restaurant enjoys a wonderful lack of formality. You can also eat on a balcony looking out to sea, or in the terraced garden.

Noted for very fresh fish and a commitment to local produce, the Port Gaverne succeeds admirably in balancing good food and hospitality to all comers, with a wholly acceptable degree of Cornish idiosyncracy. Dinner could be smoked salmon and avocado pâté, roast turbot with tomato and orange coulis or sirloin steak with brandy, cream and mushroom sauce, and a selection of regional cheeses. Upgraded bedrooms have a fresh, comfortable look and gleaming modern bathrooms. There are wonderful coastal-path walks and magical summer sunsets.

Rooms: 15. Double/twin room from £80, single from £50, family from £80.
Prices: Set dinner £27. Sunday lunch £10.95. Bar main course from £4.95. House wine £11.95.
Last orders: Bar: 23.00. Food: lunch 14.30; dinner 21.30.
Closed: 24-28 December.
Food: Traditional/modern British.
Real ale: Bass, Sharp's Doom Bar Bitter.
Other points: Smoking area. Children welcome. Dogs welcome in the bar and overnight. Garden. Car park.
Directions: Signposted from the A30 north of Camelford and the A389 from Wadebridge via the B3314. Follow the signs to Port Isaac. (Map 3)

...for competitions

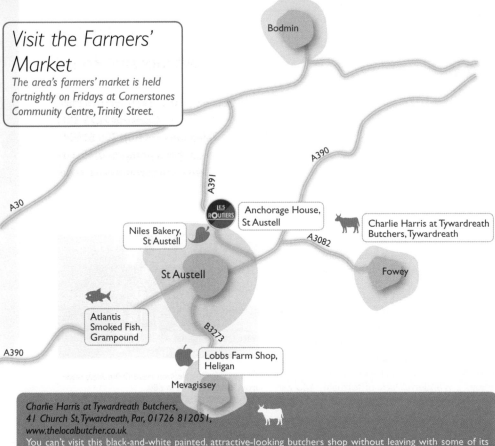

Visit the Farmers' Market

The area's farmers' market is held fortnightly on Fridays at Cornerstones Community Centre, Trinity Street.

Bodmin

A391

A390

A30

Anchorage House, St Austell

Niles Bakery, St Austell

Charlie Harris at Tywardreath Butchers, Tywardreath

A3082

St Austell

Fowey

Atlantis Smoked Fish, Grampound

A390

B3273

Lobbs Farm Shop, Heligan

Mevagissey

Charlie Harris at Tywardreath Butchers,
41 Church St, Tywardreath, Par, 01726 812051,
www.thelocalbutcher.co.uk
You can't visit this black-and-white painted, attractive-looking butchers shop without leaving with some of its famous sausages. Anchorage House features its Greenback bacon, sausages, special black puddings, fillet steaks and tender duck breasts on its menu.

Atlantis Smoked Fish,
Fore Street, Grampound, 01726 883201,
www.atlantisfoods.co.uk
Try its smoked trout, kippers, haddock, eels, roe, duck, chicken, ham and sausages – the tremendous flavour comes from smoking over hardwood, mostly oak.

Lobbs Farm Shop, The Lost Gardens of Heligan,
Heligan, St Austell, 01726 844411,
www.lobbsfarmshop.com
Not only can you buy the freshest local organic produce, including fresh fruits and vegetables, this shop also has a well-stocked butchers counter and delicatessen and grocery lines.

Niles Bakery,
Morven Road, St Austell, Cornwall, 01726 72798
Long-established family-run baker specialising in homemade pasties, saffron cake and excellent breads – tomato bread and cheese-and-onion being favourites of Jane's at the Anchorage.

St Austell

Anchorage House

Bed and breakfast

'The interior has been decorated with verve and passion, and with comfort in mind.'

Nettles Corner, Boscundle, Tregrehan Mills, St Austell, Cornwall PL25 3RH
Telephone: +44(0)1726 814071
stay@anchoragehouse.co.uk
www.anchoragehouse.co.uk

Jane and Steve Epperson's Georgian-style lodge offers home-from-home comforts, with the bonus of having a 15-metre-long pool in its landscaped gardens. The interior has been decorated with verve and passion, and with comfort in mind. The spacious lounge, with its open fire and antique furnishings, is perfect for relaxing: dip into the abundant reading matter or settle in with a pre-dinner complimentary sherry. This room leads off to the informal, plant-filled conservatory, where breakfast and dinner are served around one large mahogany table.

Breakfast is a feast of yogurts, berries, fruits, cereals and the full traditional British, newspapers included. Four-course dinners are served by prior arrangement. Jane and Steve are welcoming, and refreshingly laid-back hosts, and they have improved the property to deluxe standards. Each of the bedrooms is individually styled. The two-storey loft suite comes with luxury touches: chocs, biscuits, flowers, a turn-down service, king-size and super-king-size beds. Magnificent bathrooms have large baths and power showers. There's also a Jacuzzi and a gym.

Rooms: 3. Double room from £50 per person, single from £80.
Prices: Four-course dinner by prior arrangement from £35. Main course from £22. Unlicenced.
Last orders: Food: 19.30.
Closed: December-February.
Other points: No smoking. Garden. Car park. Spa treatments, gym and indoor heated swimming pool.
Directions: A30/A391. Two miles east of St Austell on the A390; take the turning for Tregrehan across from the St Austell Garden Centre, then immediately turn left into the driveway leading into the courtyard of the lodge. (Map 3)

St Austell

Auberge Asterisk

Restaurant-with-rooms

Mount Pleasant, Roche, St Austell,
Cornwall PL26 8LH
Telephone: +44(0)1726 890863
ferzan@L-auberge.freeserve.co.uk
www.auberge-asterisk.co.uk

'The cosy atmosphere and the simple, rustic furniture make this a laid-back place to dine.'

Rooms: **3. Double room from £54.50, single from £35.75.**
Prices: **Main course from £13.75. House wine £12.**
Last orders: **Food: dinner 21.00 (Wednesday-Saturday for non-residents).**
Closed: **Rarely.**
Food: **Modern European.**
Other points: **No smoking. Garden. Car park. Wheelchair access to the restaurant/pub.**
Directions: **On the A30. 2 miles west after Innisdown roundabout (Bodmin bypass). About five miles from the Eden Project. (Map 3)**

In an area that has become increasingly short of bed space since the success of the Eden Project, this warm and friendly restaurant-with-rooms offers very good value. Ferzan Zola's French-style auberge is a cream-coloured, squarely solid old house that wouldn't look out of place in rural France. It's a simple restaurant-with-rooms run with dedicated enthusiasm by Ferzan. The cosy atmosphere and the simple, rustic furniture make this a particularly laid-back place to dine.

Fresh produce delivered daily is used superbly in his eclectic menu, which delights with classics and interpretations of modern dishes. A starting point could be a seafood terrine of the day or filo and feta 'made to Mama's recipe'. Follow with a fillet of local beef cooked with ginger, black beans and veal stock or Dover sole braised with shallots in wine and vermouth. Puddings are also a speciality, and Ferzan has a flair for meringues, soufflés and profiteroles. The wine list is short, but wide ranging, and prices are a steal. Upstairs are three neat and tidy en-suite bedrooms with lovely views.

www.routiers.co.uk

St Austell

Highland Court Lodge

Bed and breakfast

'Elegant bedrooms ooze comfort and cosseting extras, from fresh flowers to private patios.'

Biscovey Road, Biscovey, near St Austell,
Cornwall PL24 2HW
Telephone: +44(0)1726 813320
enquiries@highlandcourt.co.uk
www.highlandcourt.co.uk

'With its understated yet pure design, inspirational setting and relaxing atmosphere, Highland Court Lodge successfully brings together luxury, style and good taste' – so says the owner on the website for this classy B&B. Every word is true, for the beautifully furnished lodge continues to surprise even the most discerning of guests, thanks to the owner's meticulous attention to detail and passion for the business. The lodge stands in two acres of tranquil gardens, with views across unspoilt countryside to Carlyon Bay.

Elegant, individually styled bedrooms ooze comfort and cosseting extras, from fresh flowers and Egyptian cotton sheets to plasma TVs, DVD and CD players, mini-bars, and private patios to relax on. Bathrooms boast Jacuzzi baths, invigorating showers, fluffy bathrobes and top-notch toiletries – perfect for pampering prior to sampling one of the imaginative set dinners. Using organic and local produce, a typical meal may feature scallops with pancetta and sweet-chilli dressing, beef fillet with tomato and garlic, and dark-chocolate truffle with loganberries. The Eden Project is within walking distance.

Rooms: 5. Double room from £45. Family room from £55. Prices are per person per night.
Prices: Set dinner £38. House wine £12.95.
Last orders: Dinner by prior arrangement.
Closed: Never.
Food: Modern European.
Other points: Totally no smoking. Garden. Children welcome. Car park. Wheelchair access (not WC).
Directions: Exit 31/M5. A30 to Bodmin and A391 to St Austell. Turn left onto the A390 through St Blazey. Turn right into Biscovey Road. (Map 3)

...for special offers

MEMBER
36
ENTRY

St Breward

The Old Inn and Restaurant

Country pub

Churchtown, St Breward, Bodmin Moor,
Cornwall PL30 4PP
Telephone: +44(0)1208 850711
darren@theoldinn.fsnet.co.uk
www.theoldinnandrestaurant.co.uk

'The strongly traditional interior exudes charm and atmosphere.'

Prices: **Main course from £7.95. House wine £11.95.**
Last orders: **Bar: 21.00. Food: lunch 14.00; dinner 21.00.**
Closed: **Never.**
Food: **Traditional British/Cornish.**
Real ale: **Sharp's Ales. Two guest beers.**
Other points: **Smoking area. Children welcome. Dogs welcome in the bar. Garden. Car park. 120-seat restaurant available for functions. Wheelchair access.**
Directions: **Follow the signposts to St Breward from the A30. The Old Inn is adjacent to the village church. The village is also signposted off the B3266 Bodmin to Camelford road. (Map 3)**
See pub walk on page 456

A low, white-painted stone cottage that claims, at 700ft, to be the highest pub in Cornwall, set on the edge of Bodmin Moor in a true Cornish village. Parts of the bar date back over 1,000 years, when it was an alehouse for the builders constructing the parish church. The strongly traditional interior exudes charm and atmosphere, with slate floors, part-exposed walls, thick beams, oak settles, and a roaring winter log fire in the granite fireplace.

The food is wholesome, unpretentious and not for the faint-hearted – portions are very generous! Walkers, locals and moorland trippers tuck into hearty pub favourites, such as ploughman's lunch, homemade pies and Charlie Harris's sausages and chips, all washed down with a tip-top pint of Sharp's local ale. Locally reared beef provides the excellent steaks, and fresh fish, notably the huge battered cod, is landed along the north Cornish coast. The menu also includes braised lamb shank and local venison with Cumberland sauce. A lovely summer garden backs on to moorland and the views from the well-placed benches are super.

St Ives

The Gurnard's Head

Country Inn

'Expect convivial surroundings, easygoing service, and unpretentious but high-quality food.'

Treen, Zennor, St Ives,
Cornwall TR26 3DE
Telephone: +44(0)1736 796928
enquiries@eatdrinksleep.ltd.uk
www.gurnardshead.co.uk

On the rugged north-west edge of Cornwall, with the sea on one side and the moors on the other, stands this sturdy old coaching inn. Respected pub operators Charles and Edmund Inkin, who own the coolest gastropub-with-rooms in Wales, The Felin Fach Griffin at Brecon (see entry), bought this isolated pub in April 2006 and have started to work their magic here. Expect a happy formula of relaxed convivial surroundings – bright paintwork, stripped pine and old oak furnishings, sofas by the fire – easygoing service, and unpretentious, high-quality food.

Daily menus are sensibly short, descriptions to the point and the cooking style simple to allow the flavours of ingredients to shine through. Emphasis is on the best produce available locally, notably fish from Newlyn and farm-reared meats. This translates to crab-and-fish stew, grilled langoustine, red mullet, fennel salad and gazpacho sauce, rib-eye steak with red-onion marmalade, rhubarb brûlée, and local Carn Brea goat cheese served with homemade soda bread. Already perfectly acceptable bedrooms will be stunning following winter refurbishment.

Rooms: 7. Double/twin room from £72.50, single from £45.
Prices: Restaurant main course from £9.50. Bar main course from £9.50. House wine £11.50.
Last orders: Food: lunch 14.30; dinner 21.30
Closed: Rarely.
Food: Modern British.
Real ale: St Austell Tribute, Skinner's Betty Stogs, Skinner's Cornish Knocker Ale.
Other points: Smoking area. Children welcome. Dogs welcome in the bar and overnight. Garden. Car park.
Directions: M5/A30. A30 to Penzance, B3311 to St Ives. After 1/2 mile take the left turn signposted to Heamoor and Newmill, then the next right to Newmill. After about 3 miles on this road, take a left at the T-junction. The Gurnard's Head is directly ahead. (Map 3)
See pub walk on page 458

...for the latest news

St Ives

The Garrack Hotel and Restaurant

Seaside hotel

Burthallan Lane, St Ives,
Cornwall TR26 3AA
Telephone: +44(0)1736 796199
les@garrack.com
www.garrack.com

'Relax on the sun terrace, or use the indoor pool, sauna, solarium and gym.'

Rooms: 18. Double room from £118, single from £72.
Prices: Set dinner £26.50 (four courses). House wine £11.95.
Last orders: Food: dinner 21.00.
Closed: Rarely.
Food: Modern English.
Other points: No smoking. Children welcome. Dogs welcome overnight by arrangement. Garden. Car park. Wheelchair access.
Directions: From the A30, follow the signposts to St Ives on the A3074. At the second mini-roundabout, take the first left, the B3311, signposted to St Ives. In St Ives, at the first mini roundabout, take the first left and follow the signs for the hotel. (Map 3)

The Kilby family have owned and run this delightful former gentleman's residence for 40 years and they have perfected its offering. Set above Porthmeor Beach with views of 30 miles of coastline, the Garrack Hotel is a fantastic base from which to explore Cornwall, simply relax on the sun terrace, or use the indoor pool, sauna, solarium and gym, which are surrounded by two acres of gardens. Bedrooms in the main house are decorated in an unfussy country fashion, while rooms in the sea-facing, lower-ground-floor wing cater for those wanting something more contemporary. Some rooms have four-posters and spa baths.

In the restaurant, chef Phil Thomas adopts a classic modern British approach, using fish caught locally in St Ives or nearby Newlyn. There is a separate section for the many lobster options. A typical starter may be smoked chicken and sun-blush tomato crostini, followed by a main course of roast loin of Cornish lamb. The wine list is carefully selected from various suppliers to offer a global choice and the good local Camel Valley wines.

Tolverne

Smugglers Cottage of Tolverne

Restaurant

'The fruit crumble with local Rodda's clotted cream is unmissable.'

Tolverne, Philleigh, Truro, Cornwall TR2 5NG
Telephone: +44(0)1872 580309
tolverne@btconnect.com
www.tolverneriverfal.co.uk

Set on the beautiful Roseland Peninsula, this thatched 15th-century cottage on the banks of the River Fal is a truly unique place and a byword for good home cooking and hospitality. Steeped in history, the Americans used it as an embarkation point for the D-Day landings, and General Eisenhower visited the troops here. One of the dining rooms is devoted to the SS Uganda. The Newman family has run the restaurant and tea gardens since 1934, and it has gained a well-deserved reputation for its Cornish specialities.

The menu changes daily and uses fresh ingredients, which are cooked in an Aga. At lunch, tuck into a proper Cornish pasty, the Smugglers' Special of soup with a filled baguette, fish pie or jacket potatoes and salad. The fruit crumble with local Rodda's clotted cream is unmissable and there is a fine selection of scones and muffins served warm from the oven for afternoon tea. There are non-smoking dining rooms and the bar has a collection of more than 100 malt whiskies. Take the boat to this Cornish gem – much more fun and picturesque than coming by car.

Prices: **Main course from £6. House wine £11.**
Last orders: **Food: 17.30 (Summer 20.30).**
Closed: **November-May.**
Food: **Modern British.**
Other points: **Smoking area. Children welcome. Tea gardens. Car park.**
Directions: **Near the King Harry car ferry, on the Roseland Peninsula, on the banks of the river Fal. (Map 3)**

...for recipe ideas

MEMBER 40 ENTRY

Ambleside

Borwick Lodge

Bed and breakfast

Outgate, Hawkshead, Ambleside,
Cumbria LA22 0PU
Telephone: +44(0)15394 36332
info@borwicklodge.com
www.borwicklodge.com

'As Lake District beauty spots go, it's hard to beat the position of this elegant lodge.'

Rooms: **6. Double/twin room from £72, single from £43.**
Closed: **Never.**
Other points: **No smoking. Children over eight welcome. Garden. Car park.**
Directions: **Exit 36/M6. Take the A591 to Windermere and Ambleside. From Ambleside, take the A593 to Coniston and then the B5286 to Hawkshead. After one mile, turn right for Tarn Hows. Borwick Lodge is on the left after two miles. (Map 12)**

As Lake District beauty spots go, it's hard to beat the position of this elegant lodge. Not only is it set in its own three acres of landscaped gardens, filled with colourful camelias, azaleas and rhododendrons, but the magnificent surrounding panorama ranked Beatrix Potter, Coleridge and Wordsworth among its admirers. The air of tranquillity and timelessness ensure a relaxing break. Views are down to Hawkshead and Windermere, and Tarn Hows, considered the 'Jewel of the Lakes', is close by. Inside the white-washed Victorian house, all is elegance and comfort, and the MacFarlanes provide a warm welcome.

Breakfast – a feast of homemade muesli, breads and preserves, plus local eggs, bacon and sausages, kippers, or scrambled egg and salmon – is served in the sunny dining room. Most of the bedrooms are reached via the impressive hall staircase, and they reflect the style of the house, with their tasteful colours and furnishings. The lodge has a friendly, family feel, and the fabulous views that are enjoyed from nearly all the bedrooms are the sort you'll never tire of.

www.routiers.co.uk

Appleby-in-Westmorland

Tufton Arms Hotel

Town-centre hotel

'The evocative 16th-century building has been beautifully restored.'

Market Square, Appleby-in-Westmorland,
Cumbria CA16 6XA
Telephone: +44(0)1768 351 593
info@tuftonarmshotel.co.uk
www.tuftonarmshotel.co.uk

The evocative 16th-century building, which became a coaching inn in Victorian times, has been beautifully restored by the Milsom family. The ambience of that period is reflected in the attractive wallpapers, lots of prints in heavy frames, drapes, old fireplaces and large porcelain table lamps. Bedrooms vary from suites with period fireplaces, antique furnishings and large old-style bathrooms to more conventional well-equipped en-suite rooms with good proportions.

Light lunch and supper menus are served in the clubby bar, with a more formal choice available in the stylish restaurant with its conservatory extension. Cooking is of a high standard, be it rack of Cumbrian fell-bred lamb with mint jus, locally reared beef fillet with Madeira gravy, or wild venison with mixed-berry sauce. Fish is delivered from Fleetwood, to create, perhaps, pan-fried sea bass with lemon-butter sauce, and a special fish pie. There is a French accent to the carefully selected, well-annotated wine list of 160 bins. Many are reasonably priced at under £20.

Rooms: 22. Double/twin room from £105.
Prices: Restaurant main course from £9.75. Bar main course from £7.95. House wine £10.80.
Last orders: Bar: 23.00. Food: lunch 14.00; dinner 21.00.
Closed: Rarely.
Food: Traditional English/French.
Real ale: Boddingtons, Worthington's Best.
Other points: Smoking throughout. Children welcome. Dogs welcome overnight. Car park. Licence for civil weddings/partnerships. Wheelchair access (not WC).
Directions: Exit 38/M6. Take the B6260 to Appleby via Orton. (Map 12)

...for events

Bassenthwaite Lake

Ouse Bridge Hotel

Hotel

Bassenthwaite Lake, Dubwath,
Cockermouth, Cumbria CA13 9YD
Telephone: +44(0)17687 76322
enquiries@ousebridge.com
www.ousebridge.com

'Relax and admire the lovely views.'

Rooms: 11, 2 with private bathroom. Double/
twin room from £36 per person, single from
£30, family from £82. Seasonal variations
may apply.
Prices: Set dinner £17 and £14 (two courses).
House wine £9.75.
Last orders: Dinner served between 19.15
and 20.00.
Closed: Never.
Food: Modern/traditional British.
Other points: No smoking. Children welcome.
Car park.
Directions: Exit 40/M6. Take the A66 towards
Keswick for 25 miles. Turn right on to the
B5291 and Ouse Bridge is 50 yards along on
the left. (Map 11)

Set on the shores of Bassenthwaite Lake, this family-run Lakeland hotel enjoys breathtaking views of Skiddaw and is an ideal base for exploring the Lake District. Owners Stephen and Kate Barrie make every effort to ensure your stay is relaxing and comfortable. The interiors have been updated, giving the hotel a fresh look and feel. The lounge and small bar with their pale leather sofas are ideal spots to relax and admire the lovely views. Bedrooms and en-suite bathrooms are pristine, uncluttered and comfortable, and many have lake views.

Stephen is passionate about food and takes time to source good local produce. The daily changing menu might be concise, but reflects the best of what's available, and it doesn't stint on flavour. Start with leeks with Parma ham in cheese sauce and move on to pan-fried lemon sole with tarragon butter, beef cooked in Jennings ale, or Ouse Bridge chicken pie, and there is always a good vegetarian option, perhaps red-lentil curry. A simple, good-value wine list should satisfy all tastes. Breakfast includes local meats and free-range eggs from a local farm.

Scafell Hotel

Hotel

'The scenery is breathtaking.'

Rosthwaite, Borrowdale, Cumbria CA12 5XB
Telephone: +44(0)17687 77208
info@scafell.co.uk
www.scafell.co.uk

Wordsworth and Coleridge stayed at this elegant, 19th-century hotel and walked the surrounding fells. It's easy to see the appealing mix of the hotel's attractions; the scenery is breathtaking and the food is along contemporary lines. Miles Jessop, who has been here for 40 years, is a welcoming host. Most of the bedrooms have good views; all are comfortable and furnished in country style.

A tempting table d'hôte is served in the dining room, and showcases local ingredients, including farm chicken and Cumbrian pork and lamb. A typical dinner may take in cream of fennel soup to start, followed by pork fillet with white wine and cream sauce and lemon-and-ginger cheesecake. A simple cocktail bar is set in one room around an open fire, while at the rear of the hotel is the public bar, which has slate floors and outdoor seating. Here you find some good bar food, ranging from Cumbrian ham-and-mustard sandwiches and smoked-chicken salad to game casserole, poached Seathwaite trout with parsley butter, and sirloin steak with pepper sauce. Wash it down with a cracking pint of Black Sheep or Theakston Bitter.

Rooms: 24. Double room from £145, single from £72.50 dinner, bed and breakfast. Seasonal price variations apply.
Prices: Set lunch £10.95 and dinner from £20.50 to £24.50 (five course). Restaurant main course from £9.50. Bar meal from £6.50. House wine £12.95.
Last orders: Bar: 23.00. Food: lunch 14.00; dinner 21.00.
Closed: Never.
Food: British/global.
Real ale: Black Sheep Ales, Theakston Best, Theakston Old Peculier. Three guest beers.
Other points: No smoking. Children welcome. Dogs welcome. Garden. Car park. Licence for civil weddings/partnerships. Wheelchair access.
Directions: Exit 40/M6. Take the A66 towards Keswick and then the B5289. (Map 11)

...for competitions

Cockermouth

Winder Hall Country House

Country-house hotel

Low Lorton, Cockermouth,
Cumbria CA13 9UP
Telephone: +44(0)1900 85107
nick@winderhall.co.uk
www.winderhall.co.uk

'The new summerhouse has a sauna, hot tub and great views.'

Rooms: **7. Double room from £50, single from £75.**
Prices: **Set dinner £29.50 (four courses). House wine £11.25.**
Last orders: **Food: dinner 19.00-20.00.**
Closed: **Occasional family holiday.**
Food: **Modern British.**
Other points: **No smoking. Children welcome. Garden. Car park. Licence for civil weddings. Fishing rights. Wheelchair access to the restaurant.**
Directions: **Exit 40/M6. From Keswick, take the A66 west to Braithwaite, then the B5292 Whinlatter Pass to Lorton. Take a sharp left at the B5289 signed to Low Lorton. (Map 11)**

Nick and Ann Lawler's historic manor house may date back to the 15th-century, but it has all the comforts of a small hotel. Upgrading of bedrooms and bathrooms continues apace and you can expect a warm and friendly atmosphere. The small lounge with sink-into sofas and an open fire is inviting, while each of the en-suite bedrooms is individually decorated in tasteful colours and fabrics. The food is good, too, with dinner being served in the oak-panelled Arts and Crafts dining room, complete with a log fire.

The menu incorporates local ingredients, organic meats and home-grown free-range eggs and pork, and is flavoured with spices and fresh herbs. The choice may be limited, but what they cook, they do exceptionally well. Start with sweet-pepper and garlic soup and follow with organic pork medallions or poached salmon with hot cucumber butter. Desserts may include warm lemon tart with raspberry coulis or a selection of local cheeses. The wine list offers value and character and is divided into helpful style categories. The new summerhouse has a sauna, hot tub and great views.

Eskdale

The Boot Inn

Country inn

'The route may not be the most accessible, but it is well worth the detour.'

Boot, Eskdale, Cumbria CA19 1TG
Telephone: +44(0)1946 723224
lesley@bootinn.co.uk
www.bootinn.co.uk

The route to this old Lakeland inn via the coast or, for the more adventurous, over the terrifying Hardknott Pass may not be the most accessible, but it is well worth the detour; the Eskdale Valley is a beautiful, lush and unspoilt part of western Cumbria. Originally built as a farm in 1578, the typical Lakeland inn was converted in 1764 and new owners Lesley and Francis Dantinnes, who took over in January 2006, are sprucing up the bar and bedrooms. Providing a comfortable base for exploring the area, rooms are simply furnished in a bright, rural style and enjoy views over the surrounding fells.

Hearty homemade food is served in both the homely bar, with its log fire, dark-wood furnishings and excellent ales, and in the cosy, cottagey restaurant. Dishes range from an impressive lunchtime sandwich choice to the likes of steak, kidney and mushroom pie, Woodall's famous Cumberland sausage with red-onion and red-wine jus, local Penny Hill Farm lamb's liver and bacon casserole, Cumbrian beef steaks, and hake-and-prawn pie. Across the Esk are bridleways to Eel Tarn and Wasdale Head.

Rooms: **9. Double/twin room from £54.50, single from £54.50. Children £15. Prices quoted are per person for dinner, bed and breakfast.**
Prices: **Restaurant main course from £6.95. Bar main course from £6.95. House wine £10.95.**
Last orders: **Bar: 23.00. Food: 21.00.**
Closed: **Rarely.**
Food: **Traditional British.**
Real ale: **Robinson's Ales. At least one guest beer.**
Other points: **Smoking area. Children welcome. Dogs welcome in the bar and overnight. Garden. Car park.**
Directions: **Exit 36/M6. Follow the A590 to Broughton-in-Furness. Take the Fell Road via Ulpha, signposted to Eskdale and then The Boot. Inn (Map 11)**
See pub walk on page 460

...for special offers

MEMBER
46
ENTRY

Grange-over-Sands

The Hazelmere Café and Bakery

Seaside café

1 Yewbarrow Terrace, Grange-over-Sands,
Cumbria LA11 6ED
Telephone: +44(0)15395 32972
hazelmeregrange@yahoo.co.uk
www.hazelmerecafe.co.uk

'Cake fans are spoilt, and everyone should try a piece of the Cumbrian rum nicky.'

Prices: **Main course from £6.25. House wine £2.10 for a glass.**
Last orders: **Food: 14.30 (Winter 16.00).**
Closed: **Rarely.**
Food: Traditional English.
Other points: **No smoking. Children welcome. Dogs welcome. Wheelchair access.**
Directions: **Exit 36/M6, then take the A590, then the B5277, signposted to Grange-over-Sands. Pass Grange Station and, at the mini roundabout, take the first exit. The café is 25 yards along on the right. (Map 9)**

Ian and Dorothy's long-established (1897) café and fantastic bakery has just about everything going for it. It's well worth the detour for the 30-40 different breads, and goods – from Lakeland plum bread, vanilla slices and strawberry tarts to authentic French sticks and ciabatta. Next door in the café, which has a traditional, gentle feel, an array of these homemade goodies and other local produce is on offer, plus an impressive selection of speciality teas.

Tea is Dorothy's passion and she is a globetrotter when it comes to sourcing the 30 or so single-estate teas on her list. Cake fans are spoilt, and everyone should try a piece of the Cumbrian rum nicky – a sweet pastry case filled with cherries, dates, rum butter, spices and stem ginger. The menu also offers a tempting range of savoury dishes and all the produce used is local, from lamb tattie pot and rabbit casserole to light meals of potted Morecambe Bay shrimps and smoked wood pigeon breast with Cumberland sauce. They also have sandwiches, amazing homemade preserves and Lakes ice creams. Children have their mini menu of adult dishes.

English Lakes Ice Cream,
The Old Dairy, Gilthwaiterigg Lane, Kendal, 01539 721211, www.lakesicecream.com
Run by Peter and Frances Fryer for the past 20 years, who have a passion for supreme traditional ice cream, the company produces Double Jersey Ice Cream using only natural ingredients – whole milk, Jersey cream and butter. They also make sorbets using fruit and fruit juice rather than colours and flavourings.

Higginsons Butchers,
Main Street, Grange-over-Sands, 015395 34367
Renowned across Cumbria and among Britain's best butchers, this is where the café sources quality meats, notably salt-marsh lamb, Herdwick lamb, locally reared beef and pork, and Higginsons award-winning Cumberland sausage.

Cartmel Valley Game Supplies & Smokehouse,
High Bank Side, Cark-in-Cartmel, 015395 36413
Set up 14 years ago by former Holker Hall Estate gamekeeper Jonathan Stott and his wife Susan, the business sources and supplies game to more than 150 customers across Cumbria, including top hotels, restaurants, butchers and delicatessens. In season, they can supply pheasant, rabbit, pigeon, wild duck and venison, all from Cumbrian estates. They also supply fresh fish and smoked salmon, game and butter in two smoking units in a converted byre.

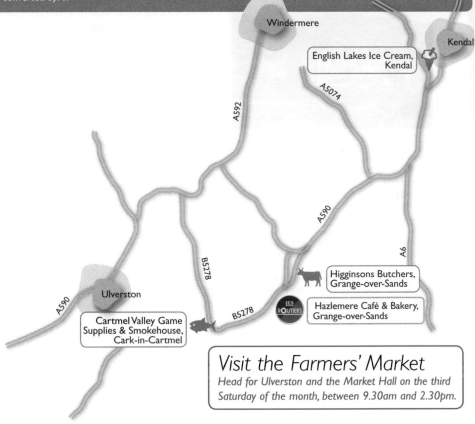

Windermere

English Lakes Ice Cream, Kendal

Kendal

A5074

A592

A590

A6

B5278

Ulverston

A590

Higginsons Butchers, Grange-over-Sands

B5278

LES ROUTIERS

Hazlemere Café & Bakery, Grange-over-Sands

Cartmel Valley Game Supplies & Smokehouse, Cark-in-Cartmel

Visit the Farmers' Market
Head for Ulverston and the Market Hall on the third Saturday of the month, between 9.30am and 2.30pm.

Grange-over-Sands

Netherwood Hotel

Country-house hotel

Lindale Road, Grange-over-Sands,
Cumbria LA11 6ET
Telephone: +44(0)15395 32552
enquiries@netherwood-hotel.co.uk
www.netherwood-hotel.co.uk

'Hotel frontages don't come more impressive than this stately Victorian mansion.'

Rooms: **32. Rooms from £80 per person. Family room from £160.**
Prices: **Set lunch £16. Bar lunches available. House wine £14.**
Last orders: **Food: lunch 14.00; dinner 20.30.**
Closed: **Never.**
Food: **Global.**
Other points: **No smoking. Children welcome. Dogs welcome in the bar and overnight. Garden. Car park. Licence for civil weddings. Wheelchair access.**
Directions: **Exit 36/M6, then take the A590 for Barrow-in-Furness. Turn left at the roundabout onto the B5277, then left again at Lindale roundabout. The hotel is on the right before the train station. (Map 9)**

Hotel frontages don't come more impressive than this stately Victorian mansion with fine mullioned windows. Run by the Followfield family for 40 years, it stands in terraced formal gardens with sweeping views across Morecambe Bay. The interiors are just as pleasing. Its relaxed country-house feel is complemented by the modern amenities of a gym, pool and business and function facilities. Updated public rooms are designed for comfort and feature open fires, big sofas and oak panelling. Spacious, individual bedrooms are refurbished on a rolling basis and boast elegant furnishings and immaculate bathrooms.

Dining is a pleasure, from the imaginative set menus to the stunning views over the gardens to Morecambe Bay. Local produce includes Kendal Roughfell lamb, game from Holker Hall and locally landed fish and shellfish. From the traditional menu, start with homemade pâté with Cumberland sauce, then opt for corn-fed duck with raspberry sauce or beef fillet with red wine jus. Luscious desserts, such as ginger sponge pudding or blueberry cheesecake, add a fitting flourish of extravagance.

www.routiers.co.uk

The Jumble Room

Café and restaurant

'A far cry from the usual run-of-the-mill lunchtime fare.'

Langdale Road, Grasmere,
Cumbria LA22 9SU
Telephone: +44(0)15394 35188
eat@jumbleroom.co.uk
www.thejumbleroom.co.uk

'Food from the sun' is the culinary motto of this modern Lakeland café-restaurant. The Jumble Room has been in Andy and Chrissy Hills' family for more than 50 years. It started life at the beginning of the 18th century as Grasmere's first shop where, among other things, Grasmere Rushbearing Gingerbread was made. During the day, the café serves snacks, sandwiches and light meals, with the emphasis on local and organic produce. Tomato-and-lemongrass soup, Balinese fish curry and Spanish frittata are a far cry from the usual run-of-the-mill lunchtime fare.

In the evening, The Jumble Room dresses for dinner: vinyl tablecloths are replaced with crisp linen, and dining is by candlelight. The global menu has influences from Troutbeck to Thailand, with starters such as warm lobster and fresh salmon terrine, followed by mains of Graythwaite game pie, Goosnargh corn-fed chicken, or asparagus and mushroom potato rösti. The puds change frequently and all are truly indulgent. There's an eclectic mix of wines from around the world, with six European organics at good-value prices.

Prices: Restaurant main course from £10. Bar main course from £5. House wine £10.95.
Last orders: Food: lunch 16.30; dinner 22.30.
Closed: Monday, Tuesday, from 23 to 27 December and lunchtimes during the winter.
Food: Global.
Other points: No smoking. Children welcome. Wheelchair access.
Directions: From Ambleside, take the A590 and turn left into Grasmere. Turn left again at the church and take the first right opposite the tourist information centre. The Jumble Room is 200 yards along on the right. (Map 12)

...for the latest news

MEMBER ENTRY

Orton

New Village Tea Rooms

Orton, Penrith, Cumbria CA10 3RH
Telephone: +44(0)1539 624886

Tea room

'The open fire and a dresser laden with homemade bakes add to its country charm.'

Prices: **Lunchtime special from £5.50.**
Last orders: **Food: 17.00 (Winter 16.30).**
Closed: **Sunday before 25 December to 2 January.**
Food: **Teashop fare.**
Other points: **No smoking. Garden. Car park. No credit cards accepted. Unlicenced.**
Directions: **Exit 38/M6, then take the road signposted to Appleby. In Orton, take the Shap Road in front of the George Hotel. New Village Tea Rooms is situated straight ahead, opposite the post office. (Map 12)**

Appetising alternatives to motorway services can be hard to find, but this tearoom in the pretty village of Orton fits the bill perfectly. Christine Evans has honed her menu to suit locals and passing trade over the decade she has been in business. Her home cooking attracts regulars for lunch, tea, or to buy her homemade ready meals. The tearooms were originally four separate rooms for farm labourers, but have been cleverly converted in this homely, Lakeland-style café.

The cream walls, open fire, wooden tables with dark green and lace cloths and a dresser laden with homemade bakes add to its country charm. The printed menu is packed with goodies, such as scones, sandwiches, toasties, jacket potatoes and Lakeland ice cream. There's also a chalkboard detailing the day's specials, which include soups such as lentil and bacon or curried parsnip; hearty bakes of chicken and broccoli, or broad bean, onion and tomato; and homemade desserts of sticky toffee pudding or chocolate-and-orange crumble. Cakes and a large choice of take-away frozen ready-made meals are available.

Penrith

Alan's Café Restaurant

Café and restaurant

'The right ambience for a special night out.'

Poets Walk, Penrith, Cumbria CA11 7HJ
Telephone: +44(0)1768 867474
alanschef@btinternet.com

A café on weekdays, serving cakes and light lunches, Alan's becomes a stylish restaurant on Friday and Saturday evenings. Chef-owner Alan Potter pulls off both of these guises with aplomb. The modern décor – light colours and whitewashed wood furniture – is an inviting setting in which to enjoy the fine selection of teas, coffees, freshly baked breads, cakes and scones, or you can opt for one of the lunchtime specials, such as hot chicken-and-bacon salad or grilled avocado and brie with a cranberry dressing and salad.

At weekends, the atmosphere becomes more sophisticated, with soft lighting and subtle background music creating the right ambience for a special night out. The fixed-price evening menu offers four or five choices per course and includes a fair selection of meat, fish and vegetarian options. Cream of parsnip soup or pan-fried scallops served on egg noodles kick things off, and might be followed by fillet of beef Wellington, venison steak or paupiette of lemon sole. Round off with a wicked traditional dessert, such as bread-and-butter pudding with apricot coulis or crème brûlée with fresh strawberries.

Prices: **Set dinner £25. Restaurant main course from £11.50. Bar main course from £7. House wine £11.50.**
Last orders: **Lunch 14.30; dinner served from 19.00 (Friday and Saturday only).**
Closed: **Monday to Thursday evenings and all day Sunday.**
Food: **Modern British.**
Other points: **No smoking. Children welcome. Wheelchair access.**
Directions: **Exit 40/M6. Just off the Market Square in the town centre. (Map 12)**

...for recipe ideas

MEMBER
51
ENTRY

Penrith

The Highland Drove Inn

Country inn

Great Salkeld, Penrith,
Cumbria CA11 9NA
Telephone: +44(0)1768 898349
highlanddroveinn@btinternet.com
www.highland-drove.co.uk

'The pub is renowned for its conviviality and popular food.'

Rooms: **3. Soon to be 5. Double/twin from £60.**
Prices: **Restaurant main course from £9.95. Bar snack from £4.95. House wine £10. 95.**
Last orders: **Bar: afternoon 15.00; evening 23.00 (all day Saturday). Food: lunch 14.00; dinner 21.00 (Sunday 20.30).**
Closed: **Monday lunchtime.**
Food: **Eclectic bistro.**
Real ale: **John Smith's Cask, Theakston Black Bull. One guest beer.**
Other points: **Smoking area. Children welcome. Dogs welcome in the bar. Garden. Car park. Wheelchair access to the restaurant/pub (not WC).**
Directions: **Exit 40/M6. Take the A66 eastbound, then the A686 towards Alston. After four miles, turn left on to the B6412 for Great Salkeld. (Map 12)**

The Newton family's good all-round country inn, set close to the church in this picturesque Eden Valley village, has expanded its appeal with the welcome addition of a new lounge extension and a bar menu. This old drovers' inn resembles an old farmhouse, with its wooden porch and abundance of flowers. Within, there are rustic tables and settles in the locals' bar, while the new wood-floored lounge sports smart leather chairs, an open fire and additional dining space.

The pub is renowned for its conviviality and popular food. Kyloe's Restaurant upstairs has a hunting-lodge feel and is the core of the business. Utilising local produce, the kitchen produces satisfying country cooking that takes in scallops and black pudding with saffron-and-mustard beurre blanc, then a main dish of beef fillet with creamy pepper sauce, with plum mousse to finish. Downstairs, you can now tuck into a homemade burger, beer-battered haddock and various meat and fish platters with a cracking pint of Theakston Black Bull. Bedrooms are small but nicely decorated and very well equipped for a country inn.

Cumbrian Lodge

Restaurant-with-rooms

'Sink into super-comfortable light goose-down duvets with Egyptian linen to watch the flat-screen TV.'

Gosforth Road, Seascale,
Cumbria CA20 1JG
Telephone: +44(0)19467 27309
cumbrianlodge@btconnect.com
www.cumbrianlodge.com

David Morgan has brought good taste in food and furnishings to this grand old house that sits on the attractive West Cumbrian coast. It became a hotel in 1999, and David's additional refurbishments combine 21st-century comforts and contemporary touches. In recently upgraded bedrooms, you can sink into super-comfortable, light, goose-down duvets with Egyptian linen to watch the flat-screen TV. Bathrooms boast thick towels and smart toiletries.

Downstairs you can enjoy the finer things, too: wine is served in Riedal wine glasses and much thought has gone into sourcing quality local food – meats from Wasdale Head Hall Farm and dairy produce from Crofton Dairies. The bar (with its maple woodwork and faux-suede seating) is relaxing and plush. Dine in the restaurant on lunches of light snacks, hearty traditional Cumbrian hotpots or Swiss specialities, such as rösti and rahm schnitzel, or from an expansive dinner menu that brings together local produce. The knowledgeable wine list offers a good selection of interesting New World wines as well as the French stalwarts.

Rooms: **6. Double room from £80, single from £72.50, family from £87.50.**
Prices: Restaurant **main course from £9.95. Bar main course from £6.95. House wine £12.95.**
Last orders: **Bar: afternoon 14.00; evening 23.00. Food: lunch 14.00; dinner 21.30. No food Monday and Saturday lunchtime and all day Sunday.**
Closed: **Rarely.**
Food: **Modern British/Swiss.**
Real ale: **Hawkshead Ales.**
Other points: **Smoking area. Children over 12 welcome. Garden. Car park. Wheelchair access to the restaurant/pub.**
Directions: **Exit 36/M6. Take the A590 west to Greenodd, then the A595 towards Whitehaven. Near Gosforth, turn left on the B5344. The hotel is two miles further on.**
(Map 11)

...for events

Sedbergh

The Dalesman Country Inn

Country inn

Main Street, Sedbergh, Cumbria LA10 5BN
Telephone: +44(0)15396 21183
info@thedalesman.co.uk
www.thedalesman.co.uk

'An ideal stop-over for walkers tackling the Dales Way.'

Rooms: **7. Rooms £30 per person.**
Prices: **Set lunch £10 and dinner £18. Main course from £8. House wine £8.**
Last orders: **Bar: 23.00. Food: lunch 14.00 (Friday, Saturday, Sunday 14.30); dinner 21.00 (Friday and Saturday 21.30).**
Closed: **Rarely.**
Food: **Modern British/traditional pub food.**
Real ale: **Black Sheep Best (on bank holidays), Tetley's Bitter, Dalesman. One guest beer.**
Other points: **Smoking area. Children welcome. Car park. Wheelchair access (not WC).**
Directions: **On the A684 in the village centre; 11 miles east of Kendal; 5 miles from Exit 36/M6. (Map 12)**

Situated in an old market town and close to scenic walks along the River Dee and up on the Howgill Fells, the Dalesman is an unassuming, comfortably modernised 16th-century inn, festooned in summer with rampant floral displays. Stripped stone and beams, farmhouse chairs and log-effect gas fires set the scene in the rambling bar and dining room where you can enjoy good homemade food prepared from local produce. Arrive early for the excellent-value lunchtime menu that features beer-battered fish and chips, and hot bacon rolls.

Evening bar food ranges from terrines and tiger-prawn starters to chargrills and lamb shank with red-wine gravy. Influenced by the seasons, the evening carte may extend the choice to organic Aberdeen Angus steak with pepper sauce, and an excellent choice of fresh fish in summer. For pudding, choose steamed ginger pudding, or Wensleydale cheese with cranberry sauce. Seven spacious and comfortably furnished bedrooms are gradually being upgraded, and most have new en-suite bathrooms. An ideal stop-over for walkers tackling the Dales Way.

www.routiers.co.uk

Silloth-on-Solway
Café 14/16

Café

'Customers recognise the quality and emphasis on flavours.'

14-16 Eden Street, Silloth-on-Solway, Wigton, Cumbria CA7 4AD
Telephone: +44(0)1697 332541
fourteensixteen@waitrose.com

Former hoteliers Jay and Morven Anson have brought their flair and passion for authentically good food to their café, which offers an extensive all-day lunch menu. The café is simply decorated and has a welcoming atmosphere. In chillier weather, a fire roars in the original Victorian marble fireplace. It's popular not only because it offers great value, but customers recognise the quality and emphasis on flavours, and, with only 24 tables, it's best to arrive early for lunch.

You can start the day with breakfast, then there's tea or coffee (Fairtrade) with homemade scones and jam, or homemade soups such as organic tomato, basil and courgette with home-baked organic bread, made using Little Salkeld's organic flour, and plenty of sandwich and wrap options. Main dishes include gratin of Solway shrimp, salmon and cod in a parsley sauce topped with a king scallop, free-range corn-fed chicken with a Cumberland honey-mustard, brandy and five-spice sauce, and various casseroles and fish specials, mainly made with organic ingredients. A bring-your-own-wine policy keeps the bill well within budget.

Prices: **Restaurant main course from £8. Snacks from £4.50.**
Last orders: **Café: Lunch 14.30 (Sunday 14.00).**
Closed: **Monday.**
Food: **Traditional/modern British.**
Other points: **No smoking. Children welcome. Garden. Credit cards not accepted. Wheelchair access.**
Directions: **Exit 41/M6. Take the B5305 to Wigton, then the B5302 to Silloth. Turn left at the tourist information centre, then right on to Eden Street. (Map 11)**

...for competitions

Ullswater

Brackenrigg Inn

Country inn

Watermillock, Lake Ullswater, Penrith,
Cumbria CA11 0LP
Telephone: +44(0)1768 486206
enquiries@brackenrigginn.co.uk
www.brackenrigginn.co.uk

'A sound local reputation for well-executed, contemporary food is certainly deserved.'

Rooms: 17. Double room from £28 per person, single from £33. Superior rooms and suites also available.
Prices: Set Sunday lunch £11.95. Set dinner £24.95 (including coffee). Restaurant main course from £10.50. Bar main course from £8.25. House wine £10.95.
Last orders: Bar: 23.00. Food: lunch 14.30; dinner 21.00.
Closed: Never.
Food: Modern British.
Real ale: Black Sheep Ales, Jennings Cumberland Ale, Tirril Ales, Theakston Ales, Coniston Bluebird. Three guest beers.
Other points: Smoking area. Children welcome. Dogs welcome in the bar and overnight (some rooms). Garden. Car park. Wheelchair access.
Directions: On the A592 south-west of Penrith; six miles from Exit 40/M6, overlooking Ullswater. (Map 12)

The sweeping views across Lake Ullswater and the fells from the tranquil setting of the Brackenrigg are second to none. The vista is matched by an appealing homely feel throughout the unpretentious interior of this 18th-century inn. This is thanks, in part, to the attractive panelled bar with its polished floorboards, open log fire and cracking local ales from Jennings, Tirril and Coniston breweries. Both the relaxing dining rooms have been refurbished and feature polished wooden tables and high-backed chairs, as well as those grand lake and fell views.

A sound local reputation for well-executed, contemporary food is certainly deserved. The bar menu is built around local produce and is also available in the lounge and terrace. Choices include a speciality sandwich filled with Cumberland sausage and red-onion marmalade, and local lamb braised in red wine, mint and garlic. The restaurant table d'hôte may list asparagus with feta and pine nuts, followed by calves' liver with Woodall's dry-cured bacon. En-suite bedrooms are cosy and cottagey in the inn, while rooms in the converted stables are more spacious suites.

Richard Woodall Ltd,
Waberthwaite, 01229 717237, www.richardwoodall.com
Famous for its traditionally cured hams, bacon and sausages, the seventh and eigth generation of family
members use the same recipes and techniques as the Woodalls of over 170 years ago. The company farms its
own herd of around 180 sows in large, straw-filled barns with natural light and fresh air, and in a completely
chemical- and preservative-free environment.

Jennings Brewery, Castle Brewery,
Cockermouth, 0845 1297190, www.jenningsbrewery.co.uk
The brewery stands in an idyllic spot beside the River Derwent in the shadow of Cockermouth Castle and
specialises in the production of cask ale, from the malty Jennings Bitter to the well-balanced, dark-brown
mild and the complex fruit, malt and roast flavours of the strong, dark-brown Sneck Lifter. Be sure to take a
brewery tour and visit the shop.

Tirril Brewery Co,
Brougham Hall, Brougham, Penrith, 01768 863219,
www.tirrilbrewery.co.uk
A century after Siddle's Brewery ceased brewing beer in the village of Tirril in 1899, the landlord of The
Queen's Head revived the brewery behind the pub. Recently, it moved to the original 1823 Brewing Rooms
at nearby Brougham Hall. It's possible to take a brewery tour by arrangement.

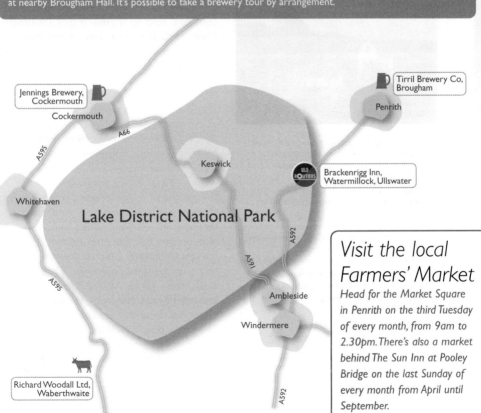

Jennings Brewery, Cockermouth

Cockermouth

A66

A595

Keswick

Whitehaven

Lake District National Park

A595

Tirril Brewery Co, Brougham

Penrith

Brackenrigg Inn, Watermillock, Ullswater

A592

A591

Ambleside

Windermere

Richard Woodall Ltd, Waberthwaite

A592

Visit the local Farmers' Market

Head for the Market Square
in Penrith on the third Tuesday
of every month, from 9am to
2.30pm. There's also a market
behind The Sun Inn at Pooley
Bridge on the last Sunday of
every month from April until
September.

Ulverston

Dusty Miller's Tea Shop

Teashop

Gleaston Water Mill, Gleaston,
near Ulverston, Cumbria LA12 OQH
Telephone: +44(0)1229 869244
dustymillers@watermill.co.uk
www.watermill.co.uk

'Not only serves good food, but has an excellent shop selling homemade goodies and crafts.'

Rooms: **Self-catering cottage £225 per week low season, £330 per week high season.**
Prices: **Main course from £5.99. House wine £7.95.**
Last orders: **Food: 16.45.**
Closed: **Monday (except public holidays).**
Food: **Traditional British.**
Real ale: **Hawkshead Ales.**
Other points: **No smoking. Children welcome. Patio. Car park. Wheelchair access.**
Directions: **Exit 36/M6. Travel west on the A590. At Ulverston, turn left onto the A5087 and take the coastal route towards Barrow. Follow the Brown Gleaston Water Mill signs from Aldingham. (Map 9)**

Centred at a working, Grade II-listed water corn mill next to the ruins of 13th-century Gleaston Castle, this culinary cornucopia not only serves good food, but has an excellent shop selling homemade goodies and crafts. Cumbrian foodies Vicky and Mike Brereton have made it a must-visit place. Visitors can see the restored 18-foot wooden water wheel in action, as well as honey being made at its observation hive (free bee-keeping courses run on Saturdays throughout late spring and summer).

A highlight of a visit, though, is the teashop, housed in the former cow shed. Brunch is served from 10.30am, which can be a light bite or the full Country Brunch, including Richard Woodall's famous dry-cured bacon and Cumberland sausages. Through the week, they serve hearty lunch dishes of, say, vegetarian bakes such as courgette-and-ginger loaf, salad platters, and a good selection of sandwiches and cakes as well as a good choice of country wines, local beers and soft drinks. Their traditional Sunday lunches are popular and the Miller's Apprentice menu offers children's portions.

Bed and breakfast

'The bedrooms are havens of calm and very spacious.'

1 Park Road, Windermere,
Cumbria LA23 2AW
Telephone: +44 (0)15394 42107
enquiries@1parkroad.com
www.1parkroad.com

A stylish Victorian villa that certainly stands out from the more traditional guesthouses in the town. Owners Mark and Alexandra Soden have a good eye for interiors and have made the most of the building's attractive features. Its elegant rooms are decorated with art deco and art nouveau prints and ornaments. The wonderful tiled hall floor and the pine wood features are beautifully polished, but the period pieces, that include ornate fireplaces and 19th-century stained glass, don't overwhelm and the overall feel is contemporary and uncluttered.

The bedrooms are havens of calm and very spacious, with extras including plasma screens, DVD and CD players. En-suite shower rooms are pristine and the beds especially comfortable. Mark is also a talented cook and devises an Italian-themed, candlelit-dinner menu daily. All the ingredients are sourced locally and everything is freshly prepared. Starters offer a soup or garlic mushrooms, followed by a choice of main courses, perhaps chicken in red wine, oregano and basil sauce or pasta with chorizo, tomato and onion sauce. The sticky toffee pudding is a must.

Rooms: **6. Double/twin room from £35 per person, single from £60, family from £105. House hire also available.**
Prices: **Set dinner £16.95. Restaurant two courses from £14.50. House wine from £7.95.**
Last orders: **Pre-order dinner for night of arrival.**
Closed: **Never.**
Food: **Modern European and seasonal specials.**
Other points: **No smoking. Children welcome. Car park.**
Directions: **Exit 36/M6. In the centre of Windermere village. (Map 12)**

...for the latest news

Windermere

Fayrer Garden House Hotel

Hotel

Lyth Valley Road, Bowness-on-Windermere,
Windermere, Cumbria LA23 3JP
Telephone: +44(0)15394 88195
lakescene@fayrergarden.com
www.fayrergarden.com

'Comfort, from the downstairs rooms to the spacious bedrooms overlooking the lake, is assured.'

Rooms: **29. Double/twin room from £66 per person, single from £75.**
Prices: **Set dinner (five courses) £35. House wine £14.50.**
Last orders: **Food: dinner 20.30.**
Closed: **First two weeks in January.**
Food: **Modern British.**
Real ale: **Jennings Ale.**
Other points: **Smoking area. Children over five welcome. Dogs welcome in some rooms. Five acres of grounds. Licence for civil weddings and partnerships. Wheelchair access.**
Directions: **Exit 36/M6. Take the A590/1 to Kendal for eight miles. At the roundabout, turn left on the B5284 onto Crook Road for eight miles. At the end, turn left onto Lyth Valley Road for a quarter of a mile. (Map 12)**

The Wildsmith family, who now run this former Victorian residence formerly owned by the Fayrers, strictly adhere to their motto of, 'We try not to overlook anything but the lake'. They have developed this stunning house in a glorious setting and have already won awards for the magnificent gardens. But the quality extends throughout this hotel, without any stuffiness or fussiness, from the furnishings to the food. The style is country house, which has been updated sensitively to give a feeling of freshness.

Comfort, from the downstairs rooms to the spacious bedrooms overlooking the lake, is assured. In fine weather, the terrace is a great place to take in the views. Equally good vistas can be enjoyed from the dining room, which offers a superb daily set menu that showcases quality local game, meats and fish. Dishes such as fillet of black bream, Grizedale venison with game sauce, and roast sirloin of beef with red-wine jus are prepared with flair. Ditto puddings such as steamed chocolate-and-orange pudding and the memorable breakfasts. The well-sourced wine cellar will please in its selection and pricing.

Windermere

Jambo Restaurant

7 Victoria Street, Windermere,
Cumbria LA23 1AE
Telephone: +44(0)15394 43429
kevatjambo@aol.com
www.jamborestaurant.co.uk

Restaurant

'Quality ingredients, complementary flavours and fine cooking raise this restaurant to a special level.'

Once a corner shop, this unprepossessing building is now home to some remarkably fine cooking, care of the talented Master Chef of Great Britain, Kevin Wyper. He runs this restaurant with his partner Andrea and they have put together a menu based on homegrown fruit, vegetables and meat, mainly from local producers. The décor is simple, with tables laid with shining cutlery and glasses.

The menu displays a real understanding of how to prepare seasonal produce to the best effect and dishes are well presented. Starters offer roast quail on mustard mash with herb salsa, or chicken-liver parfait with red-onion confit. Mains take in game such as pan-roasted Grizedale wild venison, roast rack of Cumbrian lamb, honey-glazed Goosnargh duck breast, and a daily fish special, to name but a few. For pudding, there's rhubarb cheesecake with rhubarb compote, or chocolate marquise with raspberry coulis. However, it's the combination of quality ingredients, complementary flavours and fine cooking that raises this restaurant to a special level.

Prices: **Main course from £14.50. House wine £11.95.**
Last orders: **22.00.**
Closed: During the day (open from 18.30), all day Thursday, 25-26 December and two weeks in January.
Food: **Modern British.**
Other points: **No smoking.**
Directions: **From the M6, take exit 36 heading for Windermere/Bowness. On reaching Windermere, turn left into the village. Pass the tourist information centre and the restaurant is 100 yards along on the left.**
(Map 12)

...for recipe ideas

MEMBER
60
ENTRY

Castle Donington

The Nags Head

Village Inn

Hill Top, Castle Donington,
Derbyshire DE74 2PR
Telephone: +44(0)1332 850652
thenagsheadinn@tiscali.co.uk
www.thenagsheadinn.co.uk

'Positively bustles with activity.'

Rooms: **6-8 rooms from December 2006.
Double/twin room from £55, single from £45.**
Prices: **Set dinner £25. Sunday lunch £11.50.
Restaurant main course from £11. Bar main
course from £6.50. House wine £11.**
Last orders: **Food: lunch 14.30; dinner 21.30
(Sunday 19.30). Food served all day at
weekends.**
Closed: **Rarely.**
Food: **Modern British.**
Real ale: **Marston's Pedigree, Mansfield Bitter.**
Other points: **Totally no smoking. Dogs
welcome in the bar. Garden. Children welcome.
Car park. Wheelchair access.**
Directions: **Exit 23a/M1. Follow the signs to East
Midlands airport and then to Castle Donington
racetrack. (Map 8)**

Due to its close proximity to East Midlands Airport, Castle Donington motor-racing circuit, and the M1, this 19th-century miners' pub positively bustles with activity. Andy and Kylie Smith, who took over in Spring 2005, have renovated the exterior and gardens, and en-suite rooms are open for business from December 2006. Inside, there's a traditionally furnished bar, with low-beamed ceiling and glowing coal fires, while adjoining dining areas have a smart, contemporary feel, with sea-grass floors, colour-washed walls, darkwood furnishings, and several aquariums. Expect a relaxed and informal atmosphere.

Interesting menus embrace modern and traditional pub dishes. At lunch, order a light snack from the list of paninis and baguettes, or tuck into duck-leg confit, Thai green curry or seafood jambalaya from the bistro menu (also served 5.30-7pm). Fresh fish features strongly on the dinner menu, perhaps lemon sole with vanilla sauce, alongside the likes of venison with blueberry sauce. Meat comes from a local farm and game from nearby shoots. Popular jazz evenings and excellent Sunday lunches complete the picture.

Derby

The Three Horseshoes Inn

Country pub

'Whether it be snacks or inventive mains, well-executed food has gained Ian quite a following.'

Breedon-on-the-Hill, Derby,
Derbyshire DE73 8AN
Telephone: +44(0)1332 695129
contact@thehorseshoes.com
www.thehorseshoes.com

After making a huge success of The Nag's Head at nearby Castle Donington, talented chef-landlord Ian Davison has revitalised The Three Horseshoes. Staff and loyal diners have followed him to this Grade II-listed village local, formerly a farrier's, which now blends the classic and the contemporary throughout its comfortably refurbished interior. Layers have been stripped back to reveal original features – imposing fireplaces, exposed brick, tiled floors – with a modern ambience reflected in seagrass matting, chunky tables and chairs and an eclectic mix of memorabilia decorating the walls.

The real draw, however, is Ian's food, which is freshly prepared from local produce, notably game from shoots, and traditional Derbyshire cheeses. Whether it be snacks of beef stir-fry with rice, or bacon and poached-egg salad, or inventive mains such as blackened swordfish with crème fraîche and lime, or fillet of beef in Cajun spices, this well-executed food has gained Ian quite a following. Desserts are of the homemade, comforting variety – bread-and-butter pudding, perhaps, or chocolate-whisky trifle.

Prices: **Restaurant main course from £13.95. Bar snack from £4.50. House wine £11.95.**
Last orders: **Bar: afternoon 14.30; evening: 23.00. Food: lunch 13.45; dinner 21.00 (no food on Sunday).**
Closed: **Never.**
Food: **Modern British.**
Real ale: **Courage Directors Bitter, Caledonian Deuchars IPA, Theakston Ales, Marston's Pedigree.**
Other points: **Smoking area. Dogs welcome in the bar. Garden. Car park. Wheelchair access.**
Directions: **Exit 23a/M1. Follow signs to Ashby, and Breedon church is easily visible from the A453. The Three Horseshoes is in the middle of the village. (Map 8)**

...for events

Hardwick

Hardwick Inn

Country pub

Hardwick Park, Chesterfield,
Derbyshire S44 5QJ
Telephone: +44(0)1246 850245
batty@hardwickinn.co.uk
www.hardwickinn.co.uk

'There is a delightful summer garden with super views.'

Prices: Set lunch £13.25 and dinner £14.25 in the carvery restaurant. Bar main course from £6.95. House wine £8.25. Plus an extensive bar menu.
Last orders: **Bar: 23.00. Food: lunch 21.30 (Sunday 21.00).**
Closed: **Rarely.**
Food: **Traditional British.**
Real ale: **Theakston Old Peculier, Theakston XB, Ruddles County Ale, Marston's Pedigree, Green King Old Speckled Hen.**
Other points: **No smoking. Children welcome. Garden. Car park. Wheelchair access to the restaurant/pub.**
Directions: **Two and a quarter miles from Exit 29/M1. Take the A6175, then in a quarter of a mile, turn left and follow the tourist-board signs to the pub. (Map 8)**

Dating from around 1600 and built of locally quarried sandstone, this striking building was once the lodge for Hardwick Hall, which is owned by the National Trust, so the inn draws much of its trade from visitors exploring the magnificent park and lovely Elizabethan hall. The inn, owned by the Batty family for three generations, has a rambling interior that features good period details, such as mullioned windows, oak ceiling beams, large stone fireplaces with open fires, and a fine, 18th-century, carved settle.

Traditional bar food takes in ploughman's lunches, and a whole range of steaks, jacket potatoes and sandwiches, with daily chalkboard specials offering hearty homemade pies (steak-and-kidney), casseroles (game and ale) and, a feature of the pub, fresh fish delivered daily from Scarborough. Look out for beer-battered haddock or cod, and crab and lobster salads, or opt for one of the daily carvery roasts, usually including topside of beef and Hardwick Estate lamb. With Theakston ales on tap and a delightful summer garden with super views, the pub is a useful pit stop for weary M1 travellers.

Bideford

Riversford Hotel

Hotel

'Public rooms include the light, airy restaurant with lovely garden views.'

Limers Lane, Northam, Bideford,
Devon EX39 2RG
Telephone: +44(0)1237 474239
riversford@aol.com
www.riversford.co.uk

The Jarrard family run their homely hotel with style and simplicity, and have built up loyal support over the last 30 years. As well as offering quality accommodation and food, the hotel is well placed and there are good family beaches nearby. All 15 en-suite bedrooms are well appointed and individually decorated in light, relaxing colours; the suites have four-poster beds. Public rooms include the light, airy restaurant with lovely garden views to the River Torridge and beyond.

Nigel Jarrard presides over the kitchen and is to be praised for sourcing quality local ingredients. Game comes from local shoots, Somerset and Dorset cheeses are from Hawkridge Farm, vegetables are grown locally, meat comes from a local supplier and cream is from Definitely Devon Dairies. The menu is strong on the traditional, with dishes such as mixed grill, an impressive choice of steaks, and pork chops with mustard sauce. Fish is a speciality, and local sea bass could be teamed with dill-and-orange sauce or whole Dover sole with saffron-and-cream sauce. The short selection of wines continues the good-value theme.

Rooms: 15. **Double room from £80, single from £50.**
Prices: **Set lunch £14, set dinner £18. Main course from £8. House wine £12.**
Last orders: **Food: lunch 15.00; dinner 21.30.**
Closed: **Never.**
Food: **Specialises in fresh produce and local seafood.**
Other points: **Smoking area. Children welcome. Dogs welcome overnight. Garden. Car park. Wheelchair access.**
Directions: **Exit 27/M5. One mile north of Bideford on the A386, Limers Lane is on the right. (Map 3)**

...for events

MEMBER
64
ENTRY

Chagford

Sandy Park Inn

Country inn

Sandy Park, Chagford,
Dartmoor National Park,
Devon TQ13 8JW
Telephone: +44(0)1647 433267
sandyparkinn@aol.com
www.sandyparkinn.co.uk

'Those booked in for the night are in for a treat.'

Rooms: **5, 3 with private bathroom. Double/ twin room from £38, single from £45.**
Prices: **Set Sunday lunch £12. Restaurant main course from £12. Bar main course from £6. House wine £10.75.**
Last orders: **Bar: 22.30. Food: lunch 14.30; dinner 21.00.**
Closed: **Rarely.**
Food: **Traditional British.**
Real ale: **St Austell Tribute, Otter Bitter. Guest beers, changing weekly.**
Other points: **Smoking area. Children welcome in the restaurant. Well-behaved dogs welcome in the bar and overnight at £5 per night. Car park. Wheelchair access to the pub.**
Directions: **Exit 31/M5. From the A30 go through Whiddon Down and turn left towards Moretonhampstead. After five miles, the inn is on the right. (Map 4)**
See pub walk on page 462

This thatched 17th-century inn north of Chagford is the perfect Dartmoor hideaway, close to fabulous fishing on the River Teign, Castle Drogo (National Trust), and miles of moorland walking. Follow an invigorating day out on Dartmoor with a pint of Otter Bitter in the traditional, yet comfortably refurbished bar, replete with a glowing log fire, rugs on worn flagstones and a warm green-and-terracotta décor. The cosy 'snug' room is ideal for groups gathering to drink and dine.

Chalkboards list the beers on tap, the wines by the glass, and the short, creative menu that reflects the seasons and the rich supply of locally sourced foods. At lunch, tuck into hearty sandwiches, pasta meals or warm duck-and-bacon salad. Local meats and fish delivered daily from Devon ports translate to venison casserole, roast leg of lamb with mint sauce, and roast cod on spring onions and tomatoes on the evening menu. Those booked in for the night are in for a treat as the good-value bedrooms are well above pub average – expect a large bed, flat-screen TV, CD player, super bathroom, and views across rolling Devon countryside.

MEMBER
65
ENTRY

Stoke Lodge Hotel

Country-house hotel

Cinders Lane, Stoke Fleming, Dartmouth,
Devon TQ6 0RA
Telephone: +44(0)1803 770523
mail@stokelodge.co.uk
www.stokelodge.co.uk

'A tremendous holiday base, and there's plenty to keep the children amused.'

Set high above Start Bay, this charming country-house hotel has magnificent sea views. The south-facing building, which is mainly 17th-century with an 18th-century façade, has been sympathetically extended, and has much to offer: lawns, terraces, tennis court, an outdoor and indoor swimming pool, plus a sauna and spa. You can't fail to be impressed by the comfortable décor in the lounge-cum-bar and restaurant, and by the relaxed ambience and friendly welcome. Several of the individually designed bedrooms have four-poster beds, and all are bang up to date.

The Garden Restaurant offers an extensive set dinner menu of classic country-house cooking that takes note of quality local ingredients. Traditional but superbly executed dishes may include broccoli-and-stilton soup, braised beef in red-wine and mushroom sauce and lemon sole with parsley butter. Old favourites appear on the dessert menu, notably sticky toffee pudding and lemon tart with fruit coulis. This makes a tremendous holiday base, and there's plenty to keep the children amused.

Rooms: **25. Double room from £89, single from £61.**
Prices: **Set lunch £15.95 and dinner £22.50. Main course from £12.95. House wine £10.75.**
Last orders: **Food: lunch 13.45; dinner 21.00.**
Closed: **Never.**
Food: **Modern British.**
Other points: **Children welcome. Dogs welcome overnight. Garden. Car park. Indoor and outdoor swimming pools.**
Directions: **M5/A38. From the M5 at Exeter, take the A38 towards Plymouth. Turn off at Buckfastleigh and follow the signs to Totnes and then Dartmouth (A381 or A3122). Turn right to Stoke Fleming. (Map 4)**

...for competitions

Holbeton

The Dartmoor Union Inn

Fore Street, Holbeton, Plymouth,
Devon PL8 1NE
Telephone: +44(0)1752 830288
info@dartmoorunion.co.uk
www.dartmoorunion.co.uk

Country pub

'A classy and very comfortable dining pub.'

Prices: **Set lunch £12.95. Restaurant main course from £9.95. Bar meal from £6.95. House wine £9.95.**
Last orders: **Bar: afternoon 15.00; evening 23.00 (Sunday 22.30). Food: lunch 14.00 (Sunday 15.30); dinner 21.00.**
Closed: **Rarely.**
Food: **Modern British/French.**
Real ale: **Dartmoor Union Ales. Two guest beers.**
Other points: **Smoking area. Children welcome. Dogs welcome in the bar. Garden. Car park. Wheelchair access.**
Directions: **Turn left off the A38 at Ivybridge and, at the roundabout, take the last exit over the flyover. Turn left through Ermington on to the A379 towards Plymouth, then take a left turn to Holbeton. (Map 4)**

To locate this thriving, award-winning gastropub, first negotiate the winding lanes through Holbeton and then look for a polished brass plaque on the wall of a grey stone building – there is no swinging pub sign! Step through the solid wooden front door into a different world, for this is no rustic Devon village local. Totally revamped in 2004, this 16th-century building is now a classy and very comfortable dining pub.

Polished wooden floors and leather sofas fronting a blazing log fire in the bar set the scene for some first-class bar meals – crab-and-parmesan baguette, scrambled eggs with Dartmouth smoked salmon – accompanied by a pint of home-brewed Union Pride. Alternatively, opt for the excellent-value set lunch menu – chicken-and-tarragon risotto followed by beef-and-horseradish pie. A meal in the inviting dining room, with its red walls and subtle lighting, may take in roasted-tomato soup with basil oil, local lamb noisettes with Madeira jus, and sticky toffee pudding with caramel sauce. A passion for local foods, some excellent-value wines and courtyard seating complete the picture.

MEMBER
67
ENTRY

Bed and breakfast

Langleigh Park House

Langleigh Park, Ilfracombe,
Devon EX34 8BG
Telephone: +44(0)1271 862158
joan@langleigh.co.uk
www.langleigh.co.uk

'Walking, views and atmosphere: Langleigh Park House ticks all the right boxes.'

Walking, views and atmosphere: Langleigh Park House ticks all the right boxes for those after a relaxing and scenic break. This former Victorian guesthouse, known as the 'castle on the hill', exudes grandeur, but up close, has a welcoming, homely feel that immediately puts you at ease. The splendour of the entrance hall is matched by eight individual upstairs bedrooms, and while they may not score highly in the fashion or furnishing stakes, they have a traditional appeal – some have four-posters – and a pleasing, comfortable lived-in feel.

And there's plenty to do here. When you're not exploring nearby Ilfracombe town or taking a coastal walk, cycling or fishing, soak up the atmosphere of the large lounge or the bar with log fire. Clay shooting is also an option in the woodlands of Langleigh's 18-acre grounds; gun-cleaning facilities are available. Indoor diversions include a pool table, darts and TV. Home-grown and local produce make up most of the menu, and breakfast is a hearty affair of farm eggs and local bacon, or something continental.

Rooms: **8.** Double/twin room from £25, single from £35. Family suites from £25.
Closed: October to March.
Other points: Smoking area. No smoking in bedrooms. Children welcome. Dogs welcome overnight. Garden. Car park.
Directions: Exit 27/M5. Take the A361 to Barnstaple, Braunton and Ilfracombe. Turn left into Church Hill, which leads to Langleigh Road and Langleigh Park. (Map 3)

...for the latest news

Lynton

Highcliffe House

Bed and breakfast

Sinai Hill, Lynton, Devon EX35 6AR
Telephone: +44(0)1598 752235
info@highcliffehouse.co.uk
www.highcliffehouse.co.uk

'Sit back and take it all in from the comfort of this charming house.'

Rooms: **6. Double/twin room from £38 per person, single from £56.**
Prices: **Set dinner £24.50 by prior arrangement.**
Closed: **December and January.**
Other points: **No smoking. Garden. Car park.**
Directions: **Exit 27/M5. From north Devon, take the A361 to South Molton, then the A399 to Blackmoor Gate and the A39 to Lynton and follow the signs to the Old Village. (Map 4)**

Stunning views can be savoured from this former Victorian gentleman's summer residence, situated in an elevated position in the Exmoor National Park. If you're not a keen walker, simply sit back and take it all in from the comfort of this charming house, which has retained its suaveness and its bold furnishings in the sitting room. En-suite bedrooms create a distinctive period style, with their Rococo, Tudor, Colonial or French themes, and each features a huge hand-carved bed. There are useful extras, too, such as DVD/CD players and perfumes.

The warm welcome starts on arrival as you unwind with coffee and biscuits in the quiet room. Breakfast is served in the dining room, and at weekends, you can return later to enjoy a candlelit menu that changes daily. Start with pheasant, redcurrant and port pâté with homemade bread and then move on to roast Brixham sea bass with lemon-and-thyme butter, or pork medallions in cider and cream. And don't worry about tucking into the homemade puds and West Country cheeses – there are plenty of walks and National Trust gardens to explore nearby.

St Vincent House Hotel & Restaurant

Hotel

'The bedrooms, named after ships, give a nod to its nautical heritage.'

Castle Hill, Lynton, Devon EX35 6JA
Telephone: +44(0)1598 752244
welcome@st-vincent-hotel.co.uk
www.st-vincent-hotel.co.uk

The Grade II-listed house, built in 1834 by Captain Green who served with Admiral Nelson, is named after the battle of St Vincent off the coast of Portugal. Tastefully and elegantly furnished throughout, you'll find it easy to feel at home at this smart hotel. The bedrooms, named after ships, give a nod to its nautical heritage, as does the artwork and the design of the upper-floor bedrooms which resemble roomy cabins. All have en-suite bathrooms, broadband access and tea-making facilities.

Some fine food is served in the breakfast/dining room. The menu draws on local, seasonal produce: fish is landed at Appledore, and venison, beef and lamb is from Exmoor. Jean-Paul, who is Belgian, includes some of his country's specialities in his menu as well as his homegrown herbs, and there are imaginative combinations, such as lamb marinated in olive oil and fresh herbs, served with Mediterranean roasted vegetables, whole sea bass grilled with fennel, and saffron-and-parmesan risotto cakes with herb butter. There's a well-chosen wine list, Belgian beers, and a Somerset apple brandy.

Rooms: 5. Double/twin room from £65, single from £40.
Prices: Set dinner £24.95. House wine £11.
Last orders: Food: Dinner 21.00.
Closed: Lunch and January to Easter.
Food: Belgian and French specialities.
Real ale: Duvel, Kriek, Leffe, Chimay.
Other points: No smoking. Children over 12 welcome. Garden. Car park. Free wi-fi broadband.
Directions: Exit 27/M5. Take the A361 to South Molton. Turn right at the roundabout, and take the A399 to Lynton at Blackmore Gate. Turn right on to the A39 to Barbrook and then left at the petrol station, continuing towards Lynmouth. Up the hill, take the second left and the hotel is adjacent to the Exmoor Museum. (Map 4)

...for recipe ideas

Modbury

The California Country Inn & Restaurant

Country pub

California Cross, Modbury, Ivybridge,
Devon PL21 0SG
Telephone: +44(0)1548 821449
california@bellinns.entadsl.com
www.californiacountryinn.co.uk

'Reminders of its famous past can be seen in the old prints, photographs and artefacts that adorn the walls.'

Prices: **Set lunch £16.50. Set dinner £26.50. Restaurant main course from £13.95. Bar main course from £7.50. House wine £10.95.**
Last orders: **Bar: afternoon 14.00; evening 21.00. Restaurant: dinner 21.00 (Sunday 20.30).**
Closed: **Never.**
Food: **Modern/traditional British.**
Real ale: **Fuller's London Pride, Greene King Old Speckled Hen, Bass, Coachman's IPA.**
Other points: **Smoking area. Children welcome. Dogs welcome in the bar. Garden. Car park. Wheelchair access.**
Directions: **M5 to Exeter. A38 exit at Wrangaton, then turn left on to Kingsbridge Road. Take the A3121 and continue on to the B3196, and the pub is on the right-hand side. (Map 4)**

A celebrated landmark throughout the 19th century, The California Inn was an important staging post between Dartmouth and Plymouth. Although much extended, reminders of its famous past can be seen in the old prints, photographs and artefacts that adorn the walls throughout the rambling, beamed and carpeted bar and in the Coachman's Restaurant.

Since taking over in 2003, the Bell family have transformed it from a 'basic drinker's pub with pool table and skittle alley' to a popular dining venue, where menus focus on quality produce sourced within 25 miles of the pub. Chef Tim Whiston offers a traditional pub menu in the bar, including home-cooked ham, ploughman's lunch and beer-battered cod and chips, while the restaurant carte and chalkboard specials list more imaginative modern dishes. Follow pan-fried scallops and smoked-bacon salad, with beef Wellington and red-wine sauce, or grilled John Dory with anchovies and caper butter, and round off with a plate of Devon cheeses.

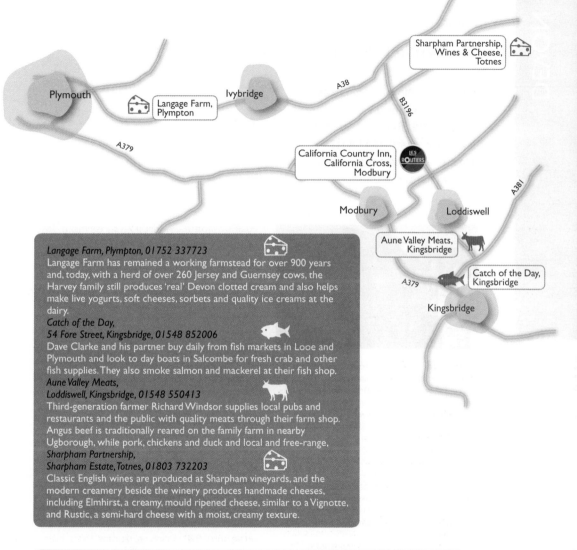

Sharpham Partnership,
Wines & Cheese,
Totnes

Plymouth

Langage Farm,
Plympton

Ivybridge

A38

B3196

California Country Inn,
California Cross,
Modbury

LES ROUTIERS

A379

A381

Modbury

Loddiswell

Aune Valley Meats,
Kingsbridge

A379

Catch of the Day,
Kingsbridge

Kingsbridge

Langage Farm, Plympton, 01752 337723
Langage Farm has remained a working farmstead for over 900 years and, today, with a herd of over 260 Jersey and Guernsey cows, the Harvey family still produces 'real' Devon clotted cream and also helps make live yogurts, soft cheeses, sorbets and quality ice creams at the dairy.

Catch of the Day,
54 Fore Street, Kingsbridge, 01548 852006
Dave Clarke and his partner buy daily from fish markets in Looe and Plymouth and look to day boats in Salcombe for fresh crab and other fish supplies. They also smoke salmon and mackerel at their fish shop.

Aune Valley Meats,
Loddiswell, Kingsbridge, 01548 550413
Third-generation farmer Richard Windsor supplies local pubs and restaurants and the public with quality meats through their farm shop. Angus beef is traditionally reared on the family farm in nearby Ugborough, while pork, chickens and duck and local and free-range,

Sharpham Partnership,
Sharpham Estate, Totnes, 01803 732203
Classic English wines are produced at Sharpham vineyards, and the modern creamery beside the winery produces handmade cheeses, including Elmhirst, a creamy, mould ripened cheese, similar to a Vignotte, and Rustic, a semi-hard cheese with a moist, creamy texture.

Visit the Farmers' Market
Kingsbridge farmers' market is held on the first Saturday of every month from 9am to 1pm.
The Ivybridge farmers' market is on the third Saturday of every month, from 9am to 1pm.

Moretonhampstead

The White Hart Hotel

Hotel

The Square, Moretonhampstead,
Dartmoor National Park,
Devon TQ13 8NF
Telephone: +44(0)1647 441340
enquiries@whitehartdartmoor.co.uk
www.whitehartdartmoor.co.uk

'Oodles of character melded with modern comforts.'

Rooms: **20. Double/twin room from £45, single from £60. Family room from £120.**
Prices: **Sunday lunch £14.50. Set dinner £19.50. Restaurant main course from £9. Bar main course from £6.50. House wine £9.95.**
Last orders: **Bar: 21.30. Food: lunch 14.30; dinner 21.30.**
Closed: **Never.**
Food: **Traditional British.**
Real ale: **St Austell Tribute.**
Other points: **Smoking area. Children welcome. Dogs welcome overnight. Garden and courtyard. Licence for civil weddings. Wheelchair access overnight. Residents' lounge and two function rooms.**
Directions: **Exit 31/M5. A30 signposted to Okehampton, then the first exit on to the B3212 into Moretonhampstead – approximately 10 miles. The hotel is in the centre of town, and parking is 50 yards from the entrance. (Map 4)**

Well located on the doorstep of Dartmoor National Park, the Grade-II listed White Hart Hotel has oodles of character melded with modern comforts. The building, dating back to 1639, was once a Georgian posting house between Plymouth and London. Recent refurbishment has enhanced its attractive original features, such as stunning marble fireplaces and the grandest entrance, and the rooms have been tastefully decorated in heritage colours, with smart fabrics adding to the quality look and feel.

Bedrooms are simply but sumptuously attired and come with nice touches, such as White Hart emblems on bed throws and tasteful art on the walls, but have all the mod cons, too – plasma-screen TVs and DVDs. After a day exploring the moors, cosy up in the flagstoned bar, with its large open fireplace, for some hearty pub food. Alternatively, settle into the smart restaurant for a menu that majors in seasonal Devon produce: fish from Brixham and beef and Dartmoor lamb from local butchers. An outside courtyard for dining is a bonus in summer and function rooms are available all year round.

Plymouth

Kubes Restaurant

Restaurant

13 Frankfort Gate, Plymouth,
Devon PL1 1QA
Telephone: +44(0)1752 266793

'Tuck into the local seafood platter with crab risotto and sauce Nero, or seared venison with chocolate and red-wine jus.'

Located on one side of the very angular Frankfort Gate, hence its name, this popular city-centre restaurant has two identities. During the day it is a casual affair, drawing in shoppers and passing trade for simple, reasonably priced lunches, while the evening sees it transformed into an intimate, fine-dining restaurant. Soft up-lighting, glowing candles, simple furnishings and huge wooden window shutters create a cosy and relaxing French bistro feel, which is proving a hit with Plymouth folk, so it's best to reserve a table.

Seasonal dinner menus make good use of local ingredients from a network of small suppliers, including game from Painter Dave on the South Hams shoot, and fresh fruit and vegetables from friends who have allotments. Linger over seared pigeon with black pudding and balsamic-and-raspberry dressing, or white-bean soup with truffle cream, and then tuck into the local seafood platter with crab risotto and sauce Nero, or seared venison with chocolate and red-wine jus. Finish with the delicious glazed rice pudding with fruit sauce. The wine list favours the New World and offers good tasting notes.

Prices: **Set lunch £7.95. Set dinner £21.95. House wine £11.50.**
Last orders: **Food: lunch 14.30 (Sunday 16.00); dinner 22.00.**
Closed: **Two weeks in January.**
Food: **Modern British.**
Other points: **No smoking. Wheelchair access (not WC).**
Directions: **In Plymouth off the Western Approach A374. (Map 3)**

...for events

73

MEMBER ENTRY

Slapton

The Tower Inn

Country inn

Church Road, Slapton, Kingsbridge,
Devon TQ7 2PN
Telephone: +44(0)1548 580216
towerinn@slapton.org
www.thetowerinn.com

'A truly atmospheric village pub.'

Rooms: **3. Double room from £60, single from £40.**
Prices: **Restaurant main course from £9. House wine from £10.**
Last orders: **Bar: afternoon 14.30 (Sunday 15.00); evening 23.00. Food: lunch 14.00 (Sunday 14.30); dinner 21.30.**
Closed: **Rarely.**
Food: **Modern British.**
Real ale: **Butcombe Bitter, St Austell Tribute, Badger Tanglefoot. One guest beer.**
Other points: **Smoking area. Children welcome. Dogs welcome overnight. Garden and courtyard. Car park. Wheelchair access to the restaurant/pub.**
Directions: **Off the A379 between Dartmouth and Kingsbridge, or off the A381 between Totnes and Kingsbridge. (Map 4)**

Visitors exploring Slapton Ley Nature Reserve and South Devon coast should venture inland to seek out this ancient inn. Tucked away behind the church and standing beside the dramatic, ivy-clad ruins of the chantry tower, the 14th-century Tower Inn is a truly atmospheric village pub. It was built to accommodate the artisans working on the monastic collegiate next door and later became the college's guesthouse.

Six hundred years on and guests continue to be warmly welcomed by Annette and Andrew Hammett. The welcome is followed by pints of local ale and plates of good modern pub food. Expect hearty sandwiches (try the local crab) and more traditional dishes, such as sausage and mash, at lunchtime. From the evening menu, there are treats along the lines of smoked haddock and bacon fishcake, followed by whole sea bass roasted with lemon and tarragon, and orange-and-treacle tart with clotted cream. Stone walls, open fires, scrubbed oak tables and flagstone floors characterise the historic interior. There are three cottage-style, en-suite bedrooms and a super rear garden.

Stokenham

The Tradesman's Arms

Country pub

'The location and views are charming.'

Stokenham, Kingsbridge, Devon TQ7 2SZ
Telephone: +44(0)1548 580313
nick@thetradesmansarms.com
www.thetradesmansarms.com

Hidden away in a sleepy Devon village, The Tradesman's Arms looks like everyone's ideal country pub. It dates from the 14th-century, has a part-thatched roof and is surrounded by rambling shrubs, plus the location and views are charming. Comprising a simply furnished main bar with stone fireplace, wood-burning stove and heavy beams, and an equally informal dining room, it is the domain of affable landlord Nick Abbot. He's passionate about offering good food and, in particular, locally sourced produce.

Meats and fish are smoked on the premises, fish is from day boats at Brixham and Plymouth, scallops are dived for in Start Bay, vegetables are grown four miles away, and Sutton Eddystone is brewed along the road. This translates to scallops with smoked bacon and red onions, smoked haddock fishcakes, whole baked sea bass, and fillet steak with red-wine sauce as well as light lunches of hot sandwiches, daily curries and various omelettes. The pub is named after the men who traded in Dartmouth and stopped at the pub for their first night en route home to Kingsbridge.

Prices: **Restaurant main course from £8.95. Bar main course from £8.95. House wine £9.95.**
Last orders: **Bar: 23.00 (all day at weekends in summer). Food: lunch 14.30; dinner 21.30.**
Closed: **Never.**
Food: **Modern British.**
Real ale: **Bass, Brakspear Bitter, South Hams Eddystone, Devon Pride. Two guest beers.**
Other points: **Smoking area. Dogs welcome. Garden. Car park.**
Directions: **Just off the A379, behind the village green between Dartmouth and Kingsbridge, one mile inland from Torcross. (Map 4)**

...for competitions

Torquay

The Orange Tree Restaurant

Restaurant

14-16 Parkhill Road, Torquay,
Devon TQ1 2AL
Telephone: +44(0)1803 213936
enquiries@orangetreerestaurant.com
www.orangetreerestaurant.com

'Pan-fried skate with a sultana, beetroot and caper butter tickles the taste buds.'

Prices: **Set dinner £28.50. Restaurant main course from £13.95. House wine £13.50**
Last orders: **Food: 21.30.**
Closed: **Never.**
Food: **Traditional British with European influences.**
Other points: **No smoking. Children over eight welcome. Wheelchair access.**
Directions: **Exit 31/M5. Take the A380 towards Torquay seafront. Turn left to the harbour and left again at the clock tower. Then take the first right and turn immediately right again. The Orange Tree is 70 yards along on the left. (Map 4)**

A bright orange canopy makes it easy to spot The Orange Tree, and it's one not to miss as its reputation for good food continues to grow. Everything from stocks and terrines to desserts, is made on the premises. It's a total dining experience, from the tastefully decorated restaurant and new conservatory to the extensive menu and wonderful service. Dishes include some of Devon's finest fish, meat and organic duck to a winning line-up of prime cheeses.

Chef Tony Fagan picks only the best and everything is skillfully executed. His venison with prunes steeped in Calvados is exemplary. The fish, say pan-fried skate with a sultana, beetroot and caper butter, or lemon sole with verjuice, tickle the taste buds, and vegetarians will love the imaginative artichoke-and-mushroom Wellington. Tony's signature dessert is the lavish Torbay Swan – a chocolate meringue swan filled with Kahlua-infused cream – but a less extravagantly turned out pear tarte Tatin with cinnamon ice cream is just as heavenly. A sensibly priced wine list complements the menu.

Country-house hotel

'Orestone Manor has a magical colonial feel and is superior in so many ways.'

Orestone Manor

Rockhouse Lane, Maidencombe, Torquay, Devon TQ1 4SX
Telephone: +44(0)1803 328098
enquiries@orestonemanor.com
www.orestonemanor.com

Elegance and comfort pervade this stylishly furnished Georgian house set on the Torbay coastline. Orestone Manor has a magical colonial feel and is superior in so many ways: views from the hotel across to Lyme Bay are superb, the bedrooms magnificent and the food and service first class. Its inspired décor successfully combines several styles, from the impressive colonial-style dining room through to the 12 lavish, individually furnished suites and bedrooms. All are en-suite and have tremendous sea views.

Dining is a real treat, chef Darren Bunn's menus offer contemporary dishes using the best seasonal local ingredients and produce from the hotel's gardens. Set lunches are superb value and include Orestone fishcakes and line-caught sea bass with mussel-and-saffron chowder. For dinner, try Start Bay scallops with roasted-cauliflower purée, followed by aged prime Devon fillet of beef with port jus, with passionfruit soufflé to finish. The 150-strong wine list includes fab options at good prices. Snacks, lunches and teas can be enjoyed in the conservatory throughout the day.

Rooms: 12. Double/twin room from £125, single from £89.
Prices: Set lunch £14.95. Restaurant evening main course from £18.50. House wine £14.95.
Last orders: Food: lunch 14.00; dinner 21.00. Open for afternoon teas.
Closed: Never.
Food: Modern European.
Other points: Smoking area. Children welcome. Dogs welcome. Garden. Car park.
Directions: From Torquay, follow the A379 (signposted Teignmouth) up Watcombe Hill. Fifty yards after Brunel Manor, turn right down Rockhouse Lane. The hotel is signposted from the top of Rockhouse Lane. (Map 4)

...for special offers

Yealmpton

The Rose & Crown & Seafood Restaurant

Country pub and restaurant

Market Street, Yealmpton, Devon PL8 2EB
Telephone: +44(0)1752 880223/880502
info@theroseandcrown.co.uk
www.theroseandcrown.co.uk

'This is the place to enjoy fresh fish delivered daily from local markets and fishermen.'

Prices: **Set lunch £12.95. Restaurant main course from £10.95. Bar main course for £4.25. House wine £9.95.**
Last orders: **Bar: 23.00. Food: lunch 14.00 (Sunday 15.30); dinner 21.30 (Sunday 21.00). Seafood restaurant: lunch 14.00; dinner 21.00 (Friday and Saturday 21.30). Seafood restaurant closed Sunday.**
Closed: **Never.**
Food: **Modern European and fish.**
Real ale: **Courage Best Bitter, Otter Bitter.**
Other points: **Smoking area in the bar. Children welcome. Dogs welcome in the bar. Garden. Car park. Wheelchair access.**
Directions: **A38. Turn off at the Ivybridge exit towards Plymouth. Follow signs to Ermington, go through the village and turn right and right again. Yealmpton is the next village, and the pub and restaurant is on the right opposite the petrol station. (Map 3)**

Reputed to be the oldest pub in the South Hams – and opposite the original Old Mother Hubbard's cottage – The Rose and Crown has been given a radical makeover from sleepy local to a modern, food-driven pub with a separate seafood restaurant. The bar area is roomy with rustic seating and tables at which to enjoy light bites and snacks by the roaring fire. Seafood features here, too, as does game and local duck. The set-lunch menu is particularly good value.

Across the driveway in a renovated outbuilding, The Seafood Restaurant is run separately with a different kitchen team. This is the place to enjoy fresh fish delivered daily from local markets and fishermen. Again, a set-lunch menu is a bargain, but choices such as diver-caught Lime Bay scallops with sweet-potato and mushroom hash and coriander oil, followed by whole Dover sole caught by a local boat, makes the à la carte menu equally irresistible. A 'secret' walled garden with water feature is highly recommended for alfresco dining in summer. Part of the successful Wykeham Inns group (see Dartmoor Union and Webbs Inn entries).

Charmouth

Fernhill Hotel

Hotel

'A genuine home from home for their guests.'

Fernhill, Charmouth, Dorset DT6 6BX
Telephone: +44(0)1297 560492
mail@fernhill-hotel.co.uk
www.fernhill-hotel.co.uk

When Wendy and Chris Satterthwaite moved into Fernhill in March 2005, they always wanted it to be a genuine home from home for their guests. Set between the beautiful Dorset village of Charmouth and the historic town of Lyme Regis, this once-faded hotel has been injected with new life by the couple. With magnificent views over the lush Dorset countryside, Fernhill has a heated swimming pool and a holistic treatment and well-being centre, where Wendy – a qualified nutritionist and therapist – offers a range of treatments.

Each of the guest bedrooms is individually and stylishly designed, with much of the furniture sourced from antique shops, auctions and trips abroad. Locally sourced produce – organic, wherever possible – forms the backbone of the menus in both the café/bar and the colonial-style restaurant, with all meat, fish and poultry coming from Dorset and Devon. Start with local Blue Vinney and nettle tart and move on to plaice with wild garlic, lemon and primroses, or rack of lamb with lentil cassoulet and braised red cabbage. Finish with lemon posset or local ice cream.

Rooms: 12. Double/twin room from £110, single from £45. Family room from £130.
Prices: Restaurant main course from £11.50.
Last orders: Food: lunch 14.00 (only during summer months) dinner 20.30.
Closed: January and first two weeks of February.
Food: Modern European.
Other points: No smoking. Garden. Children welcome. Car park. Swimming pool.
Directions: Exit 25/M5. Take the A3052 just off the large roundabout on the A35, signposted to Lyme Regis. (Map 4)

...for the latest news

Corscombe

The Fox Inn

Corscombe, Dorchester,
Dorset DT2 0NS
Telephone: +44(0)1935 891330
dine@fox-inn.co.uk
www.fox-inn.co.uk

Country inn

'It's everybody's idea of the perfect country inn.'

Rooms: 4. Double room from £75, single occupancy from £55.
Prices: Main course from £8.50. House wine £10.50.
Last orders: Bar: afternoon 15.00; evening 23.00.
Food: lunch 14.00; dinner 21.00 (Friday and Saturday 21.30).
Closed: Rarely.
Food: Modern British.
Real ale: Exmoor Ale, Fox's Ales.
Other points: Smoking area. Well-behaved children welcome. Garden/conservatory. Car park.
Directions: From Yeovil, take the A37 towards Dorchester. After one mile, turn right towards Corscombe and follow the lane for five and a half miles. Alternatively, take the A356 from Crewkerne to Maiden Newton for five miles. (Map 4)

'No chips or microwaves' is the rule at this pretty little thatched pub of stone and cob, built in 1620 as a cider house and lost down a web of narrow lanes deep in unspoilt Dorset countryside. It's everybody's idea of the perfect country inn, with roses above the door and two charming beamed bars, one with a huge inglenook fireplace, stone-flagged floors and gingham-clothed tables, the other filled with old pine furniture and chatty locals quaffing pints of Exmoor Ale. No modern-day intrusions here or in the plant-festooned rear conservatory, with its sturdy, long wooden table.

Food at the Fox is country-pub cooking at its best, with all dishes freshly prepared from quality produce, including local-estate venison with a rich game sauce, and rack of Dorset lamb with rosemary jus, and the chalkboard features fresh fish from West Bay, in such dishes as sea bass with fennel and dill and grilled lobster. Homemade desserts include sticky toffee pudding, while lunchtime ploughman's lunch and baguettes are good hearty snacks. Tucked under the thatch are four cottagey en-suite bedrooms.

www.routiers.co.uk

Studland Bay

Manor House

Country-house hotel

'En-suite bedrooms are charming, light and spacious, with period furnishings and atmosphere.'

Beach Road, Studland Bay,
Dorset BH19 3AU
Telephone: +44(0)1929 450288
themanorhousehotel@lineone.net
www.themanorhousehotel.com

The early 18th-century Gothic manor house stands in 20 acres of secluded grounds with delightful views over Studland Bay, and makes for an elegant and comfortable stay. Despite its olde-worlde charm, it offers the latest conveniences and top-notch service. The baronial-feel, oak-panelled dining room with fireplace and dark-wood furniture and its adjoining bright conservatory and comfortable, country-style lounge all have sea views. En-suite bedrooms are charming, light and spacious with period furnishings and atmosphere, and many have sea or garden views. There are five four-poster suites.

Rooms: 21. Double room from £82 per person, single £107, including dinner.
Prices: **Set dinner £30 (four courses). House wine £12.**
Last orders: **Food: lunch 14.00; dinner 21.00.**
Closed: **Never.**
Food: **Modern British/European.**
Other points: **Smoking area. Dogs welcome overnight. Garden. Car park. Wheelchair access to the restaurant/pub.**
Directions: **Three miles from Swanage; three miles from Sandbanks Ferry on Beach Road. (Map 4)**

Dinner is a meal to look forward to, with chef Giuseppe Singaguglia sourcing many ingredients locally. Venison comes from local estates, while shellfish is delivered from Portland, and regional cheeses include Dorset Blue Vinney, Stinking Bishop and Somerset brie. The evening menu may include tian of crab and avocado with dill dressing, followed by pan-fried skate wing with chargrilled vegetables and red-pepper butter. Around 40 affordable wines are bolstered by a few specials.

...for recipe ideas

MEMBER
81
ENTRY

Weymouth

Vaughan's Bistro

Restaurant

7 Custom House Quay, Weymouth,
Dorset DT4 8BE
Telephone: +44(0)1305 769004
eat@vaughansbistro.co.uk
www.vaughansbistro.co.uk

'A restaurant owner who exercises good taste in all he does – from furnishings to food.'

Prices: **Sunday lunch £14.50. Restaurant main course from £10.50. House wine £11.95.**
Last orders: **Food: lunch 14.30; dinner 22.00** (during the winter, Sunday serving times may vary).
Closed: **Two weeks in January.**
Food: **Modern British.**
Other points: **No smoking. Children welcome. Wheelchair access.**
Directions: **Exit 25/M5.** Follow the signs to Weymouth and the seafront. Take the signs for Custom House Quay, Vaughan's is positioned on the harbour. (Map 4)

Mark Vaughan is a restaurant owner who exercises good taste in all he does – from furnishings to food. Recognising the potential of this former 18th-century railway storage warehouse with outstanding harbour views, he turned it into this spacious dining area that can seat 120 upstairs and down, but which maintains a convivial and cosy vibe. The integrity of flavours on his carefully drawn menu is down to the stunning local produce, particularly fish landed along the quay and Dorset farm meats.

Start with tiger prawns and Portland crab or local pan-fried scallops before moving on to a duo of West Country lamb (rack and mince faggot) with rosemary jus, or one of the day's stunning fish specials of, say, whole Weymouth lobster, or local lemon sole or sea bass, which come with delectable sauces or butters. Regulars at Vaughan's in Portland, Mark's former bistro, will be happy to learn that his signature dish of fillet of beef with bubble-and-squeak and Madeira jus is still on the menu. The compact, but pleasing, wine list spans a good price and palate range, and the house choice is a steal.

Great Dunmow

The Swan at Felsted

■★

Country pub

'Step inside to find a spacious, beautifully designed interior.'

Station Road, Felsted, Essex CM6 3DG
Telephone: +44(0)1371 820245
info@theswanatfelsted.co.uk
www.theswanatfelsted.co.uk

A mere 15 minutes from Stansted Airport, The Swan enjoys a prominent position in the picturesque village of Felsted. The imposing redbrick-and-timber pub dates from the 1900s, when the original Tudor building burnt down, and for years it was a rough boozer. Jono and Jane Clarke took on the Ridley's lease in 2002 and the transformation has been remarkable. Step inside to find a spacious, beautifully designed interior, featuring smart wooden floors, mustard-yellow walls hung with works of art, leather sofas in the bar, and a high-ceilinged dining area filled with chunky tables and high-backed dining chairs.

The food is sourced locally and the imaginative menus offer a good choice of dishes, from lunchtime salads and sandwiches to main-menu classics such as fish pie, the Swan burger, and steak, ale and mussel suet pudding, both made with Barnston beef. Alternatively, go for one of the daily specials, perhaps Helmingham Hall venison with Madeira jus and finish with chocolate risotto with a shortbread biscuit. Wines are well chosen, and there are plenty available by the glass.

Prices: **Restaurant main course from £9.50. Bar main course from £5.50. House wine £10.95.**
Last orders: **Bar: afternoon 15.00 (Sunday 16.00); evening 23.00 (Sunday 22.30). Food: lunch 14.30 (Sunday 16.00); dinner 21.30 (no food Sunday evening).**
Closed: **Never.**
Food: **Modern British.**
Real ale: **Ridley's IPA.**
Other points: **No smoking. Children welcome. Dogs welcome in the bar. Garden. Car park. Wheelchair access.**
Directions: **Exit 8/M11. Take the A120 and then the B1256 towards Colchester. Turn right on to the B1417 to Felsted. (Map 6)**

...for events

Pattiswick

The Compasses at Pattiswick

Country pub

Pattiswick, Braintree, Essex CM7 8BG
Telephone: +44(0)1376 561322
info@thecompassesatpattiswick.co.uk
www.thecompassesatpattiswick.co.uk

'Excellent wines, alfresco patio dining and wonderful sunsets add to the appeal.'

Prices: **Restaurant main course from £9.**
Bar snack from £6. House wine £9.50.
Last orders: **Food: 21.30 (Saturday 22.00).**
Sunday during winter food served until 16.00.
Closed: **Never.**
Food: **Modern European.**
Real ale: **Greene King IPA, Crouch Vale, Kelham Island.**
Other points: **Smoking area. Children welcome. Dogs welcome in the bar. Garden, including childrens' play area. Car park. Wheelchair access.**
Directions: **Exit 28/M25. A12 toward Colchester. B1024 to Coggeshall. Go through town, turn left on to the A120 towards Braintree and then second right, signposted Pattiswick. (Map 6)**

An exciting new venture for natural hosts and skilled pub operators Jono and Jane Clarke from the award-winning Swan at Felsted (see entry). They bring the same philosophy – a passion for real hospitality and honest food from local suppliers – to this impressively refurbished rural pub. Gloriously set in rolling countryside, the much-extended former estate workers' cottages have been tastefully revamped and successfully combine the traditional (beams, open fires) with the contemporary (natural materials, spotlighting, deep sofas).

Food is a notch or two above the pub norm, taking in lunchtime sandwiches and salads and an evening à la carte menu that offers a well-balanced choice of modern British dishes. Start with smoked-duck and raspberry salad, follow with whole Dover sole or roast venison with chocolate sauce, with warm apricot-and-ginger cake to finish. Great care is taken in sourcing local foods – for example, Pattiswick Estate supplies the game, and pork comes from Priors Hall farm in Lindsell. Excellent wines, alfresco patio dining and wonderful sunsets add to the appeal.

www.routiers.co.uk

Blakeney

Old Nibley Farmhouse

Bed and breakfast

'A large garden provides ample space to chill out.'

Nibley Hill, Blakeney,
Gloucestershire GL15 4DB
Telephone: +44(0)1594 516770
enquiries@oldnibleyfarmhouse.co.uk
www.oldnibleyfarmhouse.co.uk

Parts of this Grade II-listed farmhouse are 300 years old, but careful refurbishment has created accommodation that's modern, light and airy; the sitting and dining rooms are equally bright, but comfortably furnished. A large garden provides ample space to chill out, but with the Forest of Dean, Wye Valley and Severn River nearby, there is no shortage of fresh country space to explore, walk, cycle, fish and canoe. The farmhouse offers lovely views.

Bedrooms have been individually decorated and have lovely bathrooms (not all are en-suite), plus extras such as dressing gowns and hairdryers – even slippers can be provided. Thoughtful owner Marian Buckmaster has an eye for presentation, which is clearly visible in her good-taste, country-chic furnishings. And as well as being an excellent host, her talents extend to the kitchen. Breakfasts are her forte – and she can turn her hand to cooking magnificent *huevos bravas*, home-made muffins, marmalade and coconut slices, and outstanding preserves and compotes. Evening meals draw on the excellent local game, meat and fresh produce.

Rooms: **4, 2 with private bathroom. £30 per person per night.**
Prices: **Set dinner £16.**
Last orders: **Dinner served between 18.30 and 21.00.**
Closed: **November and December.**
Food: **Traditional British.**
Other points: **No smoking. Children over 12 welcome. Dogs welcome overnight. Garden. Car park.**
Directions: **Exit 21/M48. A48 northbound for 15 miles. (Map 5)**

...for competitions

MEMBER
85
ENTRY

Cirencester

Le Spa at Stratton Place

Hotel and spa

Stratton Place, Gloucester Road,
Cirencester, Gloucestershire GL7 2LA
Telephone: +44(0)1285 648730
mail@lespa.com
www.lespa.com

'Guests can make good use of the smart and well-equipped health club.'

Rooms: **9. Double/twin room from £129, single from £94. Prices include dinner and breakfast.**
Prices: **Restaurant main course from £7.95. House wine £12.75.**
Last orders: **Food: lunch 14.30, dinner 21.45.**
Closed: **Rarely.**
Food: **Traditional English.**
Other points: **No smoking. Children over nine welcome. Garden. Car park. Licence for civil weddings. Wheelchair access to all areas.**
Directions: **Exit 11a/M5. Take the A417 towards Cirencester and then the slip-road exit towards Stratton. Follow it for one mile. Le Spa is situated on Gloucester Road, on the left-hand side.** (Map 5)

Exotic skin-care range manufacturer Linda Lloyd is investing time and money in transforming Stratton Place, a grand Edwardian manor house set in beautiful landscaped grounds, into a small and luxurious Spa Hotel. The spa is very Asian orientated, with treatments including the Royal Thai coconut and sea-salt exfoliation day, and guests can make good use of the smart and well-equipped health club, with its gymnasium, swimming pool, steam room and sauna. Those desiring more than a day's pampering can stay overnight in one of the nine individually decorated en-suite bedrooms in the manor house.

Overlooking the spa sun decks and open to non-spa guests is the Orchid Restaurant, a contemporary-styled dining room that offers a traditional English menu. Lunch on warm goat's cheese salad, fish cakes with hollandaise, an Aberdeen Angus beefburger with fries, or pasta with pesto. Dinner offers similar dishes, with the addition of lamb cutlets with rosemary gravy and grilled fillet steak served with a pepper sauce. Those not on a diet can round off with hot chocolate fudge cake.

Cirencester

Wild Duck Inn

Country inn

'The bar is quintessential English pub, brimming with character and atmosphere.'

Ewen, Cirencester,
Gloucestershire GL7 6BY
Telephone: +44(0)1285 770310
wduckinn@aol.com
www.thewildduckinn.co.uk

The mellow Cotswold-stone Elizabethan inn, hidden away in sleepy Ewen, is well worth seeking out. Creeper-clad with well-tended gardens, this fine building creates a favourable first impression. The bar is quintessential English pub, brimming with character and atmosphere, with its backdrop of rich burgundy walls, covered with old portraits and hunting trophies, glowing log fires, and large comfortable armchairs creating a warm atmosphere. The restaurant's labyrinth of rooms features dark beams, more burgundy walls and wooden tables and chairs; the same printed menu is available throughout, along with chalkboard specials.

The lively repertoire draws the crowds with its modern take and realistic pricing, perhaps a one-course lunch of beer-battered cod and chips, ham-hock broth, or Old Spot ham salad. Dinner could run to smoked haddock fish cakes with lemon aïoli, lamb with thyme and garlic jus, and Thai lemon and chilli monkfish. The globetrotting wine list offers 34 by the glass, and the bar has five real ales. Twelve individually decorated en-suite rooms await those not wanting to drive home.

Rooms: 12. Double room from £95, single from £70.
Prices: Main course from £6.95. House wine £11.
Last orders: Bar: 23.00. Food: lunch 14.00; dinner 22.00 (Saturday and Sunday all day until 21.30).
Closed: Never.
Food: Modern British.
Real ale: Wells Bombardier Premium Bitter, Smiles Original, Theakston Old Peculier, Theakston XB, Greene King Old Speckled Hen.
Other points: Smoking area. Children welcome. Dogs welcome. Garden. Car park.
Directions: Exit 15 or 17/M4. From Cirencester, take the A429 towards Malmesbury. On reaching Kemble, turn left to Ewen. (Map 5)

...for special offers

Clearwell

The Wyndham Arms

Hotel

Clearwell, The Royal Forest of Dean,
Gloucestershire GL16 8JT
Telephone: +44(0)1594 833666
nigel@thewyndhamhotel.co.uk
www.thewyndhamhotel.co.uk

'If it's period features and rustic charm you're after, look no further.'

Rooms: 18. Double room from £65 to £110, single from £35 to £65.
Prices: Restaurant main course from £12.50. Bar main course from £8.95. House wine £11.25.
Last orders: Bar: 23.00. Food: lunch 14.00 (Sunday 14.30); dinner: 21.30 (Sunday 21.00).
Closed: Rarely.
Food: Modern British.
Real ale: Freeminer Bitter. Monthly guest beer.
Other points: Smoking area. Dogs welcome overnight. Garden. Car park. Licence for civil weddings. Wheelchair access.
Directions: Exit 2/M48. From the A48 at Monmouth via the A4176 and B4228, two miles from Coleford. 12 miles from Chepstow.
(Map 5)

If it's period features and rustic charm you're after, look no further than this 13th-century former manor house. Set in several acres of glorious sloping gardens, woods and lawns, Nigel and Pauline Stanley's 600-year-old traditional inn stands at the heart of this medieval village. It is filled with oak beams, flagstones and exposed original red brick, the historic and very popular bar dispensing local Freeminer beers, decent wines and a fabulous range of malt whiskies.

Local produce features prominently on both the bar and restaurant menus, which can include seasonal game from Lydney Park Estate and rare-breed meats. The Stanleys are also active in the community cooperative for supplies of vegetables, salads and herbs. Translated on the menu, this brings a bar menu with steak and Freeminer-ale casserole or poached salmon with potato and fennel salad, and a main menu in the Old Spot Country Restaurant that starts with a plate of Old Spot charcuterie, continues with Madgett's Farm breast of duck and finishes with dark-chocolate soufflé cake or a plate of local cheeses.

Fairford

Allium

Restaurant

'An uncluttered yet sophisticated dining experience with attention to detail.'

1 London Street, Market Place, Fairford,
Gloucestershire GL7 4AH
Telephone: +44(0)1285 712200
restaurant@allium.uk.net
www.allium.uk.net

An uncluttered yet sophisticated dining experience with attention to detail is of the utmost importance to proprietors James Graham (2006 Cotswold Life Chef of the Year), his wife Erica, and Nick Bartimote at their smartly contemporary Cotswold restaurant. Expect linen-clad tables, gleaming glassware, interesting sculptures and walls adorned with modern art. Comfortable sofas are an inviting proposition for drinks before the culinary delights that await, especially with a fire roaring away in the winter months.

The immaculate dining area lives up to their motto of 'relaxed fine dining' and it becomes obvious from the menu that the true focus is on the food. Everything is locally sourced where possible. An excellent set course table d'hôte is offered on Wednesday, Thursday and Friday nights, while the seasonal menus offers delights such as fricassée of rabbit and artichokes to start, followed by roasted halibut with crayfish risotto and asparagus, or confit pork belly with white beans and homemade sausage. Puddings may include banana-and-praline soufflé. The list of wines is classy and global.

Prices: **Set lunch £18.50 and dinner £32.50. Gourmand meal £45.**
Last orders: **Food: 22.00.**
Closed: **Monday and Tuesday. Sunday evening. Two weeks at the beginning of January.**
Food: **Modern British/French.**
Other points: **Smoking area. Children welcome.**
Directions: **Exit15/M4 and exit 13/M5. Between Cirencester and Lechlade on the A417. Situated on the market place in Fairford. (Map 5)**

...for the latest news

Frampton Mansell

White Horse

Country pub

Cirencester Road, Frampton Mansell,
Gloucestershire GL6 8HZ
Telephone: +44(0)1285 760960
www.cotswoldwhitehorse.com

'Brightly painted walls, modern art and chunky tables provide a fitting setting for the modern menu.'

Prices: **Restaurant main course from £10.95.
Bar main course from £4.95. House
wine £13.50.**
Last orders: **Bar: afternoon 15.00; evening 23.00.**
Food: **lunch 14.30; dinner 21.45 (Sunday 15.00).**
Closed: **Sunday evening.**
Food: **Modern British.**
Real ale: **Hook Norton Bitter, Uley Bitter. One
guest beer.**
Other points: **Smoking area. Children welcome.
Dogs welcome in the bar. Garden. Car park.**
Directions: **Exit 15/M4 or exit 13/M5. Between
Cirencester and Stroud on the A419. On
the main road, not in the village of Frampton
Mansell itself. (Map 5)**

It may not be much to look at from the outside, but Shaun and Emma Davies's stone pub is a welcome beacon along the busy A419. The pair revived the pub's fortunes with a smart makeover but, more importantly, with their excellent food and drink. Brightly painted walls, modern art and chunky tables provide a fitting setting for the modern menu built around fresh produce from quality local suppliers. Rare-breed meat comes from Butts Farm butchers near Cirencester, game is from local shoots, and fish from Cornwall.

Seafood has become quite a focus, especially since a large lobster tank was installed. As with other seafood, the lobster is simply served, as the quality speaks for itself. Fine dining begins with scallops, apple and horseradish mash, black pudding and chive-cream sauce, or rock oysters, then moves on to mains of leg of Cotswold lamb with roasted shallots, garlic and rosemary jus, or halibut with crayfish tail and chive butter. Puddings are equally delectable, perhaps including dark-chocolate and cherry crème brûlée. Lunchtime snacks include salads and baguettes. Global wines focus on smaller growers.

Butts Farm Shop, South Cerney,
Cirencester, 01285 862224, www.thebuttsfarmshop.com
At Butts Farm, butcher Gary Wallace and livestock breeder Judy
Hancox farm rare breeds of cattle, sheep, pigs and poultry in the
traditional way to produce meat of exceptional quality and flavour.
The rare-breed meat, home-cured bacon and sausages are
available through the farm shop and their Cotswold Gourmet
mail-order service.

Cerney Cheese,
Chapel Farm, North Cerney, Cirencester,
01285 831312, www.cerneycheese.com
Since 1983, Cerney Cheese has been producing award-winning
speciality goat's milk cheeses, most notably the Cerney Pyramid.
It is made by hand, using unpasteurised goat's milk and vegetarian
rennet and is a full-fat Valencay-type cheese coated in an oak-
ash/sea-salt mix.

Uley Brewery,
The Old Brewery, 31 The Street, Uley,
01453 860120, www.uleybrewery.com
The malty, fruity and copper-coloured bitter and the distinctive,
full-bodied red-brown Old Spot Prize Ale, among others, have
been brewed at this listed building since 1985. It draws its own
spring water and no sugar or additives are used.

Visit the Farmers' Market

The Market Place in Cirencester
holds a market on the second and
fourth Saturday of every month,
from 9am to 1pm.
Call 01453 834777 for details.

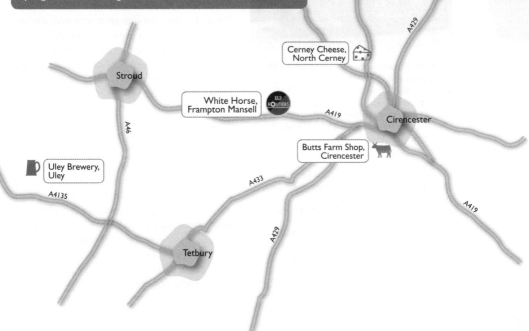

Kelmscott

The Plough at Kelmscott

Country inn

Kelmscott, Lechlade,
Gloucestershire GL7 3HG
Telephone: +44(0)1367 253543
plough@kelmscottgL7.fsnet.co.uk
www.ploughkelmscott.co.uk

'A favoured watering hole for Thames path walkers and the boating fraternity.'

Rooms: **8. Double from £75, single from £45, family from £85.**
Prices: **Restaurant main course from £9.50. Lunch and bar snacks from £4.95. Fish menu from £4.50. House wine £10.50.**
Last orders: **Bar: afternoon 15.00; evening 23.00. Food: lunch 14.30; dinner 21.00 (Saturday and Sunday all day).**
Closed: **Never.**
Food: **Classic/modern British and French.**
Real ale: **Hook Norton Ales, Wychwood Ales, Archers Best. Two guest beers.**
Other points: **Smoking area. Children welcome. Dogs welcome. Garden. Car park.**
Directions: **20 minutes from Exit 15/M5. Take the A416 from Lechlade towards Faringdon, then follow signs to Kelmscott. (Map 5)**
See pub walk on page 464

A short stroll from Kelmscott Manor, the former summer home of William Morris, and the river in a peaceful village, the 17th-century Plough has long been a favoured watering hole for Thames-path walkers and the boating fraternity. Despite its isolation, the village and the Plough bustle with visitors, and the pub does well as it operates as a gastropub-with-rooms. The interior has a stylish, contemporary rustic look, mixing original flagstones, log fires and exposed brick and timbers with modern wooden chairs and tables.

Matching the surroundings is the imaginative modern-British fare on offer. On the bar menu you may find fresh cod in beer batter and local-game casserole. Evening dishes produce confit of duck with a plum-and-peach compote, slow-roasted pork loin with apple mash and Irish cabbage, and an excellent seafood menu that may list a fresh crab platter, red snapper with Mediterranean vegetables, and scallops with coconut risotto and Pernod cream. There is a lovely garden and terrace for summer drinking, and eight en-suite bedrooms.

www.routiers.co.uk

Northleach

The Puesdown Inn

Country inn

'On a wild winter's night, this isolated former coaching inn is the perfect retreat.'

Compton Abdale,
Northleach, Cheltenham,
Gloucestershire GL54 4DN
Telephone: +44(0)1451 860262
inn4food@btopenworld.com
www.puesdown.cotswoldinns.com

On a wild winter's night, this isolated former coaching inn, situated high in the Cotswolds beside the A40, is the perfect retreat. John and Maggie Armstrong have renovated and refurbished the mellow stone pub with style, notably in the three individually designed stable-block bedrooms – two have big brass beds, all feature Egyptian cotton bedding and up-to-the-minute en-suite bathrooms with storm showers.

The rambling bar and dining areas sport oak floors, warm, rich colours and deep sofas fronting log fires. Informality is the key and the Armstrongs' hard work has paid off as the inn draws racegoers from Cheltenham, Cotswold walkers, and wine buffs and jazz fans for regular evening events. Food is freshly prepared by John, who sources quality ingredients – be it local game or fish from Brixham – for his daily menus. Expect the likes of sandwiches, ham, egg and chips, and salmon Caesar salad for lunch, while dinner options may take in ragout of lobster, langoustine and oyster, duck breast with duck-leg ravioli, Puy lentils and orange-and-juniper jus, and bread-and-butter pudding.

Rooms: 3. Double/twin room from £85, single from £50, family from £105.
Prices: Set Sunday lunch £17.75. Set weekday dinner £19.95 (Jazz evening). Restaurant main course from £14. Bar main course from £6.50. House wine £10.95.
Last orders: Bar: afternoon 15.00; evening 22.00. Food: lunch 15.00; dinner 22.00 (Sunday 21.30).
Food: Modern British.
Real ale: Hook Norton Best Bitter, Fuller's London Pride. Two guest beers.
Other points: Smoking area. Dogs welcome. Garden. Car park. Wheelchair access.
Directions: Exit 11A/M5. Follow signs to Cirencester/Stow. After 10 miles, turn right at the traffic lights on to the A40 towards Oxford. The inn is three miles along on the left. (Map 5)

...for recipe ideas

MEMBER
92
ENTRY

Northleach

The Wheatsheaf Inn

West End, Northleach,
Gloucestershire GL54 3EZ
Telephone: +44 (0)1451 860244
info@wsan.co.uk
www.wsan.co.uk

Country inn

'In summer, head for the flower-filled garden.'

Rooms: **8. Double/twin room from £60, single from £50, family from £70.**
Prices: **Main course from £7. Bar snacks from £4. House wine £10.95.**
Last orders: **Bar 23.00. Food: lunch 15.00; dinner 21.30 (Sunday 21.00).**
Closed: **Never.**
Food: **Modern British.**
Real ale: **Black Sheep. Wadworth 6X. One guest beer.**
Other points: **Smoking area. Children welcome. Dogs welcome in the bar. Garden. Car park. Wheelchair access to the restaurant/pub.**
Directions: **Exit 15/M4. The village is just off the A429 between Stow-on-the-Wold and Cirencester. (Map 5)**

Quietly situated in this celebrated Cotswold 'wool town', the pretty stone-built 300 year-old coaching inn has been revamped by brothers Caspar and Gavin Harvard-Walls. Expect classic period features – worn flagstone floors, big oak beams, blazing log fires and chunky wooden furnishings – throughout the three, light and airy front rooms. The rustic bar deals in Hook Norton and guest ales, and has a chalkboard menu.

The classy, understated dining room is marginally more formal. Modern British favourites are inspired by what is available locally, chump of local lamb with chorizo mash and redcurrant jus, for example, Bibury trout with watercress and bacon, or pork tenderloin with red cabbage, apple sauce and jus. Treacle tart, or apple crumble are classic desserts, with local cheeses making a savoury alternative. There are some impeccable choices on a globally inspired and well-annotated wine list. Eight en-suite rooms have been refurbished along cool, white, Scandinavian lines. In summer, head for the flower-filled garden. The inn is due to close for major refurbishment in winter 2006, so please call to check they are open.

www.routiers.co.uk

Painswick

Butchers Arms

Country pub

'Glorious views from the sunny front terrace.'

Sheepscombe, Painswick,
Gloucestershire GL6 7RH
Telephone: +44(0)1452 812113
bleninns@clara.net
www.cotswoldinns.co.uk

This fabulous Cotswold inn has a unique claim to fame in that its sign – showing a butcher supping a pint of ale with a pig tied to his leg – is one of the most photographed pub signs in the country. A mellow-stone pub dating from 1620, and originally a butchery for deer hunted in Henry VIII's deer park, it is worth negotiating the narrow lanes for the glorious views over the rolling Stroud Valley from the sunny front terrace. Added attractions include the good range of real ales and an interesting choice of traditional and modern pub food.

The homely, rustic bar and adjoining beamed dining room are the setting for cooking that relies on locally sourced raw materials, such as handmade sausages from local butcher Jessie Smith in Dursley and Texel lambs from Lypiatt Farm in nearby Miserden. For lunch, tuck into hearty homemade soups, decent ploughman's lunches or spinach-and-ricotta cannelloni, while at dinner choose, perhaps, from prime steaks, beef Wellington, braised lamb shank, and salmon with sesame seeds and noodles. Part of Jonny Johnston's small Blenheim Inns group of pubs.

Prices: Restaurant main course from £7.50. Bar snacks from £4.95. House wine £9.95.
Last orders: Bar: afternoon 14.30 (Saturday 15.00); evening 23.00. Open all day Sunday.
Food: lunch 14.30; dinner 21.30. Food served all day Sunday.
Closed: Never.
Food: Traditional/modern British and European.
Real ale: Three guest beers.
Other points: Smoking area. Children welcome. Dogs welcome in the bar. Garden. Car park. Wheelchair access (not WC).
Directions: Exit 11a/M5. Just off the A46 between Cheltenham and Stroud, near Painswick. (Map 5)

MEMBER ENTRY
94

...for events

Painswick

The Falcon Inn

Country inn

New Street, Painswick,
Gloucestershire GL6 6UN
Telephone: +44(0)1452 814222
bleninns@clara.net
www.falconinn.com

'Expect the likes of organic pork loin with cider and honey, and Cockleford trout with red pesto.'

Rooms: 12. Double room from £68, single from £45. Disabled bedroom available.
Prices: Set lunch £12 and dinner £16. Restaurant main course from £7.50. Bar snack from £4.95. House wine £9.95.
Last orders: Bar: 23.00. Food: lunch 14.30 (Sunday 15.00); dinner 21.30 (Saturday 22.00).
Closed: Never.
Food: Traditional/modern British and European.
Real ale: Hook Norton Best Bitter, Greene King IPA, Wadworth 6X, Otter. One guest beer.
Other points: Smoking area. Children welcome. Dogs welcome overnight. Garden. Car park. Wheelchair access (not WC in the restaurant/pub).
Directions: Exit 11a/M5. Painswick is on the A46 between Cheltenham and Stroud. (Map 5)

Set in the heart of the Cotswolds, The Falcon stands in the centre of the charming village of Painswick, close to ramblers' favourite walk the Cotswold Way. Located opposite the parish church, it is a handsome, stone-built, 16th-century coaching inn with a colourful history — it was a courthouse and the first ever Masonic ceremony was staged there. It is also the unlikely setting in which to find the world's oldest bowling green. Interconnecting bar and dining areas are full of traditional character, the scene set by stone, tiled and carpeted floors, wood panelling, log fires, and an eclectic mix of furnishings.

Jonny Johnston's careful sourcing of local produce, notably game from nearby shoots, locally grown vegetables, and butchers' meats, including belted Galloway beef, is evident in changing menus and daily chalkboard dishes. Expect the likes of organic pork loin with cider and honey, braised venison with root vegetables, and fish dishes such as organic Cockleford trout with red pesto. Individually decorated bedrooms are split between the inn and the coach house.

Winchcombe

Juri's The Olde Bakery Tea Shoppe

Tea rooms and restaurant

'Their traditional cakes, particularly their scones, will have you swooning.'

High Street, Winchcombe, Cheltenham,
Gloucestershire GL54 5LJ
Telephone: +44(0)1242 602469
miyawaki@ma.kew.net
www.juris-tearoom.co.uk

The Miyawaki family realised their dream in 2004 when they took over this long-established teashop, which occupies a quaint 18th-century Grade II-listed building in this pretty town. They have firmly established themselves as quality bakers, and their traditional cakes, particularly their scones, will have you swooning; enjoy them as part of the astonishingly good-value cream tea.

Juri's success stems from her insistence on using quality ingredients. She learned her trade at Raymond Blanc's Le Manoir aux Quat' Saisons. Her luscious chocolate cake incorporates the best Belgian chocolate, and most of the ingredients for the other cakes are organic. The menu kicks off with an English breakfast and scrummy things on toast, before moving on to snacks and substantial mains. There's a good choice of tea, while coffee options include a mashmallow and cream-topped special. Juri's parents run the front of house efficiently, and here, light lunches such as Japanese-style beef curry, creamy fish pie and Sheepdrove organic sausages are on offer. Lunch can be accompanied by a glass of wine, sherry or saké.

Prices: **Daily lunch specials from £6.50. Toasted sandwiches from £4.20. Cream tea £4.50. House wine £10.**
Last orders: **Food: 16.30.**
Closed: **Monday (open bank holidays), Tuesday and January.**
Food: **Modern European with Japanese influences. Homemade patisserie and scones.**
Other points: **No smoking. Garden. Conservatory. Wheelchair access.**
Directions: **Exit 9/M5. Take the A46, B4077 and then B4632 signposted to Winchcombe. From Cheltenham and the South, take the B4632 towards Broadway, which takes you directly into Winchcombe. (Map 5)**

...for competitions

MEMBER
96
ENTRY

Winchcombe

The White Hart Inn

Town-centre inn

High Street, Winchcombe, Cheltenham,
Gloucestershire GL54 5LJ
Telephone: +44(0)1242 602359
enquiries@the-white-hart-inn.com
www.the-white-hart-inn.com

'A slick Swedish elegance runs through the minimalist dining room and the beautifully decorated bedrooms.'

Rooms: **8. Double from £70, single room from £55**
Prices: **Set lunch £12.95 and dinner £17.95. Restaurant main course from £11.95. Bar main course from £5.95. House wine £10.95.**
Last orders: **Food: 22.00.**
Closed: **Rarely.**
Food: **Modern British with Scandinavian specialities.**
Real ale: **Greene King Old Speckled Hen, Wadworth 6X, Greene King IPA, Stanway Stanney Bitter.**
Other points: **Smoking area. Children welcome. Patio. Car park. Meeting facilities.**
Directions: **Exit 9/M5. In the centre of Winchcombe on the B4362 Cheltenham to Stratford road. (Map 5)**
See pub walk on page 466

For a pub with such a classically English look, it comes as something of a surprise to step inside this 16th-century Cotswolds town-centre inn to find such a warm Scandinavian welcome. Stylishly refurbished by Nicole Burr, who hails from Stockholm, a slick Swedish elegance runs through the minimalist dining room and upstairs to the eight beautifully decorated bedrooms. It also influences the contemporary menus.

What is traditional, though, is the 'pubby' front bar, where regulars quaff pints of real ale and tuck into baguettes, open sandwiches, burgers or the house-speciality smorgasbord platter – Swedish cold meats, seafoods and salads. In the restaurant, start with sliced smoked duck and follow it with sliced venison on a bed of parsnip and vodka-marinated lingonberries. Beef and lamb come from the Sudeley Castle Estate. The Stable Bar Pizzeria offers Italian-style pizzas to eat in or take away, including the special Swedish hotdog, mozzarella cheese, tomato and mild mustard. Individually designed and decorated bedrooms offer a high level of comfort.

The Cross at Eversley

Village pub

'Very much the hub of the community.'

The Green, Reading Road, Eversley Cross,
Hampshire RG27 ONS
Telephone: +44(0)118 9731126
eversleycross1@aol.com
www.thecrossateversley.com

The Cross dates back to the early 1800s and is situated opposite the village pond and England's oldest working cricket ground, and was once known locally as The Toad and Stumps. Very much the hub of the community, it hosts weekly live-music nights, skittle-alley evenings, summer barbecues and classic-car meetings, and becomes a popular meeting place during the cricket season. The bar is traditionally furnished and is the place to quaff some decent ale – Adnams Broadside, Wells Bombardier, Fuller's London Pride and a changing guest beer.

Accompany a pint with a hearty bar meal – perhaps a filled baguette, pasta carbonara or homemade game pie. In the homely restaurant, tuck into black pudding with mustard sauce or mussels with white wine and garlic. Follow with lamb shank with red-wine sauce or herb-crusted salmon with lemon butter, and round off with lemon-and-lime torte or a plate of interesting cheeses. There's a secluded rear garden for summer sipping, and benches to the front from where avid cricket fans can follow the action.

Prices: Set lunch £15. Set dinner £25. Restaurant main course from £8. Bar main course from £7.50. House wine £9.50.
Last orders: Food: lunch 14.30 (Sunday 17.00); dinner 21.30. No food Sunday and Monday evening.
Closed: Never.
Food: Traditional British.
Real ale: Wells Bombardier Premium Bitter, Adnams Broadside, Fuller's London Pride, Hogs Back Hair of the Hog.
Other points: Smoking area. Dogs welcome in the bar. Garden. Car park. Wheelchair access (not WC).
Directions: Exit 4b/M3. Off the B3237. (Map 5)

...for special offers

Fordingbridge

Rose and Thistle

Rockbourne, Fordingbridge,
Hampshire SP6 3NL
Telephone: +44(0)1725 518236
enquiries@roseandthistle.co.uk
www.roseandthistle.co.uk

Country pub

'Tuck into pork with oyster mushrooms and garlic sauce, local venison with chestnuts and spring onions, and fresh fish.'

Originally two 17th-century cottages, this delightful, long, low, whitewashed inn enjoys a tranquil setting in one of Hampshire's most picturesque downland villages. The low-beamed interior boasts two huge fireplaces with winter log fires and tasteful furnishings, and country-style fabrics, dried flowers, and magazines enhance the civilised atmosphere.

Quality pub food is up-to-date, and sensibly light and simple at lunchtimes. Note the daily homemade soup, 'elegant' Welsh rarebit, smoked salmon and scrambled egg, and ploughman's lunches. Evening dishes are more elaborate, featured on a monthly changing menu and daily specials board. Typically, tuck into pork with oyster mushrooms and garlic sauce, local venison with chestnuts and spring onions, and fresh fish (also available lunchtimes), such as wild sea bass with prawns and capers. There is traditional sticky toffee pudding and seasonal game from local shoots. Also worth mentioning, Sunday roasts, good ales and wines, plus a lovely rose-filled garden. Well placed for Rockbourne's Roman Villa, Salisbury and the New Forest.

Prices: Restaurant main course from £11. Bar main course from £7.45. House wine £11.25.
Last orders: Bar: afternoon 15.00; evening 23.00 (Sunday 20.00, October-March). Food: lunch 14.30; dinner 21.30. No food Sunday evening in winter.
Closed: Rarely.
Food: Modern British.
Real ale: Fuller's London Pride, Strong's Best Bitter, Palmers Copper Ale. One guest beer.
Other points: Smoking area. Children welcome. Dogs welcome. Garden. Car park. Wheelchair access.
Directions: From Salisbury, take the A354 and turn off at the signpost to Rockbourne. From Fordingbridge, take the Sandleheath road and, at the crossroads, turn right to Rockbourne. (Map 5)

MEMBER
99
ENTRY

Hamble

The Bugle

Village pub

'Views of bobbing boats on the River Hamble can be enjoyed from the front terrace.'

High Street, Hamble,
Hampshire SO31 4HA
Telephone: +44(0)2380 453000
manager@buglehamble.co.uk
www.buglehamble.co.uk

To the delight of locals and visiting sailors, Hamble's famous Bugle pub, an ancient hostelry celebrated by the sailing fraternity the world over, reopened in June 2005 following extensive renovation by the team behind the White Star Tavern in Southampton (see entry). The beautifully remodelled 16th-century pub features impressive green oak beams and wall timbers, stripped-back brick fireplaces with open fires, natural flagstone floors, and polished floorboards.

Away from the hustle-and-bustle of the bar is the understated main dining area, just a handful of old dining tables topped with glasses and cutlery. 'The Captain's Table' on the first floor is an intimate private dining room with views up the village street. You can sit at the bar with a pint of Deuchars IPA and nibble on a pork pie, while first-class, classic pub meals take in a homebaked ham, egg and chips, and Angus steak burger and relish. The evening menus offer more inventive dishes, perhaps spiced calves' liver with pancetta mash, and fish from local boats. Views of bobbing boats on the River Hamble can be enjoyed from the front terrace.

Prices: **Restaurant main course from £7.50. Bar bites from £4.50. House wine £11.50.**
Last orders: **Food: lunch 14.30 (Friday 15.00); dinner 21.30 (Friday and Saturday 22.00, Sunday 21.00). Food served all day at weekends.**
Closed: **Never.**
Food: **Traditional British.**
Real ale: **Calendonian Deuchars IPA, Courage Best Bitter. Guest beers from local micro-breweries.**
Other points: **Smoking area. Children welcome. Dogs welcome in the bar. Terrace. Wheelchair access. Private dining room,**
Directions: **Exit 8/M27. Follow the signs for Hamble across the mini roundabout and down the one-way cobbled high street. The Bugle is at the end on the right. (Map 5)**
See pub walk on page 468

...for the latest news

Lymington

Maine Restaurant & Bar

Restaurant

Ashley Lane, Lymington,
Hampshire SO41 3RH
Telephone: +44(0)1590 672777
www.mainerestaurantandbar.co.uk

'An all-round pleasing experience.'

Prices: **Set lunch £13 and dinner £21.**
Restaurant main course from £15. House wine
£11.50.
Last orders: **Food: lunch 14.00; dinner 21.30**
(Saturday and Sunday 22.00).
Closed: **Sunday, except evenings prior to a bank**
holiday, and 25 December.
Food: **Modern British.**
Other points: **Smoking area. Children welcome.**
Dogs welcome. Wheelchair access.
Directions: **Exit 1/M27. Take the A337 to**
Lymington and follow the signs to the town
centre. Maine is just off the High Street on
Ashley Lane, opposite Boots. (Map 5)

Initially, one of the most striking features about Maine is its unusual setting – a former 18th-century church schoolhouse replete with original features. Yet despite its leaded windows and lofty height – the restaurant is set over three levels – it's the minimalist, beach-style decor that creates a relaxing laid-back vibe that grabs you. Take a drink in the downstairs bar before heading to tables with banquettes or moving upstairs for views down into the rest of the building.

A big draw at Maine has to be its good-value two- or three-course dinner. The classic but imaginative menu offers starters of butternut squash, parmesan-and-sage risotto and Jerusalem artichoke soup, followed by guinea fowl, lamb rump or pumpkin ravioli, plus a host of tempting specials using well-sourced local ingredients – there's excellent seafood, good local meats and speciality cheeses. Delicious puds and a well-priced and fine wine drinks list go towards making this an all-round pleasing experience, especially if you tie it into a trip around the active sailing town of Lymington or the nearby New Forest.

Petersfield

Langrish House

Langrish, Petersfield,
Hampshire GU32 1RN
Telephone: +44(0)1730 266941
frontdesk@langrishhouse.co.uk
www.langrishhouse.co.uk

Country-house hotel

'In the spring, 27,000 daffodils come into bloom in the gardens.'

Rooms: 13. Double room from £94.50, single from £72, family from £120.
Prices: Set lunch £12.50 and dinner £27.95. House wine £15.95.
Last orders: Bar: afternoon 14.00; evening 23.00. Food: lunch 14.00; dinner 21.00.
Closed: Rarely.
Food: Modern British.
Other points: Smoking area. Children welcome. Dogs welcome. Garden. Car park. Licence for civil weddings. Wheelchair access.
Directions: Exit A31. Follow the A272, Langrish House is signposted. (Map 5)

Apart from a 26-year gap, Langrish House has been in the Talbot-Ponsonby family since 1842. Nigel and Robina are the current incumbents of this converted 16th-century farmhouse, and it's all that a country-house hotel should be: elegant, but not pompous. All 13 spacious rooms are individually decorated to a high standard, and have peaceful pastoral views. Frederick's Restaurant, named after a larger-than-life family member born in the 19th century, is an intimate place to dine, or you can eat in the Old Vaults, which were dug by prisoners of war.

Frederick's serves a variety of dishes, with fresh produce carefully prepared by head chef Duncan Wilson. Start with pheasant terrine with pickled red cabbage, then follow with an updated classic, say, beef fillet with seared foie gras and oyster-mushroom risotto. Desserts are a dream selection, perhaps white chocolate and sultana pudding, or there's a fine selection of cheeses. A well-selected, interesting wine list complements the menu. In the spring, 27,000 daffodils come into bloom in the gardens – a splendid spot for a wedding.

Southampton
Salt Bar & Kitchen

29 Shamrock Way, Hythe Marina,
Southampton, Hampshire SO45 6DY
Telephone: +44(0)2380 845594
tim@saltbarandkitchen.co.uk
www.saltbarandkitchen.co.uk

Bar and restaurant

'Salt Bar & Kitchen benefits from a huge, sunny terrace and views across the water.'

With its fabulous marina location in Hythe, Salt Bar & Kitchen benefits from a huge, sunny terrace and views across the water. The spacious bar affords a comfortable and relaxed ambience for enjoying a beer from the excellent Ringwood brewery in Hampshire or one of the many cocktails on offer. The dining area is partitioned off on a raised timber deck with chunky pine furniture. This is the place to enjoy a modern European menu that touches all bases.

A large selection of sandwiches, paninis and baguettes, salads and meat or fish specials, perhaps rib-eye steak with peppercorn sauce or beer-battered cod with hand-cut chips, are perfect for a light lunch. The more inventive dishes on the à la carte are conjured from good local ingredients. Start with New Forest wild-mushroom risotto with white truffle oil and follow it with spiced duck confit, sweet-and-sour jus and honey-glazed noodles, or red mullet with dragon-fruit risotto. For dessert, who could resist fresh strawberries, vanilla sabayon and pink champagne sorbet? The kitchen accommodates diners with food allergies.

Prices: **Set lunch £18.95. Set dinner £24.95. Restaurant main course £9.50. Bar main course from £6.95. House wine £12.25.**
Last orders: **Bar: 23.00. Food: lunch 14.30 (Saturday and Sunday 16.00); dinner 21.30. No food Sunday evening.**
Closed: **Never.**
Food: **Modern British.**
Real ale: **Ringwood Best Bitter, Ringwood Fortyniner.**
Other points: **Smoking area. Children welcome. Balcony. Car park. Wheelchair access.**
Directions: **Exit 2/M27. Follow signs for Fawley and then Hythe and the Marina Village. (Map 5)**

...for recipe ideas

Southampton

The White Star Tavern & Dining Rooms

28 Oxford Street, Southampton,
Hampshire SO14 3DJ
Telephone: +44(0)2380 821990
manager@whitestartavern.co.uk
www.whitestartavern.co.uk

Bar and restaurant

'Southampton's first gastropub continues to thrive.'

Prices: **Restaurant main course dinner from £11.50, lunch from £4. House wine £13.50.**
Last orders: **Lunch 14.30 (Friday and Saturday 15.00, Sunday 21.00); dinner 21.30 (Friday and Saturday 22.00).**
Closed: **Rarely.**
Food: **Modern British.**
Real ale: **Fuller's London Pride.**
Other points: **Smoking area. Children welcome weekends during the day. Wheelchair access.**
Directions: **Exit 14/M3. Take the A33 to Southampton and head towards the Ocean Village and Marina. (Map 5)**

Southampton's first gastropub, in a former seafarers' hotel close to Ocean Village and West Quay, continues to thrive, thanks to the drive and enthusiasm of young owners Mark Dodd and Matt Boyle. Smart front-bar lounge areas sport modern brown leather banquettes and cream walls adorned with shipping photographs and retro mirrors, yet retain the original flagstone floors and the period open fireplaces. Beyond lies the spacious, wood-floored and panelled dining rooms. This fabulous combination draws both a lively drinking crowd and discerning diners.

Good use of fresh produce from Hampshire suppliers can be seen in the traditional lunchtime carte, with goat's cheese and roasted vine-tomato tart, and beef-and-mushroom casserole. In the evening, seared scallops with cauliflower purée, confit shoulder of lamb with braised cabbage and bacon, and sirloin steak with Café de Paris butter, show the imaginative style, as do the homemade breads and puddings. There is an impressive list of cocktails, champagnes and wines by the glass. Under the same ownership as The Bugle in Hamble (see entry).

White Lion

Village inn

'Traditional pub food cooked from carefully sourced ingredients is the key to its popularity.'

Fullerton Road, Wherwell, Andover,
Hampshire SP11 7JF
Telephone: +44(0)1264 860317

At the heart of an unspoilt village in the Test Valley lies this coaching inn, parts of which date back to 1611. Legend has it that when Oliver Cromwell was fighting the Stuarts, shots fired from his cannon at Wherwell Priory fell short. One cannon ball is said to have hit the front door of The White Lion, while another fell down the chimney and can still be found at the pub. Just a short stroll from the River Test, this thriving community local has a loyal trade.

It is also a popular lunchtime destination with walkers and cyclists exploring this beautiful valley. Traditional pub food cooked from carefully sourced ingredients is the key to its popularity. Eat in the beamed bar where a warming log fire burns in winter, or in one of the two homely dining rooms. Sample smoked trout from the Chilbolton Estate, handmade sausages from the renowned John Robinson butchers in Stockbridge, or homemade specials such as steak-and-mushroom pie or pork-and-apple casserole cooked in cider. There are salad platters, ploughman's lunches, home-baked ham, egg and thick-cut chips, and popular Sunday roasts.

Rooms: 3. Double room from £52.50, single from £42.50.
Prices: Restaurant main course from £8.95. Bar main course from £5.75. House wine £12.25.
Last orders: Bar: afternoon 14.30 (Saturday and Sunday 15.00); evening 23.00. Food: lunch 14.00; dinner 21.00 (Sunday 20.30).
Closed: Rarely.
Food: Traditional English.
Real ale: Ringwood Best Bitter, Bass.
Other points: Smoking area. Dogs welcome. Garden. Car park. Folk club.
Directions: A303/M3 towards Andover. Turn left at Andover on to the A3057 or the B3048 to Wherwell. From Stockbridge, turn right off the A2057 at Testcombe/Fullerton. (Map 5)

...for events

Craswall

The Bull's Head

Country inn

Craswall, Hereford,
Herefordshire HR2 0PN
Telephone: +44(0)1981 510616
info@thebullsheadpub.com
www.thebullsheadpub.com

'Truly a special place in our rapidly changing world of pubs.'

Rooms: **3. 1 en-suite. Double room from £60, family room from £60.**
Prices: **Restaurant main course from £8.95. Bar meal from £5.75. House wine £11.99.**
Last orders: **Bar: 23.00. Food: 21.00.**
Closed: **Monday in winter.**
Food: **Traditional/modern British.**
Real ale: **Wye Valley Bitter, Spinning Dog.**
Other points: **Smoking area. Children welcome. Dogs welcome. Garden. Corrall for horses. Camping.**
Directions: **From Hay-on-Wye, take Forest Road and follow it for approximately four miles. At the fork, turn left and follow the road on to the high moors. After approximately three miles, there is a signpost for Craswall. Keep going to the T-junction. (Map 5)**

Truly a special place in our rapidly changing world of pubs. Lost down single-track lanes in wonderful walking country, six miles from Hay-on-Wye and just a short hike from the Offa's Dyke Path, this famous old drovers' inn clings to its ancient roots. It's a classic, unspoilt country inn, stone-built 400 years ago and totally unpretentious, with time-worn flagstones, antique settles, rickety chairs, low oak beams and logs burning in an old cast-iron stove. Even the beer – from the Wye Valley or Spinning Dog breweries – is drawn straight from the cask.

New owner Sandra Durose is content to make only a few changes – simple bedrooms have been brought up to date, without losing their charm, and a passing nod to modernity has been made in the revamped dining rooms. In keeping with the rustic surroundings, food is classic country cooking using fresh local produce. Here you can tuck into game casserole, pot-roasted rabbit with dumplings, the famous Craswall pie or freshly battered fish and chips. There's a brookside meadow for camping.

www.routiers.co.uk

The Cottage of Content

Country inn

'Ancient settles at farmhouse tables and blazing winter log fires complete this bucolic setting.'

Carey, Hereford,
Herefordshire HR2 6NG
Telephone: +44(0)1432 840242
admin@cottageofcontent.co.uk
www.cottageofcontent.co.uk

A secluded setting in remote countryside has preserved this treasure of a pub more or less intact for over 500 years. Tucked away at the bottom of a plunging sunken lane, the pretty building stands amid a handful of other cottages, facing a bridge over a stream. Within are flagstone floors and timbered alcoves with hops hanging from the beams. Ancient settles at farmhouse tables and blazing winter log fires complete this bucolic setting.

Since Paul and Svenia Franklin took over in early 2005, they have upgraded the bedrooms, which feature sloping floors under their heavy roof timbers. Food has improved markedly, with the emphasis on sourcing locally and organically – most seasonal fruit and vegetables come from a farm 200 yards away. Typically, choose chicken-liver parfait with red-onion jam to start and follow with Herefordshire beef fillet with watercress mash and Madeira jus, or brill stuffed with salmon mousse with a lemon, tarragon and butter sauce, and finish with walnut tart with local clotted cream. Wash it all down with an exceptional pint of Wye Valley Butty Bach

Rooms: **3. Double/twin room from £50, single from £35.**
Prices: **Restaurant main course from £9.95. House wine £10.95.**
Last orders: **Bar: afternoon 14.30; evening 23.00. Food: lunch 13.45, dinner 21.00.**
Closed: **Sunday evening, all day Monday. One week in January and one week in September.**
Food: **Modern English and French.**
Real ale: **Hook Norton Best Bitter, Wye Valley Butty Bach.**
Other points: **Smoking area. Dogs welcome in the bar. Garden. Car park. Wheelchair access to bar and restaurant.**
Directions: **Follow the A49 to Ross-on-Wye and go left to Hoarwithy for 2 miles. Go through Hoarwithy and turn right (to Kings Caple) and then left to Carey. The inn is about 1 1/2 miles down this road. (Map 5)**

...for competitions

Hereford

The Salutation Inn

Market Pitch, Weobley, Hereford,
Herefordshire HR4 8SJ
Telephone: +44(0)1544 318443
salutationinn@btinternet.com
www.thesalutationinn.co.uk

'A friendly welcome for drinkers and diners alike.'

Rooms: 4. Double/twin room from £80, single from £53. Family room from £105.
Prices: Restaurant main course from £15. Bar main course from £9. House wine from £15.
Last orders: Bar: 23.00. Food: lunch 14.30; dinner 21.30.
Closed: Rarely.
Food: Modern British.
Real ale: Spinning Dog Herefordshire Light Ale, Wye Valley Butty Bach, Goff's Jouster.
Other points: No smoking (inside or outside on decking). Children welcome. Dogs welcome in the public bar and courtyard. Garden. Car park. Wheelchair access restricted.
Directions: Off the A4112, south-west of Leominster or from the A44 north-west of Hereford. (Map 5)

Nestling in the centre of the medieval village of Weobley, this wonderfully evocative black-and-white timber-framed inn dates back over 500 years and commands the view down picturesque Broad Street to the parish church. A perfect base for exploring the Welsh Marches and the Wye Valley, this ancient ale-and-cider house boasts the usual beams, open fireplaces and a friendly welcome for drinkers and diners alike. Owner Mike Tai divides his time between a busy GP practice and running The Salutation, and his staff are confident and well drilled.

The dining room is separated from the bar by beamed walls, and tables are clothed with more formal settings than the bare-topped tables in the bar. To the rear, there's a conservatory and attractive outside terrace for summer dining. Whereas solid pub dishes such as steak-and-ale pie or calves' liver and bacon appear on the bar menu, the à la carte restaurant choices take in pan-seared Cornish king scallops or fillet of Herefordshire beef with whisky and blue cheese sauce. Finish with Weobley Jersey cream panna cotta and rhubarb-and-rosewater compote.

www.routiers.co.uk

Hereford

The Wellington

Country pub

'The menu is a triumph of good culinary taste.'

Wellington, Hereford,
Herefordshire HR4 8AT
Telephone: +44(0)1432 830367
thewellington@hotmail.com

If you are travelling on the A49 between Hereford and Leominster and are in need of sustenance, then the half-mile detour to Wellington and this thriving hostelry will be a deserved reward. The rather austere Victorian brick exterior conceals a well refurbished bar area with crackling log fires in original fireplaces, antique rural artefacts on the walls, and local Hobsons and Wye Valley ales and farm ciders on tap.

The former stables have been tastefully converted in a rustic, rural style and now house the dining area. The menu is a triumph of good culinary taste and uses lots of fresh local produce – fruit and vegetables from surrounding farms, and locally reared beef, venison and pork. Chef-owner Ross Williams offers a daily changing menu; begin with grilled figs with Shropshire Blue and walnuts, move on to oxtail braised in a deliciously rich red-wine sauce or Herefordshire rib-eye with tarragon butter and red-onion marmalade. Finish with a plate of English farmhouse cheeses. In the bar, tuck into hearty soups or steak-and-kidney pie. Summer barbecues are held in the attractive rear garden.

Prices: Restaurant main course from £12.75. Bar snacks from £4.95. House wine £10.95.
Last orders: Food: lunch 14.00; dinner 21.00. No food Sunday evening or Monday lunch.
Closed: Rarely.
Food: Modern British.
Real ale: Hobsons Best, Wye Valley Butty Bach.
Other points: Smoking area. Children welcome. Dogs welcome. Garden. Car park.
Directions: Take the A49 from Hereford towards Leominster. Turn left to Wellington village centre and the pub is halfway along on the right. (Map 5)

...for special offers

Hoarwithy

Aspen House

Bed and breakfast

Hoarwithy, Hereford,
Herefordshire HR2 6QP
Telephone: +44(0)1432 840353
sallyandrob@aspenhouse.net
www.aspenhouse.net

'Everything handmade, organic and personal.'

Rooms: **4. Double/twin room from £70, single from £39.**
Prices: **Set dinner £22.50. Aspen House 'Special' £55 for 2 people.**
Closed: **Rarely.**
Food: **Mediterranean/Polish/Middle Eastern.**
Other points: **No smoking. Garden. Car park.**
Directions: **Exit 4/M50. Take the A49 Ross-on-Wye to Hereford road. Hoarwithy is signposted from the A49. Aspen House is at the T-junction in the centre of the village. (Map 5)**

Responding to an increasing trend for people to eat local food in the right season, Robert Elliot and Sally Lawrance have gone that extra mile and decided to source everything locally, from the butter and water to all meat and vegetables. They are against everything mass-manufactured, industrial and unseasonal and in favour of everything handmade, organic and personal. They have achieved just that at this 18th-century farmhouse.

The most important thing about this guesthouse is the ethos. They have made a real feature out of the garden, which has been terraced to provide a number of secluded lawns, and the coach house at the back has been converted into a self-contained unit. The sitting room and dining room are quite simply furnished, but everything is good quality. Their culinary inspiration comes from Robert's Polish mother, but there are also Mediterranean, North African and Indian influences. The daily menu could include mackerel gravadlax to start, followed by a roast loin of wild boar from Usk Castle or home-cured duck-leg confit. The wine list is an interesting, affordable selection.

www.routiers.co.uk

The Stagg Inn & Restaurant

Country inn

'Some of the best pub food in the land.'

Titley, Kington, Herefordshire HR5 3RL
Telephone: +44(0)1544 230221
reservations@thestagg.co.uk
www.thestagg.co.uk

Steve and Nicola Reynolds's rustic rural local stands in tiny Titley, amid unspoilt Welsh border country. The Stagg plays host to farmers quaffing pints of Hobsons Bitter and avid foodies, the latter here for some of the best pub food in the land. Local boy and Roux-trained chef Steve has a real passion for food, delving deep into the fine raw materials that the Welsh Borders has to offer, notably rare-breed meats and game from local organic farms, producing seasonally influenced menus. He makes just about everything on the premises.

With Steve's assured, yet restrained touch, dishes could include veal sweetbreads with smoked bacon, saddle of venison with horseradish gnocchi and braised fennel, and John Dory with bouillabaisse sauce. Puddings bring a chocolate tart with cardamom ice cream and a wonderful selection of 21 local, mostly unpasteurised, cheeses. Alternatively, in the pine-furnished bar, tuck into organic pork sausages with a pint of Ralph's Radnor cider. Retire to one of the three en-suite bedrooms, or stay at the Old Vicarage, where Steve's mum also has three charming rooms.

Rooms: **6. Double room from £80, single from £60.**
Prices: **Restaurant main course from £12.50. Bar main course from £8.50. House wine £12.90.**
Last orders: **Food: lunch 14.00; dinner 22.00.**
Closed: **Sunday evening, Monday, first two weeks of November, Tuesdays after a bank holiday and May Day.**
Food: **Modern British.**
Real ale: **Hobsons Town Crier, Black Sheep Best. Up to two guest beers.**
Other points: **Smoking area. Children welcome. Dogs welcome overnight. Garden. Car park.**
Directions: **On the B4322 between Kington and Presteigne. (Map 5)**
See pub walk on page 470

...for the latest news

Ledbury

Seven

11 The Homend, Ledbury,
Herefordshire HR8 1BN
Telephone: +44(0)1531 631317
jasonkay@btconnect.com

Restaurant-with-rooms

'Subtle low lighting and comfortable sofas for soaking in the atmosphere.'

Rooms: **3. Double/twin room from £85, single from £65.**
Prices: **Set lunch (12.00-14.30 Monday to Friday) and early dinner (17.00-19.00 Monday to Wednesday) £12.95. Restaurant main course from £9.50. Bar meal from £5.90.**
House wine £12.
Last orders: **Bar: 23.00 (Sunday 22.00). Food: 22.00 (Sunday 21.00).**
Closed: **Rarely**
Food: **Modern British.**
Other points: **Smoking area. Children welcome. Dogs welcome. Garden. Wheelchair access to the restaurant. Fine foods shop on premises.**
Directions: **Exit 2/M50. Follow signs to Ledbury town centre. Seven is located in the centre of the town. (Map 5)**

It's the oldest coaching inn in Ledbury and Grade II-listed, but this chic restaurant-with-rooms comes with more than its share of contemporary touches. The current owner may still be in his first year, but has already made a mark. The bar area is now decked out in new oak, has subtle low lighting and comfortable sofas for soaking up the atmosphere. The renovations, however, have been sympathetically carried out to tie in with the olde-worlde structure and ambience.

The high-ceilinged dining room is the place to sample the substantial daytime and dinner menus, with the likes of herb-crusted cod cooked on rich creamy leeks with imaginative vegetable accompaniments or homemade fish cakes or lasagne on offer. Meats are sourced from award-winning local butchers, Wallers, plus this is the place to sample this season's much-lauded cheese, Stinking Bishop. The wine list, supplied by Tanners of Hereford, would also please sophisticated buffs. Guest accommodation runs to three oak-beamed and pleasant en-suite rooms. All in all, Seven is well located to take in Ledbury's sights and culinary delights.

www.routiers.co.uk

Ledbury

Wall Hills House

Bed and breakfast

'Scribbled notes inside the menu folder inform guests of specials such as pigeon, hake or hare, sourced that morning.'

Hereford Road, Ledbury,
Herefordshire HR8 2PR
Telephone: +44(0)1531 632833
wallhills@tiscali.co.uk
www.wallhills.com

Set amid rolling fields and woodland high above Ledbury with fabulous views across the valley below, Wall Hills House is a fine Georgian red brick house surrounded by ancient farm buildings. Owned by David and Jennifer Slaughter, it is very much a family home, offering traditional comforts in three spacious, light and prettily decorated bedrooms, which reflect the elegant Georgian era and enjoy stunning rural views. They are all TV-free zones due to poor reception.

What draws folk down the half-mile long drive, other than the peace and quiet of this rural idyll and the warm welcome, is David's excellent cooking. Using locally produced meat and game, and wonderful seasonal vegetables from the walled kitchen garden, his daily menus offer, surprisingly, up to six choices at each course. Scribbled notes inside the menu folder inform guests of specials such as pigeon, hake or hare, sourced that morning. Begin with crab, salmon and coriander ravioli, follow with wild rabbit and root-vegetable casserole, and finish with a plate of local cheeses. Not bad for a small B&B, and the wine list is pretty good as well.

Rooms: **3. Double/twin room from £75, single from £55.**
Prices: **Set dinner £17.50. House wine £9.75.**
Last orders: **Dinner served at 20.30.**
Closed: **Rarely.**
Food: **Modern British with French and Italian influences.**
Other points: **No smoking. Children welcome. Garden. Car park.**
Directions: **Exit 2/M50. Take the A417 towards Ledbury. Follow Hereford Road (A438). At the fifth roundabout, turn left. The entrance to the drive is on the left, 200 yards after the roundabout. (Map 5)**

...for recipe ideas

MEMBER ENTRY

Wye Valley Brewery,
Stoke Lacy, 01885 490505, www.wyevalleybrewery.co.uk
Founded in 1985, the Wye Valley Brewery is committed to using traditional methods while using only the best-quality raw materials. Brewery tours can be arranged, during which you can see (and taste) the award-winning Wye Valley, Butty Bach and Dorothy Goodbody's Golden Ale being made.

Bower Farm Dairy,
Grosmont, 01981 240219
Clotted Jersey cream is sourced from Val Collinson's pedigree Jersey herd at Bower Farm. She has developed a good local market for her dairy product and also produces rare-breed Gloucester Old Spot pork, which chef Jon Rix uses on the Lough Pool menu.

Huntsham Farm Pedigree Meats,
Goodrich, Ross-on-Wye, 01600 890296, www.huntsham.com
Rare-breed Longhord beef and Middlewhite pork come from Richard Vaughan at Huntsham Farm, who specialises in producing the finest meat from pedigree animals. The animals are reared, fed and cared for to a very high standard, and the beef is hung for nearly five weeks.

Seasonal fruits and vegetables
Biddlestone Orchard near Ross-on-Wye supplies the inn's apples and pears, while soft fruit and vegetables come from Whitehorn Farm at Carey and local growers, and herbs are picked from the pub's garden.

Visit the Farmers' Market

Hereford's market is on the first Saturday and third Thursday of every month, from 9am to 2pm. Ross-on-Wye's market, below the Market Hall, is on the first Friday of every month, from 10am to 2pm.

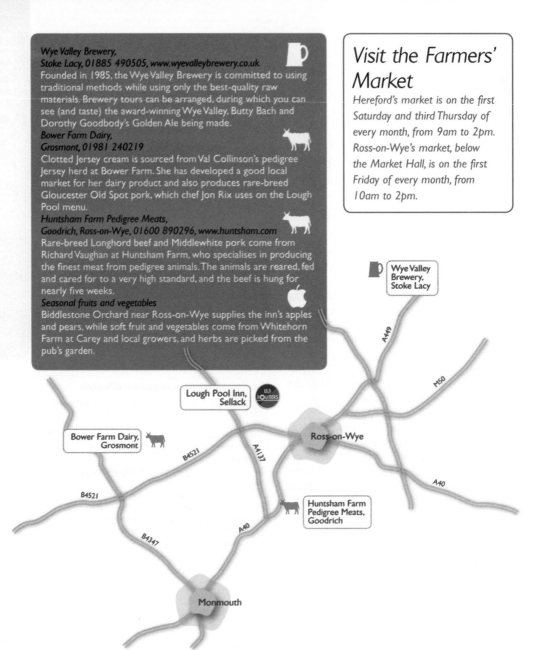

Ross-on-Wye

Lough Pool Inn at Sellack

Country pub and restaurant

'The key appeal, other than its olde-worlde charm and rural seclusion, is the availability of first-class local produce.'

Grove Common, Sellack, Ross-on-Wye,
Herefordshire HR9 6LX
Telephone: +44(0)1989 730236
david@loughpool.co.uk
www.loughpoolinn.co.uk

Experienced publicans and former Routiers award winners David and Janice Birch swapped Dorset for Herefordshire in April 2005 and bought the high-flying Lough Pool Inn, a black-and-white, 16th-century timbered pub hidden away down narrow lanes close to the River Wye. The key appeal, other than its olde-worlde charm and rural seclusion, is the availability of first-class local produce, such as organic meats, fruit and vegetables.

Still very much a pub, little has changed in the delightfully unspoilt bar, with its low beams, slate floors, huge stone fireplace and rustic scrubbed tables. There is an attractive wood-floored dining room and a tranquil garden with smart tables under weeping willows for summer alfresco eating. Chef Jon Rix successfully blends traditional and modern cooking on daily menus that may list twice-baked Herefordshire Hop cheese soufflé with cider cream, chargrilled rib-eye with hand-cut chips and mustard hollandaise, and dark-chocolate fondant with orange ice cream. Expect top-notch ales from Wye Valley Brewery and a well-chosen list of wines with 10 by the glass.

Prices: **Restaurant main course from £10.25. Bar main course from £10.25. House wine £14.**
Last orders: **Food: lunch 14.15; dinner 21.00.**
Closed: **Rarely.**
Food: **Modern British and European.**
Real ale: **Wye Valley Bitter, John Smith's Cask, Wye Valley Butty Bach.**
Other points: **Smoking area. Children welcome. Dogs welcome in the bar. Garden. Car park. Wheelchair access (not WC).**
Directions: **Exit 4/M50. Take the A49 towards Hereford, then follow the signs for Sellack and Hoarwithy. (Map 5)**

Ross-on-Wye

The Saracens Head Inn

Symonds Yat East, Ross-on-Wye,
Herefordshire HR9 6JL
Telephone: +44(0)1600 890435
contact@saracensheadinn.co.uk
www.saracensheadinn.co.uk

Riverside inn

'Makes the most of its splendid riverside setting.'

Rooms: **9. Double/twin room from £35 per person including breakfast. Single room from £48.50, family room from £78.**
Prices: **Set lunch £20. Set dinner £25. Restaurant main course from £9.95. Bar main course from £9.95. House wine £9.95.**
Last orders: **Bar: 23.00. Food: lunch 14.30; dinner 21.00.**
Closed: **Rarely.**
Food: **Modern British.**
Real ale: **Theakston Old Peculier, Morland Original Ale, Greene King Old Speckled Hen, Wye Valley Butty Bach, Courage Best Bitter.**
Other points: **Smoking area. Children welcome. Dogs welcome in the bar. Garden. Car park. Wheelchair access to the bar.**
Directions: **Exit 4/M50. Take the A449 towards Ross-on-Wye and Monmouth. Follow the signs for Symonds Yat East. (Map 5)**

Perched precariously on the banks of the River Wye and owned by the family who operate the adjacent passenger ferry, The Saracens Head has been transformed from drinking dive to cosy inn and one that makes the most of its splendid riverside setting. Enjoy the view from the terrace or head inside to the traditional bars for pints of Theakston or local Wye Valley beers. Beyond is the renovated dining room with slate floor and chunky wooden tables and chairs.

Long, changing menus are written up on chalkboards daily, and everything is freshly prepared using local produce, including pork from Huntsham Farm, Forest of Dean venison and smoked salmon from the Black Mountain Smokery. This translates to rack of Welsh lamb, supreme of free-range Newent chicken, and lemon sole with lime-and-cardamon beurre blanc and fennel confit. Lunch takes in a generous Ferryman's lunch – ham and Raglan pie with salad, pickles and crusty bread. Bedrooms have been refurbished with flair, especially the two superior rooms in the Boathouse Annexe, which offer space and beautiful views down the valley.

www.routiers.co.uk

Trumpet

Mainstone House

Bed and breakfast

Trumpet, Ledbury,
Herefordshire HR8 2RA
Telephone: +44(0)1531 670230
enquiries@mainstonehouse.co.uk
www.mainstonehouse.co.uk

'Plenty of home comforts, especially in the food and drink department.'

This former farmhouse has all the period charm and atmosphere you'd expect of a 17th-century Grade II-listed building. Its olde-worlde setting, with stone walls, beams and a profusion of fireplaces to keep you warm on a winter's evening, comes with plenty of home comforts, especially in the food-and-drink department. Husband-and-wife team John and Lesley Woakes put great store in using the best produce from the Herefordshire countryside, much of it organic.

Set dinners in the impressive dining hall are a feast of fresh fruit and vegetables, meat and cheeses, washed down with excellent English wine, local bottled ales (Butty Bach, Town Crier and Old Henry), ciders (Dunkerton's premium organic) or flavoured gins and liqueurs. Main meals focus on British classics, cooked in a robust, home-cooked style, say Hereford beef in ale. Puddings are unctuously good. Upstairs are four well-presented, spacious rooms, with the two-linked-roomed Hellens suite being ideal for families. Mainstone is on the main Ledbury-Hereford road, so touring the countryside, especially the Malvern Hills, is within easy reach.

Rooms: **4. 1 en-suite. Double/twin room from £29, single from £29. Family room from £70.**
Prices: **Set dinner £25. House wine £9.95.**
Last orders: **Pre-booked evening meals, last orders 20.30. One sitting only Saturday 19.30.**
Closed: **Never.**
Food: **Modern British.**
Other points: **No smoking. Children welcome. Garden. Car park. Wheelchair access.**
Directions: **Exit 2/M50. Follow the A438 and the signs for Hereford. Mainstone House is on the main crossroads of the A438 and A417. (Map 5)**

...for events

MEMBER ENTRY

Walterstone

Allt-yr-Ynys Hotel

Walterstone, Abergavenny,
Herefordshire HR2 0DU
Telephone: +44(0)1873 890307
reception@allthotel.co.uk
www.allthotel.co.uk

Country-house hotel

'Boasts a fine restaurant, indoor heated and spa pools and lush-lawned gardens.'

Rooms: 21. Double room from £85, single from £65.
Prices: Set lunch £16.95 and dinner £25.
Main course from £11. House wine £14.75.
Last orders: Food: lunch 15.00; dinner 21.30.
Closed: Rarely.
Food: Modern British.
Other points: Smoking area. Children welcome. Garden. Car park. Licence for civil weddings. Swimming pool, spa and sauna. Clay pigeon shooting. Dogs welcome overnight. Wheelchair access.
Directions: Take the A465 Abergavenny to Hereford road. Turn off five miles north of Abergavenny at Old Pandy Inn and after 400 yards, turn right at Green Barn. (Map 5)

Set in the foothills of the stunning Black Mountains, this beautifully preserved, mediaeval, 16th-century manor house offers first-rate accommodation and food. Once owned by William Cecil, chief minister to Elizabeth I, the house boasts many of its original features, with 19 en-suite bedrooms, a fine restaurant, indoor heated and spa pools, and lush-lawned gardens leading down to the River Monnow. The comfortable sitting room boasts fine oak panelling, as does the Jacobean suite, complete with its 16th-century four-poster bed.

The luxurious bedrooms are split between the main house and converted stables and outbuildings; most have views over the mountains and woodlands. The kitchen is faithful to regional and local produce, offering Welsh lamb, beef and cheeses in starters such as fusilli pasta with smoked local ham, Welsh cheese, garlic and herbs. Mains could take in braised shank of Welsh lamb on rosemary-and-redcurrant sauce or oven-baked monkfish tail wrapped in bacon with chive-and-onion cream sauce. The delicious puddings include banana-and-caramel torte.

Berkhamsted

The Alford Arms

Country pub

'This pretty, cottage-style pub is well worth seeking out.'

Frithsden, Berkhamsted,
Hertfordshire HP1 3DD
Telephone: +44 (0)1442 864480
info@alfordarmsfrithsden.co.uk
www.alfordarmsfrithsden.co.uk

Secreted away in a tiny hamlet on the edge of the National Trust's Ashridge Estate, this pretty, cottage-style pub is well worth seeking out. Part of David and Becky Salisbury's thriving mini dining-pub empire, it offers first-class food served in an informal atmosphere. Styled 'country pub and eating' on the menu, it successfully blends a stylishly modernised interior, with its tiled-and-wooden floors and old scrubbed-pine tables, with some imaginative modern British cooking that relies on quality, local, free-range and organic produce where possible.

Listed on the à la carte or daily changing chalkboard are 'small plates' of, say, potted brown shrimps with melba toast or confit duck leg on celeriac remoulade with crispy black pudding. Eclectic main courses range from risotto with seared scallops and chargrilled fennel to rib-eye steak with garlic-and-herb butter. Rich chocolate mousse is a typical dessert. Great care is taken in presentation of dishes and flavours shine through. There are good ales and a raft of wines offered by the glass. On warm days, tables spill out on to the front terrace.

Prices: Restaurant main course from £10.25. House wine £11.50.
Last orders: Bar: 23.00. Food: lunch 14.30 (Sunday 16.00); dinner 22.00.
Closed: Rarely.
Food: Modern British.
Real ale: Brakspear, Marston's Pedigree, Marlow Rebellion IPA, Flowers Original.
Other points: Smoking area. Children welcome. Dogs welcome in the bar. Garden/terrace. Car park.
Directions: From Berkhamsted High Street, follow the signs for Potten End and then Frithsden, or, from the A4146 north of Hemel Hempstead, go to Water End and take the second left to Frithsden and Nettleden. After one mile, turn left at the T-junction and then take the next right. (Map 8)
See pub walk on page 472

...for competitions

MEMBER ENTRY

Flaunden

The Bricklayers Arms

Country pub

'Renowned for its award-winning food.'

Hog Pits Bottom, Flaunden,
Hertfordshire HP3 0PH
Telephone: +44 (0)1442 833322
goodfood@bricklayersarms.com
www.bricklayersarms.com

Built in 1722 and the oldest dwelling in the village of Flaunden, this cottagey pub is renowned for its award-winning food. Situated in a tranquil, inviting spot, especially in summer, when its country-style garden is in full flight, it becomes the perfect place to enjoy an alfresco pint of ale. On cooler days, the refurbished, timbered and low-ceilinged bar, replete with blazing log fires, old prints and comfortable traditional furnishings, are popular with both local diners and walkers for head chef Claude Paillet's highly regarded modern pub food.

Alvin and Sally Michaels have smartened up the place and offer a good range of menus with good use of local ingredients, including organic vegetables, herbs and seasonal fruits grown at the pub. In the bar, follow a country stroll with thick-cut sandwiches or tuck into half a spit-roast chicken, or fresh cod fillet cooked in ale batter. In the evening, start with a brochette of tiger prawns, follow with pan-fried duck breast with chestnut-and-port jus, and finish with hot apple-and-cinnamon tart. Don't miss the summer Sunday barbecues and live jazz in the garden.

Prices: **Restaurant and bar main course from £9.95. House wine £11.45.**
Last orders: **Bar: 23.00. Food: lunch 15.00 (Sunday 16.00); dinner 21.30 (Sunday 21.00)**
Closed: **Rarely.**
Food: **Modern British/French.**
Real ale: **Fuller's London Pride, Greene King Old Speckled Hen, Greene King IPA, Archers Best, Adnams.**
Other points: **Smoking area. Children welcome. Dogs welcome in the bar. Garden. Car park. Wheelchair access.**
Directions: **10 minutes from Exit 18 or 20/M25. Three miles south-west of Hemel Hempstead. (Map 8)**

East Cowes

Coasters Coffee Shop

Coffee shop

1 Clarence Road, East Cowes,
Isle of Wight PO32 6EP
Telephone: +44(0)1983 200009
medinamews@wight365.net
www.coasterscoffeeshop.com

'A magnet for those who want good coffee and a baguette or sandwich that are a cut above the norm.'

Prices: **House wine £7.**
Last orders: **Food: lunch 13.45 (winter); lunch 15.30 (summer).**
Closed: **Rarely.**
Food: **Modern British.**
Other points: **No smoking. Children welcome. Wheelchair access.**
Directions: **Two minutes from Cowes floating bridge. (Map 5)**

Standing proudly on the corner of Clarence Road in East Cowes, Coasters is a magnet for those who want good coffee and a baguette or sandwich that are a cut above the norm. In summer, outdoor seating extends the options. Close to the ferry port, it's an excellent place to stop pre- or post-crossing. You can even phone in your order in advance and it will be ready waiting for you.

Its special blend of Segafredo coffee beans is freshly ground every hour and attracts customers from all over the Isle of Wight, as does its fresh range of sandwiches, baguettes, wraps and paninis, which are filled with a tempting array of locally sourced ingredients – the ripest, freshest tomatoes and crispiest lettuce, meats and local vegetables. Chef-patron Kevin Dullaghan bakes the baguettes on site throughout the day. He swapped the rigours of the House of Commons to open Coasters and, with his team, can provide a varied catering service for private and corporate functions. As well as baguettes, they serve hot snacks such as pasties and homemade soups. A drinks licence means you can enjoy beer or wine with your meal.

Ventnor

The Wellington Hotel

Seaside hotel

'Stunning sea views from its elevated cliff-top position, best enjoyed from the smart, decked terrace.'

Belgrave Road, Ventnor,
Isle of Wight PO38 1JH
Telephone: +44(0)1983 856600
enquiries@thewellingtonhotel.net
www.thewellingtonhotel.net

Lovingly restored to its Victorian splendour, the beautifully upgraded Wellington Hotel brings a stylish new look to this traditional resort town. The building faces south and commands stunning sea views from its cliff-top position, best enjoyed from the smart, decked terrace and sea-facing bedrooms, which boast big private balconies. Expect a fresh, minimalist-style of décor throughout, typically, bare boards, modern artwork, open fires, spotlighting, white and cream paintwork, and contemporary furnishings. It reflects its seaside location perfectly. Stylish bedrooms sport up-to-the-minute en-suite bathrooms and crisp white linen.

The Wellington Restaurant offers a varied international menu and may include local lobster, fish landed on the quay, and local farm meats. This translates to grilled lemon sole, roast rump of lamb with honey-and-rosemary jus, pan-fried duck with wild mushrooms and port sauce, apple-and-plum crumble and the Island's famous Minghella ice creams. Come for the sea breeze and the breathtaking views, and don't forget to follow the private footpath down to the beach.

Rooms: 28. Double/twin room from £90, single from £80. Family room from £110.
Prices: Set dinner £40 (four courses). Restaurant main course from £12.90. House wine £13.95.
Last orders: Food: dinner 21.30.
Closed: Never.
Food: Modern British.
Other points: Smoking area. Children welcome. Garden. Limited off-street parking. Licence for civil weddings. Wheelchair access overnight.
Directions: A3 to Portsmouth, Wightlink Ferries crossing to Fishbourne. M3 to Southampton, Red Funnel Ferries crossing to East Cowes. (Map 5)

...for special offers

Bodsham

Froggie's at the Timber Batts

Country pub

School Lane, Bodsham, near Wye,
Kent TN25 5JQ
Telephone: +44(0)1233 750237

'Superb stuffed mussels and perfect rack of lamb with herbs are staples of the menu.'

Prices: Set Sunday lunch £18 and dinner £25. Restaurant main course from £12. Bar main course from £6. House wine £12.
Last orders: Bar: afternoon 14.30; evening 23.00. Food: lunch 14.30; dinner 21.30. No food Sunday evening.
Closed: Monday and the Tuesday after a bank holiday.
Food: Traditional French, specialising in seafood and game.
Real ale: Adnams Best, Fuller's London Pride, Harvey's Sussex Best Bitter.
Other points: Smoking area. Children welcome. Dogs welcome. Garden. Car park. Wheelchair access (not WC).
Directions: Exit 9/M20. Follow signs to Ashford. Take the A28 to Canterbury and follow signs to Wye. From Wye, carry on to Hastingleigh. Go through the village and half a mile down the hill, turn left. The pub is on the left. (Map 6)
See pub walk on page 474

Chef Joel Gross built up a great reputation at Froggie's Restaurant in Wye, so when he headed deeper into the Kent countryside to the remote, 15th-century Timber Batts, he knew they would follow. The place went from being just another rural pub frequented by the walking fraternity to one with an authentic French restaurant attached and a broader customer base. The beamed and timbered bars have blazing log fires – one in a huge inglenook – and comfortable seating. The restaurant has its own fireplace and old pine tables topped with candles.

Local favourites – superb stuffed mussels, a classic duck-confit salad, perfect rack of lamb with herbs, beef fillet with Roquefort sauce – are staples of the printed menu. Profiteroles and tarte Tatin are classic puddings and there's a chalkboard listing daily fish specials such as sea bass in white butter sauce, and bar snacks such as sausage and mash. Sourcing is impeccable – game from local shoots, locally grown vegetables – but cheeses are totally French, as is the wine list, which includes the house wine grown by Joel's cousin in the Loire Valley. Well placed for peaceful walks.

www.routiers.co.uk

The Coastguard

Seaside pub

'The pub is famous for its award-winning cheeseboards.'

The Bay, St Margaret's Bay, Dover,
Kent CT15 6DY
Telephone: +44(0)1304 853176
thecoastguard@talk21.com
www.thecoastguard.co.uk

'Between the bottom of the hill and the deep blue sea' is the motto of this coastal inn – the closest British pub to France. Set into the bottom of the cliff with steps up to a terrace with breathtaking sea views, The Coastguard is located at St Margaret's Bay and surrounded by the White Cliffs of Dover and magnificent coastal walks. Needless to say, the pub is decked out with maritime objects and maps and is a popular spot for watching the ships sailing past.

Nigel Wydymus is an enthusiastic and ambitious owner and this rubs off on his eager-to-please staff. Nigel's wife, Sam, is in charge of the food, which is simple, seasonable and as local as possible. Enjoy real ales from local breweries such as Hopdaemon, Ramsgate and Goacher's, plus wines from local Chapel Down vineyard. It's all a perfect match for the food, which includes starters of potted prawns with ginger and lime and deep-fried whitebait with lemon mayonnaise, and mains such as hot devilled crab, local beef from Goldstone Farm with garlic and black pepper butter, and fish specials. The pub is famous for its award-winning cheeseboards.

Prices: Restaurant main course from £9.50. Bar main course from £9.50. House wine £10.60.
Last orders: Bar: 23.00. Food: lunch 14.45; dinner 20.45.
Closed: Never.
Food: Modern European.
Real ale: Three guest beers.
Other points: No smoking. Children over 14 welcome in the bar, babies welcome in the restaurant. Dogs welcome in the bar. Garden. Car park.
Directions: Exit 13/M20. A258 for Dover and Deal. Follow the signs through St Margaret's at Cliffe. The Coastguard is at the bottom of the hill. (Map 6)

...for the latest news

MEMBER ENTRY

Maidstone

Who'd A Thought It

Country inn

Headcorn Road, Grafty Green,
Maidstone, Kent ME17 2AR
Telephone: +44(0)1622 858951
joe@whodathoughtit.com
www.whodathoughtit.com

'You will find food options to match your every mood.'

Rooms: 9. Double/twin room from £60,
four-poster with double Jacuzzi from £160,
with hot tub £180.
Prices: Restaurant main course from £13.
Bar snacks from £8. House wine £11.
Last orders: Bar: afternoon 15.00; evening 23.00
(all day Sunday). Food: lunch 14.30; dinner 21.30
(Sunday 19.00).
Closed: Rarely.
Food: Modern British.
Real ale: Shepherd Neame Master Brew Bitter,
Timothy Taylor Landlord, Fuller's London Pride.
Other points: Smoking area in the bar. Children
welcome. Garden. Car park. Wheelchair access.
Directions: Exit 8/M20. (Map 6)

You'll find plenty of glitz and glamour at this cosy country inn, built in the reign of Henry VIII. Whether you want a flute of Cristal or a pint of ale, you'll find your every whim catered for here. This inn is a fascinating mix of pub, champagne and oyster bar, tasteful restaurant and luxury accommodation. The rooms are finished to a very high standard. Traditional rooms have four-poster beds, while contemporary rooms sport hot tubs and leather beds; all have a DVD, hi-fi and mini-fridge.

Be it in the bar and brasserie, restaurant or attractive outside terrace, you will find food options to match your every mood. Colchester rock oysters and seafood are on offer in the brasserie. Start with crab cakes with sweet chilli-dressing, then follow with seared cod with lemon-and-chive butter, or a huge platter of lobster, crab, langoustine, king prawns and scallops (for two), plus there are gourmet meat dishes, such as beef Wellington and chateaubriand. Balsamic strawberry millefeuille makes for an indulgent finish. The extensive wine list extends to a fine choice of cognacs and cigars.

www.routiers.co.uk

The Crab & Winkle Restaurant

Seafood restaurant

'With bustling harbour views and balcony seats in summer, this is a charming place to relax.'

South Quay, The Harbour, Whitstable,
Kent CT5 1AB
Telephone: +44(0)1227 779377
www.seafood-restaurant-uk.com

Named after the first passenger railway that ran from Whitstable to Canterbury, this harbourside restaurant occupies the roof space of the fish market below. There is no shortage of fresh produce here and the menu stays broadly the same throughout the day, although the lively lunchtime atmosphere winds down to more cosy and intimate dining at night.

Starters include a Whitstable skink of smoked haddock, cockles and cream, potted brown shrimps or hot-smoked salmon blinis, dill and chive sour cream. Mains offer flaked fish, lobster and thermidor lasagne or haddock fumé with poached egg and grape and grain-mustard cream. Although predominantly fish, the daily specials allow for carnivore and vegetarian tastes. Grape, berry and rosé wine terrine with raspberry-coulis sorbet and dark chocolate, pear and walnut brownie are indulgent ways to round off. With bustling harbour views and balcony seats in summer, this is a charming place to relax over a locally sourced bottle of wine or one from the Old World collection. Diners receive a discount in the downstairs fish market.

Prices: **Set menu from £11 (two courses). House wine £10.95.**
Last orders: **Food: all day until 21.30.**
Closed: **Rarely.**
Food: **Specialises in seafood, local game and vegetarian.**
Real ale: **Shepherd Neame Spitfire, Whitstable Bay Ale.**
Other points: **Smoking area. Children welcome. Free parking after 18.00. Wheelchair access.**
Directions: **From London, go through the town centre of Whitstable towards the harbour entrance, which is on the left just as you exit the one-way system. (Map 6)**

...for recipe ideas

Cardium Shellfish,
South Quay, The Harbour, Whitstable, 01227 264769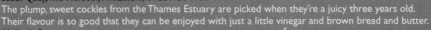
The plump, sweet cockles from the Thames Estuary are picked when they're a juicy three years old.
Their flavour is so good that they can be enjoyed with just a little vinegar and brown bread and butter.
Mallards Farm,
Waterham Rd, Hernhill, Faversham, 01227 751245
The farm supplies fresh fruit and vegetables to the restaurant all-year round. You can buy direct from
the farm shop.
Fruits de Mer,
10 The Broadway, Broadstairs, 01843 861863
When he can't get supplies from the local fisherman, Mark gets his fish supplied by this amazing fishmonger.
It's well worth a visit to stock up on the local catch.
West Whelks,
The Harbour, Whitstable
Mark recommends its whelks and oysters, which you can buy daily at the harbour.
Churchman's Farms,
Kennaways, Ospringe, Faversham, 01795 531124
The farm's free-range eggs are used to make Mark's light and airy smoked-eel soufflé.
Fisherman Brian Foad,
Whitstable
Instead of buying from the fish-market stalls, Mark buys straight from the day boats that go out from the
harbour, including lobsters from Brian Foad, and sea bass, skate and scallops from fisherman Ian Brooks.
Oysters delivered to your home
Treat yourself to the decadence of Whitstable oysters by having them delivered direct to your home.
Order them online at www.whitstable-shellfish.co.uk or by calling 01227 282375.

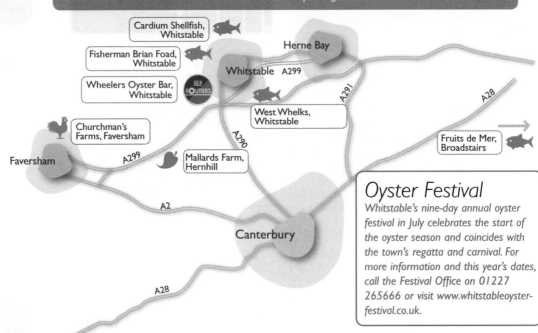

Cardium Shellfish, Whitstable

Fisherman Brian Foad, Whitstable

Wheelers Oyster Bar, Whitstable

Herne Bay

Whitstable   A299

West Whelks, Whitstable

Churchman's Farms, Faversham

Faversham

A299

Mallards Farm, Hernhill

Fruits de Mer, Broadstairs

A2

A290

A291

A28

Canterbury

A28

Oyster Festival

Whitstable's nine-day annual oyster festival in July celebrates the start of the oyster season and coincides with the town's regatta and carnival. For more information and this year's dates, call the Festival Office on 01227 265666 or visit www.whitstableoyster-festival.co.uk.

Whitstable

Wheelers Oyster Bar

Seafood restaurant

'A mini seafood paradise.'

8 High Street, Whitstable, Kent CT5 1BQ
Telephone: +44(0)1227 273311
www.whitstable-shellfish.co.uk

Whitstable is the oyster capital of Kent, and Wheelers, which celebrated 150 years of business in 2006, is a most winsome place to sample the fine local catch. Originally a simple oyster bar, the restaurant has long since branched out to become a mini seafood paradise, serving everything from cockles and crab to lobster. It's essential to book, as demand far outstrips the number of tables in the small dining room.

Chef Mark Stubbs's talent for cooking seafood speaks for itself. He cooks with the freshest seafood, but is not afraid to introduce intense and interesting flavours to his dishes. Each is carefully considered, such as roasted marinated jumbo prawns on couscous with sauce vierge, or the combination of roast halibut with a citrus-and-crab hollandaise and sweet-potato and coriander mash. But the simple native oysters unadorned are equally thrilling. A light menu is also offered: potted shrimps, whole cracked crab salad, and trout, leek and horseradish tart. In the tiny oyster bar, eat in or take-away winkles, cockles, octopus or bowls of eels. There's no licence, but no charge for corkage either.

Prices: Main course from £10. Unlicenced.
Last orders: Food: 19.30.
Closed: Wednesday, and the second and third week of January.
Food: Seafood.
Other points: No smoking. Children welcome. Credit cards not accepted. BYO. Wheelchair access.
Directions: Exit 7/M2. Turn off the Thanet Way at the roundabout to Whitstable and follow the road through town. The restaurant is at the end of the high street on the left. (Map 6)

Wingham

The Dog Inn

Canterbury Road, Wingham, near
Canterbury, Kent CT3 1BB
Telephone: +44(0)1227 720339
thedoginn@netbreeze.co.uk

Country pub

'Large leather sofas for sinking into with a pint and the weekend papers.'

Rooms: **9. Double/twin room from £69, single from £40, family from £89.**
Prices: **Set lunch £15 and dinner £20. Restaurant main course from £8.95. Bar main course from £6.95. House wine £12.95.**
Last orders: **Bar: 23.00. Food: lunch 15.00; dinner 22.00 (all day Saturday and Sunday).**
Food: **Eclectic British.**
Real ale: **Courage Best Bitter, Adnams, Greene King IPA, Marston's Bitter, Shepherd Neame.**
Other points: **No smoking. Children welcome. Dogs welcome. Garden and barbecue. Car park. Licence for civil weddings.**
Directions: **A2 to Barham/M2. Four miles from Canterbury on the A257. (Map 6)**

Realising that there was plenty of life in the 'old Dog' yet, Richard and Sherry Martin took on this ancient hostelry and have scraped away years of grime to expose the impressive features of the original building, which dates back to the 13th century. Superb heavy beams and panelling blend well with the antique oak floors throughout the character bars; one has large leather sofas for sinking into with a pint and the weekend papers. There's a historic function room and renovated en-suite bedrooms under the eaves.

Upgraded menus feature game from Godmersham Estate, organic meats from Chandler and Dunn in Ash, and fish from Whitstable. This translates as Romney Marsh lamb with rosemary jus, rib-eye steak with pepper sauce, baked trout with parsley butter, and upmarket lunchtime bar snacks, perhaps wild-mushroom ragout with toasted brioche and goat's cheese and courgette tart. The building has huge potential and there's still plenty to do, but with Richard and Sherry's enthusiasm for the place, their grand ideas should soon be realised. The new pagoda in the garden will host civil weddings.

Raffles Hotel and Tea Rooms

Seaside hotel

'A real gem and perfect for a traditional seaside break.'

73-77 Hornby Road, Blackpool,
Lancashire FY1 4QJ
Telephone: +44(0)1253 294713
enquiries@
raffleshotelblackpool.fsworld.co.uk
www.raffleshotelblackpool.co.uk

Owners Graham Poole and Ian Balmforth have a real passion for their exceptional B&B-hotel. It's a real gem and perfect for a traditional seaside break as it is just minutes from Blackpool's Tower. The standard of décor is high, the housekeeping exemplary. The atmosphere is relaxed from the moment you step over the doorstep and are served a welcoming coffee or tea in your room. At other times, morning coffees and evening drinks are served in the comfortable lounge.

All the bedrooms are compact, but not small, and meticulously decorated with flair. A do-it-yourself tea tray, TV and quality towels are standard issue in bedrooms. There's a fabulous, oriental-themed room with Thai furniture and Chinese bedspread and rooms inspired by North Africa, Egypt and India. In addition, there are two high-spec family suites, each with a spacious lounge and diner with kitchenette, and en-suite bathroom. Two rooms on the ground floor are ideal for less mobile guests. And, it is worth noting that the premises next door have been converted into a tea room where meals, as well as fluffy cakes and scones, are served.

Rooms: 17. From £30 per person.
Prices: Main course from £5.95. Starters and sweets from £1.50.
Last orders: Food: 18.00.
Closed: Rarely.
Food: Traditional/modern British.
Other points: Smoking area. Children welcome. Dogs welcome overnight. Car park. Wheelchair access.
Directions: Take the M55 towards Blackpool and follow the red signs for central car park. Leave the car park for the one-way system, Central Drive. Then turn left and Hornby Road will be the first immediate right. (Map 9)

...for events

Clitheroe

The Freemasons Arms

Village pub

8 Vicarage Fold, Wiswell, Clitheroe,
Lancashire BB7 9DF
Telephone: +44(0)1254 822218

'It didn't take long before local foodies and wine buffs were beating a path to the door.'

**Prices: Set lunch and dinner £10.95 (two
courses), time restrictions on availability.**
Last orders: **Bar: afternoon 14.00; evening 21.30.**
Food: **lunch 14.00 (Sunday 20.00); dinner 21.30.**
Closed: **Monday and Tuesday.**
Food: **Modern British.**
Real ale: **Bowland Hen Harrier, Moorhouses
Pride of Pendle, Black Sheep Best.**
Other points: **Smoking area. Children over
three welcome. Wheelchair access.**
Directions: **A59, two miles south of Clitheroe.
Take the A671 to Blackburn. After half a mile,
take the first left to Wiswell and the pub is in
the centre of the village. (Map 9)**
See pub walk on page 476

Chef-patron Ian Martin has not looked back since he arrived at the this tiny pub tucked down an unmade village lane at the foot of Pendle Hill. Originally three cottages, it became a pub in 1850 and remains a traditional village local with a cosy bar and upstairs dining area decorated in rich greens, soft reds, fresh flowers and contemporary prints. Having found room for his amazing cellar of 500 wines, which includes 120 clarets and some great vintages (at low mark-up prices), it didn't take long before local foodies and wine buffs were beating a path to the door.

The draw is Ian's exemplary cooking and his fresh, modern menu, which reflects his enthusiasm to source everything locally, including Goosnargh duck breast with spiced plum compote and red-wine jus and loin of Bowland pork with black pudding and a cider-and-mustard sauce. Come for pints of locally brewed beers and the great-value two-course lunch, or choose seared scallops with chilli jam, followed by beef fillet with foie gras, wild mushrooms and Madeira sauce. Don't miss the well-organised wine dinners.

www.routiers.co.uk

Restaurant

Clitheroe

Weezos @ The Old Tollhouse

1-5 Parson Lane, Clitheroe,
Lancashire BB7 2JP
Telephone: +44(0)1200 424478
weezos@btconnect.com
www.weezos.co.uk

'Desserts of banana spring roll with butterscotch and nougat semi freddo show innovation in the kitchen.'

Housed in what used to be the original Clitheroe Toll House at the foot of the town's ancient castle, this charming restaurant has quaint old beams and original corner stonework, but what grabs your attention are the classic and professional table settings – crisp white linen, sparkling cutlery and tall Schott Zwiesel glasses. The vast experience of Stosie and her partner shows in all areas – style, service, wine and, above all, the pair show a real understanding of good ingredients and how to make the best of them.

Stosie's cooking talent is evident from her superb spring-pea soup starter and is enhanced by tiger-prawn fritters with a vibrant cucumber and spring-onion salad with green chilli and coriander salsa, through to her pot-roasted Goosnargh spring chicken infused with local wild garlic, lemon, thyme and butter. Medallions of Bowland beef fillet appear au poivre, with crushed green and black peppercorns, flambéed in cognac. Desserts of banana spring roll with butterscotch and nougat semi freddo show further innovation in the kitchen. The wine list offers plenty of interest and good value.

Prices: Set meal plus wine on Friday-Saturday £25. Set Sunday lunch £18. Restaurant main course from £12.20. House wine £11.95.
Last orders: Lunch; 15.00 (Friday and Saturday). Dinner; 19.00 (Sunday 18.00).
Closed: Monday and Sunday night.
Food: Modern European.
Other points: Smoking area. Children welcome. Wheelchair access.
Directions: A59. Follow signs to the town centre and the castle. Go down Parson Hill and Weezos is 50 yards from the castle's main gate. (Map 9)

...for competitions

MEMBER
ENTRY
130

Mitton

The Three Fishes

Country pub

Mitton Road, Mitton, Near Whalley,
Lancashire BB7 9PQ
Telephone: +44(0)1254 826888
kaye@northcotemanor.com
www.thethreefishes.com

'A cracking gastropub – one not to be missed.'

Prices: Restaurant main course from £8.
Bar main course from £8. House wine £11.75.
Last orders: Food: lunch 14.00 (all day Sunday);
dinner 21.00 (Sunday 20.30).
Closed: Rarely.
Food: Traditional British.
Real ale: Thwaites, Bowland.
Other points: No smoking. Dogs welcome in
the bar. Garden. Children welcome. Car park.
Wheelchair access.
Directions: Exit 31/M6. From the A59 at
Whalley roundabout, follow the road to
Whalley to the mini roundabout, take the
second exit to Stonyhurst, Hurst Green and the
Trough of Bowland, then follow the road for
three miles to the village of Mitton. (Map 9)

After many years of neglect, this 400-year-old inn reopened its doors in 2004 with a blaze of publicity, following a £250,000 investment by the owners of Michelin-starred Northcote Manor. Set in the lush Ribble Valley, this long, low, rambling stone building has been simply and tastefully refurbished throughout, with stone-flagged floors, plenty of exposed brick and stone, and a grand open fireplace at one end. Business has been brisk, and instrumental to this success has been the menu, which embraces regional dishes and British classics.

All the meat, vegetables and dairy produce are sourced from a host of local suppliers – menus feature a map pinpointing the location of traders, and the interior walls feature a photo gallery of all the suppliers. Food is honest, hearty and delicious, as seen in oxtail braised in red wine and herbs, Bowland lamb Lancashire hotpot with pickled cabbage, and battered haddock with real chips and tartare sauce. Add lunchtime sandwiches and great local beers from Thwaites and Bowland and you have a cracking gastropub – one not to be missed.

Regional food heroes

The Three Fishes menu champions Lancashire's leading artisan food producers, and photographs of these local heroes adorn the walls of the pub in tribute to their dedication, enthusiasm and knowledge. A photo gallery of 33 producers, with links to websites, can be found on the pub website, wwwthethreefishes.com.

Bowland Forest Foods,
Abbeystead, Lancaster, 01524 793558, www.bowlandforest.co.uk

Farmers in the heart of the Forest of Bowland have joined together to establish and promote their own locally branded products. Lamb, beef and pork are produced in a traditional and environmentally friendly way. The pub taps into this supply of quality meat, namely beef and lamb reared by Jim Curwen at Marshaw Farm, near Abbeystead.

Fairfield Farm,
Clayton-le-Dale, Blackburn, 01254 812550, www.fairfieldfarm.co.uk

Phil and Louise Edge rear pigs using time-honoured techniques to produce quality pork products that are sold from their Farm Shop. They specialise in award-winning dry-cured gammon, sweet dry-cured bacon and homemade sausages.

Sandham's Lancashire Cheese,
Rostock Dairy, Barton, Preston, 01995 640247

Chris Sandham is a traditional cheesemaker specialising in Lancashire cheese. He makes a soft, sweet and buttery cheese using pasteurised organic milk. It graces the excellent cheeseboard and makes a delicious sandwich filling at the pub.

Visit the Farmers' Market

Clitheroe Farmers' Market is held on the first, third and fifth Tuesday of every month, from 9am to 4pm.
Call 01200 443012 for details.

Poulton-le-Fylde

Monsieurs

12d Blackpool Old Road,
Poulton-le-Fylde, Lancashire FY6 7DH
Telephone: +44(0)1253 896400

French-style takeaway

'A Mediterranean café atmosphere, where you can sit in comfortable chairs and read glossy magazines.'

Prices: Main course from £8. Snack from £5.
Last orders: Food: 17.00-21.00.
Closed: Lunchtime. Monday. The last two weeks of July and the first week of August.
Food: Traditional French/English/takeaway.
Other points: No smoking. Children welcome. Car park. Credit cards not accepted.
Directions: Exit 3/M55, then the A585 to Fleetwood. Left at the first traffic lights, then left at the second lights on to the A586, and into Poulton one-way system. Monsieurs is situated opposite the library. (Map 9)

Monsieurs is a one-stop dinner solution, offering takeaways with a difference. Now concentrating on its evening trade, this spick-and-span, upmarket eaterie dispenses fine homemade French and British 'ready' meals. The brainchild of Guy and Anita Jenkinson, it is a welcome addition to the many Chinese and Indian takeaways that are the high-street norm, and is well placed in the middle of town. Waiting for your order is a pleasant experience as Monsieurs has a Mediterranean café atmosphere, where you can sit in comfortable chairs and read glossy magazines instead of copies of the day's tabloids.

The French-style and British dishes are made from quality ingredients and are a far cry from the supermarket equivalent. Here you can tuck into French onion soup, a hearty beef bourguignon, navarin of lamb, Basque chicken and pork Dijon, with side orders of garlic sautéed potatoes, Vichy carrots and ratatouille. Pasta, vegetarian dishes and popular British desserts of fruit crumbles, and both sticky toffee and bread-and-butter pudding extend the range.

www.routiers.co.uk

Whitewell

The Inn at Whitewell

Country inn

'One of Britain's finest all-round inns.'

Forest of Bowland, Whitewell, Clitheroe,
Lancashire BB7 3AT
Telephone: +44(0)1200 448222

With his late father's vision and style, Charles Bowman, and his excellent staff, imbue this ancient hostelry with warmth, personality and a pleasing quirkiness. It's set amid the wild beauty of the Trough of Bowland, overlooking the River Hodder and stands next to the parish church. Inside, it's relaxed, with a haphazard arrangement of furnishings, bric-a-brac, open log fires, heavy ceiling beams and colourful rugs throughout the stone-floored taproom, rambling dining areas and library.

The bar supper choice may include peppered rib-eye steak with garlic butter, with salads and substantial sandwiches featuring at lunchtime. The evening carte majors on quality local ingredients, perhaps roast Bowland lamb with carrot and cumin-seed purée, fantastic puddings and British and Irish cheeses. Individual bedrooms are furnished with antiques, peat fires and Victorian baths – spacious new rooms have superb views. Eight miles of fishing, a superlative wine list an art gallery and a shop selling homemade foods complete the picture. One of Britain's finest all-round inns.

Rooms: **23. Double/twin room from £96.**
Prices: **Restaurant main course from £12. Bar main course from £7.50. House wine £9.50.**
Last orders: **Bar: afternoon 15.00. Food: lunch 14.00; dinner 21.30.**
Closed: **Never.**
Food: **Modern British.**
Real ale: **Marston's Bitter, Taylor's Ales, Copper Dragon Ales, Bowland Ales.**
Other points: **Smoking area. Children welcome. Dogs welcome in the bar and overnight. Garden. Car park. Licence for civil weddings. Fishing. Wheelchair access to the pub.**
Directions: **Exit 32/M6 to Longridge. In the centre of Longridge, follow signs to Whitewell. (Map 9)**
See pub walk on page 478

...for special offers

San Carlo Restaurant

Italian restaurant

'Good-value pizza and pasta that are a cut above the norm.'

38-40 Granby Street, Leicester,
Leicestershire LEI IDE
Telephone: +44(0)116 251 9332
www.sancarlo.co.uk

Part of a small chain of city-centre restaurants, San Carlo serves good Italian food that puts many chains in the shade. It majors in good-value pizza and pasta that are a cut above the norm. The décor is contemporary, simple and the same across the chain, which has outlets in Birmingham, Bristol and Manchester. The light and airy feel is helped by mirror-lined walls and white-tiled floors that create a sleek Mediterranean look softened by lots of potted plants and trees.

This branch ranges over three floors, and has a great atmosphere. The look inside may be modern but the food is traditional, with an extensive range of pizza and pasta (spaghetti with crab, tomato, chilli and basil), and classic trattoria dishes such as calves' liver cooked with onions and Madeira, and rack of lamb with tomato-and-rosemary sauce. Seafood is delivered once, sometimes twice daily, and the seafood specials board is updated accordingly. Sardines, dressed crab, lobster tagliolini, grilled Dover sole, and king prawn and monkfish kebab are typical examples. The wine list covers an extensive selection of Italian and French wines.

Prices: **Main course from £9. House wine £12.95.**
Last orders: **Food: 23.00.**
Closed: **Rarely.**
Food: **Italian.**
Other points: **Smoking throughout. Children welcome. Wheelchair access.**
Directions: **Situated in Leicester city centre, just outside the busy shopping area. (Map 8)**

MEMBER
134
ENTRY

Long Clawson

The Crown and Plough

Village inn

East End, Long Clawson,
Leicestershire LE14 4NG
Telephone: +44(0)1664 822322
crownandplough@btconnect.com
www.crownandplough.co.uk

'Food is clearly taken seriously here and there is some inventive cooking evident.'

Rooms: **6. Please call for prices.**
Prices: **Set lunch and dinner £13.50 (Tuesday-Thursday). Restaurant main course from £9. Bar main course from £9. House wine £10.**
Last orders: **Bar: afternoon 14.00 (Tuesday-Friday); evening 23.00 (open all day at weekends). Food: lunch 14.30 (Sunday 15.00); dinner: 21.30 (no food Sunday evening).**
Closed: **Never.**
Food: **Modern British and European.**
Real ale: **Shepherd Neame Spitfire, Marston's Pedigree, Black Sheep Best.**
Other points: **Smoking area. Children welcome. Dogs welcome in the bar. Garden. Car park. Wheelchair access.**
Directions: **Exit 21a/M1. To Kegworth and then Melton Mowbray. Follow the A606 to Nottingham. Long Clawson is signposted five miles outside Melton Mowbray. (Map 8)**

Enter The Crown and Plough and you are immediately seduced by its wonderful simplicity. Situated in one of a handful of villages on the Leicestershire and Nottinghamshire border where stilton cheese is still produced, the pub is set back from the road in two buildings. Following extensive refurbishment by new owners Allan and Caroline Stewart, the pub reopened in August 2005. The floors retain the old red quarry tiles and the farmhouse furniture is pine and distressed. The informal bar has French windows leading out to an enclosed garden. The 30-cover restaurant is intimate and welcoming, with white linen napkins adding a nice contrast.

Food is clearly taken seriously here and there is some inventive cooking evident on the daily changing menus. Start with loin of spring lamb with lime-and-chilli dressing and homemade naan bread or moules marinière. Local sourcing is showcased in dishes such as a lasagne of English asparagus served with Long Clawson stilton and wild mushrooms, and roast local partridge. Desserts include vanilla crème brûlée. Six bedrooms were due to open for buisness as we went to press.

www.routiers.co.uk

Nether Broughton

The Red House

Village inn

'Bedrooms are imaginatively designed and feature DVDs and a host of goodies.'

23 Main Street, Nether Broughton,
Melton Mowbray,
Leicestershire LE14 3HB
Telephone: +44(0)1664 822429
bookings@the-redhouse.co.uk
www.the-redhouse.co.uk

Set in the charming village of Nether Broughton, this early Victorian house is now a stylish, contemporary and highly individual pub-restaurant with rooms. Combining a relaxed atmosphere with modern luxury, the bar has a traditional feel, where chalkboards offer the day's menu, which includes local butcher Mr Bailey's pork pie, black pudding and poached-egg bruschetta and casserole of Alton Manor beef.

But modern styling distinguishes the restaurant with, for example, a bar that consists of a pine-wood frame filled with old books. Or, head for the adjoining dining room, which is filled with light from patio doors that look on to the courtyard. Here you can choose Vivian Hall's unpasteurised goat's cheese with sweet-and-sour cherry tomatoes, roast rump of Belvoir Estate lamb and rhubarb-and-custard trifle from a seasonally inspired menu that proudly names many of its local suppliers. The global wine list is expansive and keenly priced. Eight en-suite bedrooms are imaginatively designed and feature DVDs and a host of goodies. Old Stables houses both the Garden Bar and Grill.

Rooms: **8. Double/twin room from £50 per person.**
Prices: **Restaurant main course from £11. Bar snack from £5. House wine £12.**
Last orders: **Bar: 23.00 (Sunday 22.30). Food: lunch 14.30; dinner 22.00 (Sunday 17.00).**
Closed: **Rarely.**
Food: **Modern British.**
Real ale: **Two guest beers.**
Other points: **Smoking area. Children welcome. Dogs welcome in the bar. Car park. Garden bar and open kitchen. Meeting room. Marquee facility. Wheelchair access to the restaurant/pub.**
Directions: **Exit 25/M1, then the A52, then the A606 to Melton. Situated on the A606 between Nottingham and Melton Mowbray, five miles north of Melton. (Map 8)**

...for the latest news

Cropwell Bishop Creamery, 0115 989 2350
and Colston Bassett Dairy, 01949 81322
Cropwell Bishop and Colston Bassett are two of the seven dairies in the world licensed to make Stilton cheese, as it can only be made in the three counties of Derbyshire, Leicestershire and Nottinghamshire. It is still made in much the same way as it was 250 years ago. The Red Lion is a passionate supporter and, whether it's White Stilton, Shropshire Blue or the 'King of Cheese', the Blue Stilton, it always takes pride of place on its cheese platter.

Belvoir Fruit Farms
Belvoir, 01476 870286
Fresh fruits, flowers and spices grown on the farm are pressed, infused and cooked to create health-giving cordials, presses and crushes. Started in 1984, this family business is thriving, due to the demand for soft fruit that have real, honest fruit flavours. Belvoir cordials are free of artificial colours, flavours and sweeteners.

Brewster's Brewery
Strathern, 01949 861868
Just round the corner from The Red Lion, Brewster's Brewery was set up in 1998 by Sara Barton – Brewster is the old English word for a female brewer. With Sara brewing, selling and delivering the beer, the brewery developed from a five-barrel plant to a 10-barrel brewery in 2002 and now brews around eight beers.

Blackberry Farm
Clipston-on-the-Wolds, 0115 989 2260
The farm shop sells quality produce that has been naturally reared, much of it sourced from the surrounding area, with lamb, turkey and beef being fed on natural foods on their own farm. There's full traceability on individual animals, with steak joints hung for a minimum of 21 days to ensure flavour and tenderness.

Nottingham

Cropwell Bishop Creamery,
Colston Bassett

Blackberry Farm,
Clipston-on-the-Wolds

Red Lion Inn,
Stathern

A52

Belvoir Fruit Farms,
Belvoir

Grantham

Stathern

A606

Brewster's Brewery,
Strathern

A607

A46

Visit the Farmers' Market

The former poultry shed at Melton Cattle Market is the location of the Melton Mowbray farmers' market every Tuesday and Friday.

Melton Mowbray

A606

Leicester

Red Lion Inn

Village pub

'Informality, real ales, fine wines and good-quality, innovative, traditional food using local produce.'

Red Lion Street, Stathern,
Leicestershire LE14 4HS
Telephone: +44(0)1949 860868
info@theredlioninn.co.uk
www.theredlioninn.co.uk

Part of the ever-expanding mini pub empire that includes the highly regarded Olive Branch at Clipsham, this refurbished 16th-century village pub ticks all the gastropub boxes. Informality, real ales, fine wines and good-quality, innovative, traditional food using local produce sum up the philosophy of the hugely successful Rutland Inn Company. The converted skittle-alley dining room comes with low beams, terracotta walls and wood-burning stove, and the informal bar buzzes with diners and local drinkers.

As the menu indicates, there's a passion for quality suppliers: Brewster's Bitter is brewed in the village, game comes from the Belvoir estate, sausages from the village butcher, and cheese and fruits are sourced from local farms. A pub 'shop' sells chutneys and pickles made in the kitchen, as well as other locally sourced foodstuffs. There's something for everyone on the daily-changing menu, including, perhaps, wood-pigeon tartlet, roast halibut with chive mash and lobster bisque and, to finish, warm rum baba. The addition of bedrooms will only enhance the reputation of this fabulous place.

Prices: Set lunch £16. Restaurant main course from £9.25. Bar main course from £6.25. House wine £12.
Last orders: Bar: afternoon 15.00; evening 23.00. Food: lunch 14.00 (Sunday 15.00); dinner 21.30. No food Sunday evening.
Closed: Sunday evening.
Food: Modern pub food.
Real ale: Brewster Vale Pale Ale, Grainstore Olive Oil. Two guest beers.
Other points: Smoking area in the bar. Children welcome. Dogs welcome in the bar. Garden. Car park.
Directions: From the A1 follow the A52 towards Nottingham. Turn left towards Belvoir Castle for three miles; Stathern is signposted left. (Map 8)

Belvoir

The Chequers Inn

Country inn

Main Street, Woolsthorpe-By-Belvoir,
Grantham, Lincolnshire NG32 1LU
Telephone: +44(0)1476 870701
justinnabar@yahoo.co.uk
www.chequers-inn.net

'The inn boasts its own cricket and a petanque pitch.'

Rooms: 4. Double room from £59, single from £49, family from £69.
Prices: Set lunch £12.50 and dinner £15 (Monday-Friday evenings). Restaurant main course from £11. Bar snacks from £7.95. House wine £12.50.
Last orders: Bar: afternoon 15.00; evening 23.00. Food: lunch 14.30 (Sunday 16.00); dinner: 21.30 (Sunday 20.30).
Closed: Rarely.
Food: Modern British.
Real ale: Belvoir Bitter, Brewster's Marquis. Guest beers.
Other points: Smoking area. Children welcome. Dogs welcome in the bar and overnight. Garden. Car park. Wheelchair access.
Directions: A1. Take the A607 towards Melton Mowbray and follow the Heritage Trail signs towards Belvoir Castle. (Map 8)

Just a stone's throw from Belvoir's magnificent castle, the Chequers is a 17th-century coaching inn that has been stylishly refurbished by Justin and Jo Chad. Décor blends the old and new, with bold colours on the walls, leather chairs, sturdy oak tables and a blazing log fire in the smart, beamed lounge, and a light and airy restaurant lined with modern artwork. Outside, you'll find teak furniture and lovely views of the castle.

Food is taken very seriously, the philosophy being 'to use the freshest ingredients to create modern, simple dishes with exciting taste and texture'. Expect home-baked breads, herbs from the garden, lamb from neighbouring farms and game from the Belvoir Estate. Tuck into a rib-eye steak sandwich or fish and chips at lunch, with evening additions taking in clam, squid and salmon risotto, and rabbit stuffed with garlic and apricot. Accompany with first-class wines or the locally brewed Brewster's beer. The contemporary feel extends to the four en-suite bedrooms in a converted stable block. The inn also boasts its own cricket and a petanque pitch – boules are behind the bar.

Lincoln

Jocasta's Restaurant

Moor Lane, Thorpe on the Hill,
Lincolnshire LN6 9DA
Telephone: +44(0)1522 686314
enquiries@jocastas.co.uk
www.jocastas.co.uk

Restaurant

'A broad range of dishes, from the rustically simple to the fantastically complex.'

Prices: Set lunch £11.50. Restaurant main course from £12.95. House wine £10.50.
Last orders: Food: lunch 14.00 (Sunday 15.00); dinner 21.00 (Friday and Saturday 22.30).
Closed: Sunday evening and all day Monday.
Food: Global.
Other points: No smoking. Children welcome. Car park. Licence for civil weddings.
Directions: Follow the A46 from the A1 towards Lincoln. Follow the brown tourist-information signs for Whisby Nature Park. Jocasta's is opposite the golf course. (Map 8)

Sister restaurant to The Bottle and Glass at Harby, Newark (see entry), Jocasta's enjoys a stunning lakeside location in the Whisby Water Park. It's no surprise that this beautiful situation is popular with wedding parties, as well as for more intimate dining. The setting has a Hellenic ambience with its pillars, drapes and palms. Apart from a Caesar salad though, the food leans towards international, with an emphasis on using the best local produce. The week's meat suppliers are written up on a chalkboard.

Head chef David Witlea offers a broad range of dishes, from the rustically simple to the fantastically complex. Try risotto of gorgonzola, rocket and fennel salad or crispy pork belly with chive mash from the light lunch menu or, from the carte, start with pea-and-mint soup with coconut milk and sautéed crayfish and follow it with seared calves' liver and thyme-scented potato rösti. For unbeatable value, come for the set-lunch menu. An extensive wine list offers a distinctly European flavour, firmly centred around France, but with numerous New World entries.

Lincoln

The Kitchen

Restaurant and diner

'Sunday lunch is quite an event and is how The Kitchen's reputation for good food began.'

Sleaford Road, Nocton Heath, Lincoln,
Lincolnshire LN4 2AN
Telephone: +44(0)1522 811299
davidmat@tesco.com
www.thekitchenatnoctonheath.co.uk

Housed in a former RAF mess hall, this modern British diner has become a prime pit-stop for travellers and tourists in Lincolnshire. The Kitchen is a service station like no other – expect to see upmarket motors alongside the clutch of lorries in the car park, which is testament to its wide appeal. The menu focuses on local produce, most notably Lincolnshire sausages and Lincoln Red beef, as well as fresh vegetables, eggs and cheese. The main dishes are traditional and hearty, and include steaks, liver and onions, hot roasts, homemade pies, warming casseroles, and comforting puddings of the crumble or spotted dick and syrup sponge variety.

Sunday lunch is quite an event and is how The Kitchen's reputation for good food began. And it's not just the food that has been overhauled since chef-proprietor David Mathers took over; the interiors have been gutted and rebuilt to create a bright and modern space. The two dining rooms have tiled floors, local-limestone walls and neutral colours. The service is eager and friendly, and worked from a long hot counter.

Prices: Set dinner from £7.25. Restaurant main course from £5.50. Breakfast from £3.
Last orders: Food; 22.00 (Friday 22.30, Saturday 23.00, Sunday 18.00)
Closed: Rarely.
Food: Modern British.
Other points: Smoking area. Children welcome. Garden. Car park. Wheelchair access.
Directions: A15. Five miles south of Lincoln and seven miles north of Sleaford. (Map 10)

...for recipe ideas

Batemans Brewery
Wainfleet All Saints, Lincolnshire, 01754 880317 www.bateman.co.uk
One of the country's oldest family breweries is based around a 200-year-old windmill overlooking the River Steeping. It brews a classic mild and porter as well as a seasonal ale, the XB Bitter and malty XXXB, the latter two being served at the Tally Ho. A new brewhouse and visitor centre opened in 2002 and you can tour the brewery.

Dennetts Ice Cream
24-26 Boston Road, Spilsby, 01790 752573 www.dennetts.co.uk
The Dennett family have been making dairy ice cream in Spilsby since the 1920s. The current range consists of 28 flavours, with traditional family favourites as well as more adventurous flavours, including brandy and orange. Visit their ice cream parlour in Lincoln's Bailgate area.

Lincolnshire Poacher Cheese
F.W. Read & Sons, Ulceby Grange, Alford, 01507 466987 www.lincolnshirepoachercheese.com
Using unpasteurised milk from 200 Holstein cows and traditional methods, Simon Jones, a fourth generation farmer on the edge of Wolds, produces an award-winning Cheddar-style cheese. More open textured that Cheddar but with the same earthy tang, he matures the Poacher for 9-12 months and the Vintage for 12-15 months. You can buy it at local farmers markets.

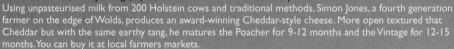

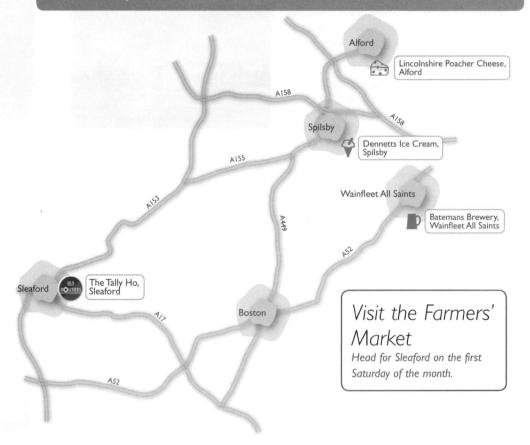

Alford

Lincolnshire Poacher Cheese, Alford

A158

A158

Spilsby

Dennetts Ice Cream, Spilsby

A155

Wainfleet All Saints

Batemans Brewery, Wainfleet All Saints

A153

A449

A52

Sleaford

LES ROUTIERS

The Tally Ho, Sleaford

A17

Boston

A52

Visit the Farmers' Market

Head for Sleaford on the first Saturday of the month.

Sleaford

The Tally Ho Inn

Country inn

'Real-ale drinkers will not be disappointed.'

Aswarby, Sleaford,
Lincolnshire NG34 8SA
Telephone: +44(0)1529 455205
james@tally-ho-aswarby.co.uk
www.tally-ho-aswarby.co.uk

Just south of Sleaford before the turning off the A15 to Aswarby stands this fine mellow stone inn, which dates back to 1750 when it was built as a working farm for the Aswarby Estate. The pleasant bar boasts exposed stone and brickwork aplenty, country prints on pastel-yellow walls, old settles, pews, an open log fire and an additional woodburner for cold winter days. A good atmosphere prevails for diners tucking into the freshly prepared meals that are listed on the traditional lunch and regularly changing evening menus.

Owners Jo and James Cartwright look to local suppliers for their produce, notably meats from Barrowby and fruit and vegetables from Osbournby. Satisfying choices may include Poacher's ploughman's, hot baguettes and beef suet pudding for lunch, with roast duck, noisettes of lamb and a range of grills among the evening menu options. A good-value Sunday lunch menu is served in the attractive, pine-furnished restaurant and real-ale drinkers will not be disappointed with the handpumped Bateman's XB. A converted stable block houses the six spacious and simply furnished en-suite bedrooms.

Rooms: 6. Double/twin room from £60, single from £40. Family room from £70.
Prices: Restaurant main course from £10. Bar main course from £10. House wine £10.
Last orders: Restaurant: lunch: 14.30; dinner 21.30.
Closed: Never.
Food: Traditional British.
Real ale: Bateman's XB Bitter, Everards Tiger.
Other points: No smoking. Children welcome. Dogs welcome in the bar. Garden. Car park.
Directions: Four miles south of Sleaford on the A15 Lincoln to Bourne and Peterborough road. (Map 10)

MEMBER ENTRY

Swinderby

The Dovecote

Country pub

Newark Road, Swinderby, Lincoln,
Lincolnshire LN6 9HN
Telephone: +44(0)1522 868206
joanne.towle@ukonline.co.uk
www.the-dovecote.com

'The Dovecote is a wonderfully rambling roadside inn steeped in history.'

Prices: Set lunch £15. Set dinner £20.
Restaurant main course from £9.95. Bar main
course from £6.95. House wine £12.95.
Last orders: Bar: afternoon 15.00; evening 23.00.
Food: lunch 15.00; dinner 21.00 (food served all
day Saturday and Sunday until 21.30).
Closed: Monday and Tuesday, except bank
holidays. First week of January.
Food: Traditional/modern British.
Real ale: Poachers Ales.
Other points: No-smoking area. Children
welcome. Garden. Car park. Licence for civil
weddings. Wheelchair access.
Directions: A46 between Lincoln and Newark.
Take the Swinderby turning at Halfway House
roundabout and then first right. The Dovecote
is 50 yards along on the right-hand side. (Map 8)

With parts dating from the 15th century, The Dovecote is a wonderfully rambling roadside inn steeped in history. Enter through the porch running along the front of the building and there is a sense of an old French farmhouse with its orange pantiles and rickety old hay wagon on the roof overlooking picnic tables at the front. The bar is divided into three distinct areas, which are all flagstoned and heavily beamed; one is adorned in a collage of press cuttings that feature the pub over the past 150 years. Geese, chickens and pigs can be seen from the lovely garden.

Bar food sticks to the traditional pub favourites – ham, egg and chips, homemade pies – but the restaurant menu is more inventive: smoked mackerel is served on a bed of buttered spinach and topped with a poached free-range egg, pork fillets from Chestnut Farm are cooked in cider with chestnut mushrooms and cream, and Taylor's lamb shank is served with rosemary, garlic and rioja sauce. Desserts are of the old-school variety: treacle sponge and custard, perhaps, or Bakewell pudding. The three Poacher ales on tap are brewed in the village.

London

Adria Hotel

Bed and breakfast

'A large, smart house with bags of character.'

44 Glenthorne Road, Hammersmith,
London W6 0LS
Telephone: +44(0)20 7602 6386
info@adria-hotel.co.uk
www.adria-hotel.co.uk

A good-value, family-run bed-and-breakfast hotel a short stroll from Hammersmith's main shopping street and conveniently located for the Tube and the concert venue the Hammersmith Apollo. It is a large, smart house with bags of character and has the edge over the more anonymous chain hotels in the area. Drivers can park opposite in the nondescript, but useful, multi-storey car park (although the hotel does have some limited parking of its own).

This attractive house is big on kerb appeal: smart, wrought-iron gates open into a tidy, paved front courtyard and polished stone steps lead up to an entrance porch boasting coloured marble tiles and video-entry intercom. The interiors are just as neat and well looked after. Up-to-date, bright, modern bedrooms, some with three beds, are available, and each has compact, modern shower rooms. Tea and coffee-making facilities and a TV are also provided in the room. Breakfast is taken in the south-facing basement room, where one can also relax at other times of the day to watch TV.

Rooms: 16. Double/twin room from £55, single from £45.
Prices: Continental breakfast £3. Full English breakfast £5.
Closed: Rarely.
Other points: No smoking. Children welcome.
Directions: 120 yards from Hammersmith Tube, exit North. (Map 1, see inset)

...for events

MEMBER ENTRY

London

Bull's Head and Stables Bistro

Pub and Thai restaurant

373 Lonsdale Road, Barnes,
London SW13 9PY
Telephone: +44(0)20 8876 5241
jazz@thebullshead.com
www.thebullshead.com

'What really pulls crowds from miles around is the top-class modern jazz.'

Prices: Main course from £4.50. Thai main course from £4.75. Wine from £10.50.
Last orders: Bar: 23.00. Food: 22.00.
Closed: Rarely.
Food: Traditional British at lunch; Thai food in the evening.
Real ale: Young's Bitter.
Other points: Smoking area. Children welcome in daytime. Wheelchair access (not WC).
Directions: Five minutes' walk along the river from Barnes Bridge station. (Map 1, see inset)

The Thamesside setting of this imposing 17th-century pub would be a draw in itself, but what really pulls crowds from miles around is the top-class modern jazz and blues groups that have made The Bull's Head internationally famous for over 40 years, including Ronnie Scott and Stan Tracy. Nightly concerts are from 8.30-11pm (also 2-4.30pm on Sundays), held in a separate room with a genuine jazz-club atmosphere. Back in the bustling bar, alcoves radiate around the island servery, which dispenses Young's ales and some 240 bottles of wine, 30 offered by the glass.

All the food is freshly cooked and served from noon until it's finished (and they will then make sandwiches). Typical choices include soup and ciabatta, roast of the day, steak-and-kidney pie, and treacle tart. The former Stables Bistro now houses Nuay's Thai Bistro, but you can also order at the bar in the pub and be served there, or order authentic Thai food to takeaway. In addition to good curry and noodle dishes, there are speciality main dishes such as stir-fried beef in oyster sauce with mixed vegetables.

Café in the Crypt

All-day eaterie

'A welcome escape from the crowds.'

Crypt of St Martin-in-the-Fields,
Duncannon Street, London WC2N 4JJ
Telephone: +44(0)20 7766 1158
ladka.cervena@smitf.co.uk
www.smitf.org

Although long established and hugely popular, this unique café remains something of a hidden gem, due to its subterranean location in a fascinating church crypt. A stone's throw from Trafalgar Square and bustling theatreland, it makes a welcome escape from the crowds. Brick-vaulted ceilings, pillars, and gravestones on the floor make for a dramatic and airy setting in which to tuck into the good-value, wholesome food. Its relaxed atmosphere is ideal for an inexpensive meal pre- or post-theatre, or before catching a train from nearby Charing Cross station.

The extensive self-service counter offers an appealing array of pick-and-mix salads, soup and daily changing meat and fish dishes listed on chalkboards. Popular choices include roquefort-and-spinach tart and chorizo tortella. For something more substantial, look to mains of slow-cooked lamb with red-wine and rosemary sauce, or chickpea and roast-vegetable ragout. But you can also just relax with a hearty sandwich and pot of tea. Allow yourself extra time to explore the gallery in the vault or to book for one of the many classical concerts.

Prices: **Main course from £5.95. House wine £11.50.**
Last orders: **Food: Monday-Wednesday 19.30 (Thursday-Saturday 22.00, Sunday 19.30).**
Closed: **Rarely.**
Food: **Traditional English.**
Other points: **Smoking area. Children welcome.**
Directions: **Nearest Tubes – Charing Cross, Leicester Square, Embankment. (Map 2)**

...for competitions

London

Food for Thought

31 Neal Street, Covent Garden,
London WC2H 9PR
Telephone: +44(0)20 7836 9072/0239
fftgarrett@aol.com

Vegetarian restaurant

'This friendly restaurant continues to serve reassuringly wholesome vegetarian food.'

Prices: **Set lunch and dinner £9.90. Main course from £4. Unlicenced, BYO welcome, no corkage charged.**
Last orders: **Food: eat in 19.50 (Sunday 16.50); take-away 20.30 (Sunday 17.00).**
Closed: **Rarely.**
Food: **Vegetarian.**
Other points: **No smoking. Children welcome.**
Directions: **Nearest Tube – Covent Garden. Head due north from the exit down Neal Street. Food for Thought is on the left. (Map 2)**

Housed in an 18th-century listed building once used as a banana-ripening warehouse, this friendly restaurant continues to serve reassuringly wholesome vegetarian food on its daily-changing menu. The snug, white-washed basement may be small and you'll probably have to share a table, but the food makes up for these inconveniences. Customers are happy to queue to partake in Vanessa Garrett's seasonal, homemade dishes made from fresh fruit and vegetables from Borough and New Covent Garden markets.

A day's offering may include a warming country-vegetable soup with poppy-seed bread or a savoury scone flavoured with sage, tomato and red onion; deep-filled broccoli and red-pepper quiche; Spanish lentils layered with aubergines, peppers and cauliflower in a tomato, paprika and oregano sauce; and stir-fried vegetables tossed in a ginger-and-tamarind sauce. Strawberry-and-banana scrunch or apple, pear and plum crumble double as puddings or afternoon-tea treats. The restaurant is unlicenced, but you can bring your own wine and there's no corkage charge

Fung Shing

Chinese restaurant

15 Lisle Street, London WC2H 7BE
Telephone: +44(0)20 7437 1539
www.fungshing.co.uk

'The Cantonese food is in the premier league.'

Despite a new generation of young pretenders opening nearby, this veteran Chinese restaurant remains one of the best in the area. The Cantonese food is in the premier league, and the extensive menu caters for all budgets and tastes. Starters range from the modestly priced vegetarian spring rolls to the more lavish braised fresh abalone or steamed scallops in their shells with garlic and soy sauce. The same applies to the main courses, with the more unusual ingredients available at a price.

But you can keep within a moderate budget by choosing prawns with chilli and black-bean sauce, or go some way to blowing it with the braised suckling pig or fried yin yan chicken. Specials of the day add plenty of interest, but you won't feel short-changed if you opt for one of the mainstream dishes, which are thoughtfully prepared. There are also a number of set-meal options offering a reassuringly familiar version of Cantonese cooking. They also put plenty of effort into the homemade puddings. The wine list covers most bases, and includes a fine wine selection.

Prices: Set menu £17. Main course from £8. House wine £14.50.
Last orders: Food: 23.00.
Closed: Rarely.
Food: Traditional Cantonese.
Other points: Smoking area. Children welcome. Two private rooms available.
Directions: Nearest Tube – Leicester Square. Behind the Empire cinema. (Map 2)

...for special offers

London

Hanoi Café

Vietnamese restaurant

98 Kingsland Road, London E2 8DP
Telephone: +44(0)20 7729 5610
hanoicafe@hotmail.com

'Exceptionally good, authentic Vietnamese food.'

Prices: Set lunch £3.80 and dinner £10.
Main course from £4.60. House wine £8.90.
Last orders: Food: 23.30 (Friday and Saturday 24.00).
Closed: Rarely.
Food: Vietnamese.
Other points: Children welcome.
Directions: In Shoreditch. Nearest Tube – Old Street or Liverpool Street. (Map 1, see inset)

Hai Nguyen has created a friendly neighbourhood restaurant with Hanoi Café. It looks basic and unassuming, but don't be fooled by its understated décor, as it serves exceptionally good, authentic Vietnamese food. The interiors may not be fancy, but nice touches, such as fresh flowers on each of the wooden tables and oriental pictures on the walls help create a pleasant vibe. The menu is a comprehensive collection of Vietnamese favourites and some less well-known dishes.

The noodles are much noted, especially the Vietnamese wonton noodle and chicken glass-noodle soups. Among the best-known dishes are stir-fries, such as beef with oyster sauce, cashew chicken and ginger, and spring-onion chicken. The more adventurous might opt for the roll-your-own summer rolls of grilled pork belly, the crispy aromatic lamb, or the enticing choice of claypot dishes. Among the list of light bites, the spare ribs are excellent, as are the crisp-wrap prawns, fried crab claws and vegetable tempura. Towards the end of the evening, it gets quite buzzy as a livelier crowd makes the most of the late opening.

www.routiers.co.uk

Hotel

'The high standard of refurbishment and the central location, make this relaxed, friendly place outstanding value.'

The Harlingford

61-63 Cartwright Gardens,
London WC1H 9EL
Telephone: +44(0)20 7387 1551
book@harlingfordhotel.com
www.harlingfordhotel.com

Situated on a graceful Georgian crescent in the heart of historic Bloomsbury, this independent and family-run hotel is boutiquey and contemporary. Modern, but with the mood of a grand Georgian townhouse, The Harlingford's elegant surroundings provide the perfect backdrop for the vibrant furnishings and bold colour schemes. The high standard of refurbishment by interiors specialist Nathalie O'Donohoe, coupled with its central location, makes this relaxed, friendly place outstanding value.

The all-white foyer creates a sense of calm, while the smart lilac sitting room that shows off Victorian paintings in a setting of modern fabrics and textures, or the hotel's private garden, are the perfect places to relax. Like many well-priced central London hotels, the rooms are not huge, but are perfectly formed. The rooms are spread over five floors, so older or infirm guests should request ground-floor accommodation. The breakfast room is dominated by an art deco stained-glass mural, while modern vases form centrepieces on tables, and splashes of colour complement the clean lines of the light design.

Rooms: **43. Double room from £99, single from £79, family from £110.**
Closed: **Never.**
Other points: **Smoking throughout. Access to tennis courts and garden. NCP car park nearby.**
Directions: **Nearest Tube – Kings Cross or Euston (a few minutes' walk from each). Turn into Mabledon Place, which turns into Cartwright Gardens. The hotel is at the bottom of the crescent. (Map 2)**

...for the latest news

London

Justin James Hotel

Bed and breakfast

43 Worple Road, Wimbledon,
London SW19 4JZ
Telephone: +44(0)20 8947 4271
info@justinjameshotel.com
www.justinjameshotel.com

'The house is smart, homely, friendly and efficiently run.'

Rooms: **20, 1 not en-suite. Double room from £80, single from £45, family from £95.**
Closed: **Rarely.**
Other points: **Smoking area. Garden. Children welcome. Car park.**
Directions: **Follow the A219 to Wimbledon. The hotel is a few minutes' walk from Wimbledon Station. (Map 1, see inset)**

Conveniently located to make the most of Wimbledon's highlights, this attractive late-Victorian hotel was originally built in the 1890s as a doctor's surgery. It's close to town-centre shops and the railway station for trains into central London, and just a leisurely uphill stroll away from pretty Wimbledon village and the many shopping, eating and drinking opportunities that it has to offer. Tennis fans will be able to walk to the All England Tennis Club, which is just over a mile away.

The house is smart, homely, friendly and efficiently run. All the well-maintained bedrooms are en suite and have cable TV, tea- and coffee-making facilities, as well as the extra perks of a hairdryer and IT connection. There is no lounge or bar, but there is a neat, small ground-floor breakfast room where you can enjoy a traditional English breakfast. This hotel makes a welcome change from the impersonal middle-market chains and compares favourably on price. Consequently, it has many returning guests, so you will need to book at least a month in advance.

Mamma

Italian restaurant

110 Kew Road, Richmond,
London TW9 2PQ
Telephone: +44(0)20 8948 8330
caffemamma@hotmail.com
www.caffemamma.co.uk

'The bar dispenses cocktails such as the Godfather – a potent mix of whisky and amaretto.'

After a brief spell in Barnes, this traditional and friendly Italian restaurant has returned to its roots in Richmond. It was first established here over 20 years ago and regulars will find that the welcoming Mediterranean atmosphere has been recreated at the new Kew Road location. The overall ambience is bright and fresh, with small wooden tables set for twos and fours and bright place settings adding a cheery note. The décor resembles an indoor patio garden, with plants and low lighting, and the bar dispenses cocktails such as the Godfather – a potent mix of whisky and amaretto – and mid-priced Italian wines.

The menu is a comprehensive selection of Italian favourites that are all reasonably priced, starting with an extensive line-up of antipasti, from bread and marinated olives to Italian cured ham with melon. Pastas, from pesto to lasagne verdi, and seconds of popular meat and fish dishes, perhaps veal with rosemary and butter sauce, form the backbone of the choice, and there are several pizza options. The desserts continue along classic lines, with tiramisu and ice creams, and there's excellent coffee to finish.

Prices: **Set lunch £9.95. Restaurant main course from £5.95. House wine £11.95.**
Last orders: **Food: 23.00.**
Closed: **Rarely.**
Food: **Italian.**
Other points: **No smoking. Children welcome. Wheelchair access.**
Directions: **Between Kew Gardens and Richmond Circus roundabout.**
(Map 1, see inset)

...for recipe ideas

151

MEMBER ENTRY

London

No 77 Wine Bar

77 Mill Lane, West Hampstead,
London NW6 1NB
Telephone: +44(0)20 7435 7787

Wine bar

'What keeps this place in the popularity stakes is simple but wholesome food.'

Prices: **Main course from £7.95. House wine £11.45.**
Last orders: **Food: lunch 15.00; dinner 23.30.**
Closed: **Rarely.**
Food: **Modern British/pan Pacific.**
Other points: **Smoking area. Children welcome. Dogs welcome in the bar. Alfresco seating.**
Directions: **Nearest Tube – West Hampstead. Ten minutes' drive from the M1.**
(Map 1, see inset)

Opened in 1982, this is an archetypal wine bar with its roots firmly in that period. However, it continues to update its wine collection and adapt its menu. Every two months, its wine list is spruced up with new bottles added to an already comprehensive list, and new recipes crop up just as often. Its ever-popular, proper beefburger, which comes with melted smoked cheese and a homemade relish of braised onions and capsicums, remains a favourite, and its daily fish special, perhaps roast salmon with sautéed potatoes and French beans – plus a small selection of meat dishes, such as chicken schnitzel, find favour, too.

At lunch, there are some light options that include Spanish tapas and Mediterranean snacks, such as houmous and flatbreads. Dine alfresco in summer, or cosy up inside around one of the small polished pine tables scattered throughout a maze of tiny quarry-tiled rooms. What keeps this place in the popularity stakes is simple but wholesome food and its wide choice of good-value wines, not forgetting the service, which is wonderfully relaxed and friendly.

www.routiers.co.uk

London

Swag and Tails

City pub-restaurant

'Well worth seeking out after a hard day's shopping.'

10-11 Fairholt Street, London SW7 1EG
Telephone: +44(0)20 7584 6926
theswag@swagandtails.com
www.swagandtails.com

You'll find this gem of a dining pub secreted away in a warren of pretty residential mews in Knightsbridge village, and it is well worth seeking out after a hard day's shopping – Harrods is just two minutes' stroll away! Beyond the magnificent, flower-adorned façade lies a civilised yet informal bar, with original panelling, stripped wooden floors, open fires and to the rear, a cosy, quieter dining area.

Business folk, shoppers and well-heeled locals quickly fill the bar at lunchtime, attracted by the welcoming atmosphere and the modern, Mediterranean-style dishes listed on the chalkboard menu. Pop in to peruse the papers over a pint of Adnams and a classic burger with red-onion pickle and shoestring fries, or linger longer over something more substantial. Follow deep-fried calamari, served with a red-pepper and lime salsa, with roast lamb shank with olive mash and sun-dried tomato sauce, and finish with fig, pear and frangipane tart with Chantilly cream, or a plate of French cheeses. A good list of wines offers 11 by the glass. Note: the pub is closed at weekends and on bank holidays!

Prices: **Main course from £10.95. Bar snacks from £7.50. House wine £12.95.**
Last orders: **Bar: 23.00. Food: lunch 15.00; dinner 22.00.**
Closed: **Saturday, Sunday, bank holidays and 10 days over the Christmas period.**
Food: **Modern British.**
Real ale: **Adnams Best, Wells Bombardier Premium Bitter.**
Other points: **Smoking area. Children welcome in the restaurant only. Dogs welcome in the bar in the evening. Wheelchair access to the pub only.**
Directions: **Nearest Tube – Knightsbridge. On the opposite side of the road to Harrods. Turn into Montpelier Street and take the first left into Cheval Place and then the second right and first left. (Map 1)**

...for events

London

Truc Vert

Restaurant and shop

42 North Audley Street,
London W1K 6ZR
Telephone: +44(0)20 7491 9988
info@trucvert.co.uk

'It's a feast for the senses and a haven of civility.'

Prices: **Set lunch £15 (two courses, Monday only). Set dinner £18.50 (Monday to Friday). House wine £12.**
Last orders: **Food: 21.00 (Sunday 15.00).**
Closed: **Bank holidays.**
Food: **Modern European.**
Other points: **No smoking. Children welcome. Patio.**
Directions: **Between Oxford Street and Grosvenor Square. Nearest Tube – Bond Street. (Map 2)**

Early risers will be pleased to note that breakfast kicks off at 7.30am (including Saturdays) at this quality deli and restaurant, just a short walk from Oxford Street. It's a feast for the senses and a haven of civility, and there is much to tempt in the shape of home-baked croissants, Danish pastries, cakes, quiches, and savoury vegetarian pasties. You can order from the menu, or make up your own selection from the shop's supplies, including stacks of pestos, salsas, sun-dried tomatoes, and delicacies such as artichoke cream, as well as free-range organic eggs and an array of French honey and top-quality cheeses.

In the early evening, Truc Vert undergoes a slick and seamless transformation into a smart restaurant. The wooden tables sport crisp white linen and the lighting is lowered for intimate dining. Try seafood-and-sausage gumbo to start, followed by chargrilled veal escalope with roast broccoli, roast fig, watercress and blue-cheese dressing, with raspberry crème brûlée to finish, and you can eat well here for less than £20 a head. A good range of French wines and delightful staff complete the picture.

Dimitris Tapas Bar and Taverna

Mediterranean restaurant

'The vibe is strongly Mediterranean, and at weekends, the atmosphere has a lively holiday feel.'

Campfield Arcade, Tonman Street,
Deansgate, Manchester M3 4FN
Telephone: +44 (0)161 839 3319
manchester@dimitris.co.uk
www.dimitris.co.uk

Good-value dining with dishes made for sharing, and cheery surroundings has been a winning formula for owner Dimitris. The vibe is strongly Mediterranean, and at weekends, the atmosphere has a lively holiday feel. The restaurant, with its brightly painted walls is warm and inviting; wooden floors and check tablecloths make for an informal atmosphere. Outside, the large heated area is perfect for alfresco dining, plus there's a separate bar and cellar bar.

Expect honest Mediterranean cooking and a menu that has something for everyone, from lunch mezzes to hearty tapas in the evening, which includes Greek taverna favourites and Spanish specialities. In the mains section, lamb kleftico and mixed seafood in spicy sauce vie for attention with chargrilled kebabs, chicken in feta sauce, new Catalan dishes, salads, vegetables, pasta and couscous. Popular dishes such as the *kalamata platas* and the mega mezzes are set menus for two or more people and are exceptional value. The wine list takes a popular global view and includes some Greek wines.

Prices: Set lunch from £11.95, set dinner from £17.35. House wine £11.35.
Last orders: Food: 23.30.
Closed: Rarely.
Food: Mediterranean.
Other points: Smoking throughout. Children welcome. Dogs welcome in the bar. Heated arcade. Wheelchair access.
Directions: At the end of Deansgate, near GMEX and Castlefield, just off the main road in the arcade. (Map 9)

...for competitions

Manchester

San Carlo Restaurant

40-42 King Street West,
Manchester, M3 2WY
Telephone: +44(0)161 834 6226
www.sancarlo.co.uk

Italian restaurant

'Everything comes pleasingly presented and in generous portions.'

Prices: **Restaurant main course from £8. House wine £12.95.**
Last orders: **Food: 23.00.**
Closed: **Never.**
Food: **Italian.**
Other points: **Smoking area. Children welcome. Wheelchair access.**
Directions: **Just off Deansgate. (Map 9)**

With successful outlets in Bristol, Leicester and Birmingham, the expanding San Carlo chain could easily fall into being formulaic, but each restaurant has its own individual menu and buzzy vibe. This smart city-centre Manchester branch majors in fish and puts its fine catch to good use in its specials and menu. The main menu focuses on popular Italian favourites using excellent ingredients, many from Italy, mixed with quality fish.

The chef has a good eye, so everything from the antipasti to the mains comes pleasingly presented and in generous portions. Antipasti of *salsiccia con ploenta* and borlotti beans and tuna carpaccio are a cut above the norm. Moving on to mains, there is a wide selection of pasta dishes, which are also strong in the fish department. *Penne con pollo gamberetti* combines chicken and prawns in a creamy garlic and peppercorn sauce, while tagliatelle Montecarlo features diced monkfish in a wine and tomato-enriched sauce. There is much else besides fish to tempt, from mushroom risotto and grilled-vegetable tortellini to fresh mussels cooked in Provençal or meunière style.

www.routiers.co.uk

The Tavern Company

Mexican restaurant and bar

'The kind of bar-restaurant every neighbourhood should have.'

621-625 Smithdown Road, Penny Lane,
Liverpool, Merseyside L15 5AG
Telephone: +44(0)151 734 5555
pennylane@tavernco.co.uk
www.tavernco.co.uk

This buzzing Mexican wine bar and restaurant makes the grade food and street-cred wise. It's just a stone's throw away from the homes of Lennon and McCartney, Strawberry Fields, Penny Lane and other Beatles-related attractions, so right on the Beatles tourist map. Its friendly vibe, thanks to American owner Keith Gurney, attracts a relaxed crowd. It serves an array of vibrant Cajun-Mexican dishes throughout the day.

In the morning, you can snuggle up in one of its many nooks and crannies with a coffee and paper, enjoy brunch that can be a full English, Mexican or continental, without the price spoiling the rest of your day, or dine upstairs in the evening on a wide-ranging budget-conscious menu, as colourful and interesting as the yellow-ochre walls with murals. Grills, sandwiches, fajitas, stuffed chillies, steaks and first-rate burgers are as good as they come, plus there's a winning line-up of fish (seafood-stuffed catfish) and vegetarian choices (halloumi sandwich). This is a steal for the amount of style and substance present, and it's the kind of bar-restaurant every neighbourhood should have.

Prices: **Set dinner £18. Restaurant main course from £6.95. House wine £9.95.**
Last orders: **Food: 22.00 (Friday and Saturday 22.30). Saturday and Sunday breakfast served until 14.30.**
Closed: **Rarely.**
Food: **Mexican and Cajun.**
Other points: **Smoking area. Children over 14 welcome. Wheelchair access.**
Directions: **Exit 4/M62. Less than three miles from the city centre at the junction of Smithdown Road and Penny Lane. (Map 9)**

...for special offers

Brancaster Staithe

The White Horse

Seaside inn

Brancaster Staithe, Norfolk PE31 8BY
Telephone: +44(0)1485 210262
reception@whitehorsebrancaster.co.uk
www.whitehorsebrancaster.co.uk

'Memorable views across breezy salt marsh are among the treats that await you.'

Rooms: 15. Double room from £90, single supplement £20 per night.
Prices: Main course from £9.95. House wine £11.20.
Last orders: Bar: 23.00. Food: lunch 14.00; dinner 21.00.
Closed: Rarely.
Food: Modern/traditional British.
Real ale: Adnams Bitter, Fuller's London Pride, Woodforde's Wherry. One guest beer.
Other points: Smoking area. Children welcome. Dogs welcome. Garden. Car park.
Wheelchair access.
Directions: Midway between Hunstanton and Wells-next-the-Sea on the A149 coast road.
(Map 10)

The evocative call of the curlew and memorable views across the breezy salt marsh are among the treats that await you at this stylishly refurbished inn on Norfolk's magical north coast. Swish bedrooms feature handsome modern furniture, simple clean lines, soft colours and up-to-the-minute en-suite bathrooms. Drinkers will find a welcoming atmosphere within the light and airy bar, kitted out with scrubbed pine. The conservatory dining room, with its adjoining summer sun deck and one of the finest views in Norfolk, is the place to linger over dinner.

Reflecting the view, colours throughout are muted and natural, and Nick Parker's modern menus focus on fresh local fish and seafood, notably cockles, mussels and oysters from the 'beds' at the bottom of the garden. In the dining room, start, perhaps, with lemon-and-dill potted salmon, move on to halibut with tarragon linguine and bisque sauce, or calves' liver with thyme jus. Bar lunches take in filled ciabattas, dressed Cromer crab, and smoked-haddock fish cakes. Top-notch Adnams and Woodforde's ales, and 12 wines by the glass complete the pleasing picture.

Catfield

The Limes

Bed and breakfast

'Bags of charm and a slightly quirky atmosphere that puts you at ease immediately.'

Limes Road, Catfield, Great Yarmouth,
Norfolk NR29 5DG
Telephone: +44(0)1692 581221
info@thelimesatcatfield.com
www.thelimesatcatfield.com

For location, location, location, it's hard to beat The Limes, a most welcoming and wonderfully positioned B&B, halfway between Norwich and the stunning beaches of North Norfolk. You'll find many historic villages to explore from this tranquil mid-Norfolk base in the village of Catfield. The Partridge family have perfected their offering over four years in this comfortable and spacious detached house with equally spacious en-suite rooms, set in extensive grounds.

The couple choose the best local ingredients and draw on their culinary flair to prepare their renowned breakfasts – from croissants and pancakes with maple syrup to the full English. Fine dinners are served by arrangement – game in season, prime meat and fish, Norfolk's finest cheeses and vegetables. The bring-your-own wine arrangement makes the already good-value set dinners even more of a bargain. Add in bags of charm (and that includes the owners, too) and a slightly quirky atmosphere that puts you at ease immediately, and you can't fail but feel you're away from it all.

Rooms: 3, 1 with private bathroom. Double/twin room from £55, single from £30.
Prices: Set dinner £17.50.
Closed: Never.
Food: Modern British.
Other points: No smoking. Garden. Car park. BYO.
Directions: Eight miles east of Wroxham on the A149. Catfield lies between Stalham and Potter Heigham, and The Limes is in the centre of the village. (Map 10)

...for the latest news

Cley-next-the-Sea

terroir

Restaurant-with-rooms

High Street, Cley-next-the-Sea,
Norfolk NR25 7RN
Telephone: +44(0)1263 740336
terroir.restaurant@virgin.net
www.terroir.org.uk

'The effort put into sourcing ingredients puts this menu in the super league.'

Rooms: 1 suite. Single nights not accepted.
Two nights for two people £340 for dinner with wine, bed and breakfast.
Prices: Set dinner £24.50 (four courses). Wines from £13.
Last orders: Dinner served Wednesday to Saturday 19.30 for 20.00 (open Sunday bank holidays). Booking essential.
Closed: Lunchtime, Sunday, Monday, Tuesday and two weeks in September/October and December through to February.
Food: Seasonal vegetable cooking – Modern British/Southern European.
Other points: No smoking. Credit cards not accepted. Wheelchair access to the restaurant (not WC).
Directions: On the A149 coast road midway between Cromer and Wells-next-the-Sea. (Map 10)

The listed brick-and-flint Georgian house may be easy to miss on the narrow High Street, but it is a well-known local landmark for outstanding contemporary vegetarian cooking. Kalba Meadows and John Curtis cook the food they enjoy and they are passionate about fresh local, seasonal and organic produce, and the effort they put into sourcing ingredients puts this menu in the super league. Credentials are impeccable and include homegrown herbs and vegetables from local organic farmers, with a few specials from farther afield, such as Neal's Yard Dairy. In fact, the menu reads like a Who's Who of Norfolk's top producers.

Dinner starts at 7.30pm and is intended to be a relaxed affair. From the set four-course dinner menus, start with Wiveton artichoke-and-potato terrine or Cley samphire with Berkswell ewes' milk cheese. Next up could be a truffled haricot and borlotti-bean cassoulet with parsnip and wild-rice cake, followed by the cheese of the day and a fabulous dessert, perhaps rhubarb, cardamom and marscapone fool with rhubarb lemonade. At the time of going to print, terrior was being sold.

www.routiers.co.uk

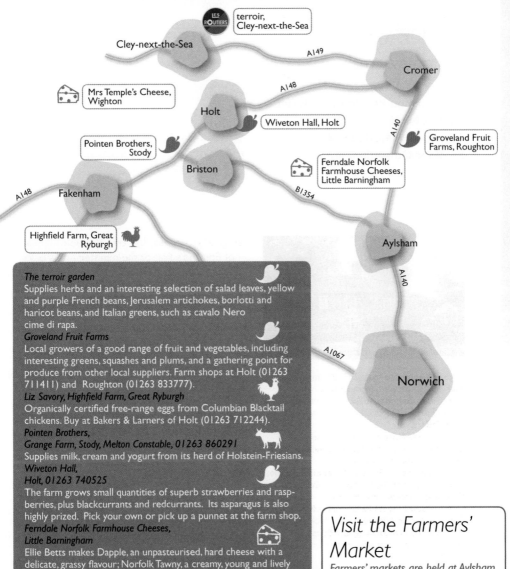

LES ROUTIERS

terroir, Cley-next-the-Sea

Cley-next-the-Sea

A149

Cromer

Mrs Temple's Cheese, Wighton

A148

Holt

A140

Wiveton Hall, Holt

Groveland Fruit Farms, Roughton

Pointen Brothers, Stody

Briston

Ferndale Norfolk Farmhouse Cheeses, Little Barningham

A148

Fakenham

B1354

Highfield Farm, Great Ryburgh

Aylsham

A140

A1067

Norwich

The terroir garden
Supplies herbs and an interesting selection of salad leaves, yellow and purple French beans, Jerusalem artichokes, borlotti and haricot beans, and Italian greens, such as cavalo Nero cime di rapa.

Groveland Fruit Farms
Local growers of a good range of fruit and vegetables, including interesting greens, squashes and plums, and a gathering point for produce from other local suppliers. Farm shops at Holt (01263 711411) and Roughton (01263 833777).

Liz Savory, Highfield Farm, Great Ryburgh
Organically certified free-range eggs from Columbian Blacktail chickens. Buy at Bakers & Larners of Holt (01263 712244).

Pointen Brothers,
Grange Farm, Stody, Melton Constable, 01263 860291
Supplies milk, cream and yogurt from its herd of Holstein-Friesians.

Wiveton Hall,
Holt, 01263 740525
The farm grows small quantities of superb strawberries and rasp-berries, plus blackcurrants and redcurrants. Its asparagus is also highly prized. Pick your own or pick up a punnet at the farm shop.

Ferndale Norfolk Farmhouse Cheeses,
Little Barningham
Ellie Betts makes Dapple, an unpasteurised, hard cheese with a delicate, grassy flavour; Norfolk Tawny, a creamy, young and lively cheese washed in Men of Norfolk Ale from the Iceni Brewery. Buy at the Picnic Fayre, Cley-next-the-Sea (01263 740587).

Mrs Temple's Cheese,
Copys Green Farm, Wighton
Catherine Temple makes several cheeses using milk from the Chalk Farm Herd; terroir takes her Binham Blue and Wighton, a soft fresh ricotta-type cheese that makes a great torte or polpettoni.

Visit the Farmers' Market

Farmers' markets are held at Aylsham on the first Saturday of the month and at Fakenham on the fourth Saturday of the month.

Itteringham

Walpole Arms

Country pub

The Common, Itteringham, Aylsham,
Norfolk NR11 7AR
Telephone: +44(0)1263 587258
goodfood@thewalpolearms.co.uk
www.thewalpolearms.co.uk

'This oak-beamed 18th-century inn attracts discerning foodies from afar.'

Prices: Main course from £10. Bar main course from £6. House wine from £12.25.
Last orders: Bar: afternoon 15.00; evening 23.00.
Food: lunch 14.00 (Sunday 14.30); dinner 21.00.
Closed: Rarely.
Food: Modern British.
Real ale: Adnams Broadside, Adnams Best, Wolf Walpole. One guest beer.
Other points: Smoking area. Children welcome. Dogs welcome in the bar. Garden. Car park. Wheelchair access.
Directions: Off the A140 Norwich to Cromer Road. Go through Aylsham, past Blickling Hall, then take the next right. (Map 10)
See pub walk on page 480

Originally owned by the Walpole family – of England's first prime minister – this oak-beamed 18th-century inn attracts discerning foodies from afar. They come for the first-class modern British and Mediterranean-inspired food served at this unspoilt brick-and-timber cottage. With talented head chef Andy Parle at the stove, daily menus reflect his passion for fresh local produce, notably Morston mussels, lamb from the Walpole estate, and venison from Gunton Hall.

Typically, starters may feature escabeche of red mullet with pine nuts, sultana and butter beans or Chinese-spice cured salmon, glass noodles, pickled vegetables and seaweed. Mains include a roast cod with chorizo-and-lemon risotto or confit duck leg, baby potatoes, green beans and pickled peach. Round off with saffron-poached pear with orange-flower rice pudding. There's the choice of dining in the rustic bar, which retains plenty of original character, or the more formal dining room. On Saturdays, a special brunch menu is served from midday and, on Sundays, there are always a couple of roasts. Excellent ales and top-notch wines.

Brummells Seafood Restaurant

Seafood restaurant

'If you want to push the boat out wine or champagne-wise, you have come to the right place.'

7 Magdalen Street, Norwich, Norfolk NR3 1LE
Telephone: +44(0)1603 625555
brummell@brummells.co.uk
www.brummells.co.uk

It's not a popular local haunt with bags of word-of-mouth recommendations for nothing. Over the 25 years that it has been in business, Brummells has built up an excellent reputation for its quality menu, which majors in fish and is matched with an exceptionally indulgent wine and champagne list. Its location is in no way as upmarket as its wares, but venture inside and you'll find its traditional, cosy ambience and well-set tables are a fitting precursor to the enticing menu.

Prepare to be wowed by creamed fish soup with coconut milk, monkfish fritters or cold-marinated octopus to start, before moving on to local lobster, skate wing pan-fried in black butter or some formidably good meat courses, such as wild red deer venison and roast neck of lamb. Vegetarians are also going to find something to thrill. Desserts are a finely put together offering of rich classics and puds with a touch of the exotic to freshen the palate. If you want to push the boat out wine or champagne-wise, you have come to the right place, as they serve high-class Cristal, Dom Perignon, top European and New World big hitters.

Prices: **Restaurant main course from £16. House wine £13.**
Last orders: **Opening hours are flexible – please telephone ahead.**
Closed: **Rarely.**
Food: **Modern European.**
Other points: **Smoking area. Children welcome. Wheelchair access (not WC).**
Directions: **In the centre of Norwich, just off St Crispins Road. (Map 10)**

...for recipe ideas

Norwich

The Wig and Pen

6 St Martins Palace Plain, Norwich,
Norfolk NR3 1RN
Telephone: +44(0)1603 625891
info@thewigandpen.com
www.thewigandpen.com

City-centre pub

'Real-ale enthusiasts are spoilt rotten.'

Prices: **Restaurant main course from £8.95. Bar main course from £3.95. House wine from £8.95.**
Last orders: **Bar: 24.00 (Friday and Saturday 01.00). Food: lunch 14.30; dinner 21.00.**
Closed: **Sunday evening and 25 December and 1 January.**
Food: **Traditional/modern British.**
Other points: **Smoking area. Children welcome by prior arrangement. Garden. Wheelchair access (not WC).**
Directions: **Adjacent to Norwich Cathedral. 100 yards from Maid's Head Hotel, Tombland. Walking distance from the River Wensum. (Map 10)**

A classic 17th-century coaching inn situated opposite the cathedral close, with super views of the impressive Norman cathedral from its large, sunny front terrace. Arrive early to bag a table here, or a window seat in the beamed front bar, where log fires blaze in winter and legal-related prints adorn the walls. The welcoming atmosphere extends through to the modern dining extension.

Expect to find lawyers and locals supping pints of ale at the bar, shoppers and tourists popping in for lunch and, in the evenings, a young, lively crowd, here for the beer and live sport on the TV. Real-ale enthusiasts are spoilt rotten. Brewery badges on the six hand-pumps may feature Buffy's Hop Loaf and Woodforde's Norfolk Nog. All are kept in tip-top condition – great beer to wash down some hearty and good-value pub food: 33 different sandwiches; ham, egg and chips; a home-cooked special, such as lamb casserole, salmon with dill-and-cucumber sauce; or cod in beer batter; and bread-and-butter pudding to follow. Fish is supplied by Howard's Fish and Game on Fye Bridge and top-notch meats by the local Thorpe Butchers.

Country pub

Bulwick

Queen's Head

Main Street, Bulwick,
Northamptonshire NN17 3DY
Telephone: +44(0)1780 450272

'Interesting bin-end wines and a delightful terrace for summer dining add to the appeal.'

In need of a rest and some sustenance while travelling on the A43? Then look no further than this quaint 17th-century pub in the heart of pretty Bulwick. Standing opposite the parish church and built of mellow local stone, it oozes charm and character. From the front door, you enter a tiny bar warmed by an open fire and dominated by plenty of timber joints and beams, with those wonky, uneven walls indicating great age. You'll find local Rockingham ales on tap, and quality pub food that utilises the best local produce.

Menus are modern British, with influences from the Mediterranean, and include imaginative offerings such as fish soup with basil pesto; roast free-range belly pork with bean and Irish white-pudding cassoulet; and red gurnard with crab, basil and roast-pepper risotto. Lunchtime meals include crab and lemon-mayonnaise sandwiches, and ham, egg and chips. Food is served in three small adjoining rooms, each strewn with rugs and furnished with classic wood furniture and knick-knacks. Interesting bin-end wines and a delightful terrace for summer dining add to the appeal.

...for events

Prices: **Restaurant main course from £10.95. Bar main course from £4.95. House wine from £10.25.**
Last orders: **Bar: afternoon 14.30; evening 23.00. Food: lunch 14.30; dinner 21.30. No food Sunday evening.**
Closed: **Monday.**
Food: **Modern British with Italian influence.**
Real ale: **Shepherd Neame Spitfire, E&S Elland, Rockingham, Newby Wyke. Three guest beers.**
Other points: **Smoking area. Children welcome. Dogs welcome in the bar. Garden. Car park. Wheelchair access.**
Directions: **Just off the A43 between Stamford and Corby. (Map 8)**

Northampton

Greens Restaurant

Windingbrook Lane,
Collingtree Park, Northampton,
Northamptonshire NN4 OXN
Telephone: +44(0)1604 663963
enquiries@greens-restaurant.com
www.greens-restaurant.com

Restaurant

'An impressive space, beautifully designed with some unique features.'

Prices: **Set lunch £12.50 (two courses).
Restaurant main course from £8.50. House
wine £11.50.**
Last orders: **Food: lunch 14.00 (15.30 Sunday);
dinner 21.30 (closed Sunday evening).**
Closed: **Rarely.**
Food: **Modern European.**
Other points: **No-smoking area. Children
welcome. Car park. Wheelchair access.**
Directions: **Exit 15/M1. Take the second exit
from the A45 and follow signs for Collingtree
Park. (Map 8)**

Greens Restaurant is located within the prestigious Collingtree Park Golf Club, overlooking the 18th hole and its impressive water features and bunkers. You don't have to play golf or have any interest in the game to dine here, as it is open to the public. Opened in June 2005, it is an impressive space, beautifully designed, with some unique features, namely elegant and chic materials, contemporary leather furnishings, big modern works of art, a trendy wine rack, subtle lighting and a stylish décor.

You can peruse the menus and ridicule the hackers from the comfort of the smart bar area. The extensive à la carte menu offers a good range of modern European dishes, from simple sandwiches, light summer salads and pasta meals, such as Caesar salad or prawn tagliatelle with shellfish cream, to more imaginative dishes such as confit Brixworth belly pork with glazed apple and mash, pan-fried sea bass with sauce vierge, and duck breast with wild-mushroom jus. Puddings include chocolate-and-rum mousse. There's also a good-value set lunch menu and a well-balanced list of wines.

Oundle

Falcon Inn

Country pub

Fotheringhay, Oundle,
Northamptonshire PE8 5HZ
Telephone: +44(0)1832 226254

'The first-class wine list offers an eclectic, esoteric and stimulating selection.'

Standing close to the grand parish church in this historic thatch-and-stone village, the Falcon is a great village pub. Candles, fresh flowers, Windsor and high-backed tapestry-covered chairs, some exposed stone, and discreet, soft colours define the bar. The double conservatory dining room provides a slightly more formal setting, filled with a mix of director's and Lloyd Loom chairs.

There's a snack menu chalked up on a board listing British classics such as Lancashire hotpot, but the printed, monthly changing menu is classic Italian in style and is offered in the bar as well as the dining room. Thus, an April meal could open with chicken-liver spaghetti with sage-and-pecorino cream. Chargrilled lamb rump with olive-oil mash, braised fava beans, morels and green garlic and salsa verde could follow, with chocolate-almond cake and zabaglione ice cream making a great finish. The first-class wine list offers an eclectic, esoteric and stimulating selection. Don't miss the magnificent church, and allow time to stroll round the site of Fotheringhay Castle, where Mary Queen of Scots was executed.

Prices: Restaurant main course from £9.95. Bar main course from £8.95. House wine £12.50.
Last orders: lunch 14.15; dinner 21.30 (Saturday 22.00).
Closed: Never.
Food: Italian in the restaurant and Classic British in the bar.
Real ale: Adnams Best, Greene King IPA. One guest beer.
Other points: No smoking. Children welcome. Garden. Car park. Wheelchair access.
Directions: The village is signposted off the A605 between Oundle and Peterborough, one mile north of Oundle. (Map 10)

...for competitions

MEMBER ENTRY
166

Wadenhoe

The King's Head

Church Street, Wadenhoe, Peterborough,
Northamptonshire PE8 5ST
Telephone: +44(0)1832 720024

Country pub

'A cosy place to retreat to for pints of locally brewed Pot Belly Aisling Ale following a hike along the Nene Valley Way.'

Prices: **Restaurant main course from £7.95.
House wine £14.25.**
Last orders: **Lunch 14.30 (Sunday 15.30); dinner 21.30 (Sunday 21.00).**
Closed: **Never.**
Food: **British.**
Real ale: **Oakham Ales.**
Other points: **No-smoking area. Dogs welcome in the bar. Garden. Children welcome. Car park. Wheelchair access.**
Directions: **A14. Take the A605 and follow signs to Wadenhoe, between Oundle and Thorpe Waterville. (Map 8)**
See pub walk on page 482

A part-thatched, 17th-century stone inn tucked away down a dead-end lane in this quaint village of mellow-stoned cottages. Peacefully situated beside the River Nene, close to the parish church, the pub's extensive garden borders the willow-fringed river and, along with the terrace, is a popular destination on fine summer days. Inside, quarry tiles, bare boards, old beams, farmhouse pine and crackling winter log fires help retain the rustic feel throughout the interconnecting bars. A cosy place to retreat to for pints of locally brewed Pot Belly Aisling Ale following a hike along the Nene Valley Way.

Food is simple and freshly prepared. The lunchtime choice offers big bowls of mussels in white wine and garlic, and decent sandwiches, perhaps lemon-and-thyme chicken. Evening options include fresh fish, local game, organic lamb and beef, rare-breed pork, and an excellent platter of English cheeses. Good-value Sunday lunches and an impressive 18 wines by the glass.

www.routiers.co.uk

The Cottage Inn

Country inn

'A hit with locals and visitors to this magnificent coastal area.'

Dunstan Village, near Craster, Alnwick,
Northumberland NE66 3SZ
Telephone: +44(0)1665 576658
enquiries@cottageinnhotel.co.uk
www.cottageinnhotel.co.uk

The transformation from a row of derelict cottages in 1975 to the Cottage Inn in 1988, has proved a hit with locals and visitors to this magnificent coastal area, with its dramatic castles and wonderful walks. New owners Malcolm and Rebecca Readman are restoring the fortunes of the pub, upgrading bedrooms and bars, buying fresh local produce, and offering real hospitality. The beamed bar, with ancient exposed brick, wood panelling, and a fireplace, is an atmospheric room, and one where drinkers and diners mingle easily.

The smokery, Robsons of Craster, supply the kippers served at breakfast, and the lunch and dinner menu's first course of kippers 'n' custard. There's also crab soup, mussels in white wine and garlic, and a ramekin of pigeon pie to start, with mains running to bouillabaisse, rabbit pie, and chargrilled steaks with a choice of sauces. Various snacks and simpler dishes are also available. Local ales from Mordue, Wylam and Hadrian breweries are complemented by a decent choice of wines. The 10 en-suite rooms are fully equipped, comfortable and good value.

Rooms: 10. Double/twin room from £30, single from £35. Prices quoted are per person and include breakfast.
Prices: Restaurant main course from £8.95. Bar main course from £5.95. House wine £9.45.
Last orders: Bar: 23.00. Food: lunch 15.00; dinner 21.00.
Closed: Never.
Food: Traditional British.
Real ale: Four guest beers.
Other points: Smoking area. Children welcome. Garden. Car park. Wheelchair access.
Directions: A1 to Alnwick, then turn off and follow the signs to Denwick and then Craster. (Map 12)

Belllingham

Riverdale Hall Hotel

Country-house hotel

Bellingham, Northumberland NE48 2JT
Telephone: +44(0)1434 220254
reservations@riverdalehallhotel.co.uk
www.riverdalehallhotel.co.uk

'The proximity to and opportunity to fish from the River Tyne explain why the restaurant fish is so good and fresh.'

Rooms: **22. Double room from £88, single from £49.**
Prices: **Set lunch £10.95 (two courses), set dinner £16.90 (two courses). House wine £10.30.**
Last orders: **Food: lunch 14.30; dinner 21.30.**
Closed: **Never.**
Food: **Traditional English.**
Real ale: **Beers change regularly. One guest beer.**
Other points: **Smoking area. Children welcome. Dogs welcome. Garden. Car park. Indoor swimming pool. Licence for civil weddings/ partnerships. Wheelchair access.**
Directions: **From the A69, take the B6320 to Bellingham. After the bridge in Bellingham, turn left. The hotel is 150 yards on the left. (Map 12)**

Run by the Cocker family for 27 years, this country-house hotel is also a popular local with a good reputation for food. The cricket field in the grounds explains much of the décor, as trophies and cricketing photos adorn many of the walls, clashing merrily with the rural-chic stencilling. The proximity to and opportunity to fish from the River Tyne explain why the restaurant fish is so good and fresh.

The kitchen draws on many top-notch local ingredients for its daily changing menu. This may include succulent Northumbrian lamb and rich Kielder venison. A selection of local cheeses is an alternative to more fancy puds such as white-chocolate panna cotta. For a less formal experience, you can eat in the bar, where the menu consists of sandwiches, jacket potatoes and steaks, or there's an extremely good-value set menu that expands the choice to include slow-cooked lamb on root mash with wine gravy, or a simply cooked fillet steak with chips. Puddings are just as good, with garden-fresh rhubarb crumble or local Northumbrian cheeses completing the picture.

Hexham

The County Hotel

Hotel

'Expect genuine Northumbrian hospitality the moment you walk through the time-honoured revolving door.'

Priestpopple, Hexham,
Northumberland NE46 1PS
Telephone: +44(0)1434 603601
info@thecountyhexham.co.uk
www.thecountyhexham.co.uk

Expect genuine Northumbrian hospitality the moment you walk through the time-honoured revolving door into the County Hotel, which commands a fine central location and provides a comfortable base from which to explore Hadrian's Wall and the Border country. Since arriving here in 2000, the Harding family have focused on the traditional core values of spotless housekeeping, warm hospitality and honest food and drink, and the results are clear to see. Restful en-suite rooms have been sensitively decorated and furnished in a fresh and uncluttered style, and are both comfortable and well equipped.

Attention to detail extends to the public rooms, where ornaments, soft furnishings and warming log fires create a relaxed and cosy atmosphere. The informal Argyle's brasserie-style bar offers a menu that reveals a kitchen dedicated to sourcing local produce, notably farm-reared meats. Dishes may include a starter of black pudding with horseradish cream and main dishes such as sea bass pan fried with lime-and-chilli butter and roast Tynedale beef with red-wine and mushroom sauce. Accompany with a pint of local ale.

Rooms: **7. Double/twin room from £67.50, single from £45.**
Prices: **Set lunch £15. Restaurant main course from £10. Bar main course from £6. House wine £10.**
Last orders: **Bar: 23.00. Food: lunch 14.00; dinner 20.30 (no food Sunday evening).**
Closed: **Rarely.**
Food: **British.**
Other points: **Smoking area. Children welcome. Wheelchair access to bar and restaurant (not WC).**
Directions: **A69. Leave at Hexham and follow the signs to the General Hospital. County Hotel is beside the mini roundabout, 200 yards west of the hospital. (Map 12)**

...for the latest news

Kielder Water

The Pheasant Inn

Country inn

'The menu delivers sound, traditional country cooking.'

Stannersburn, Kielder Water, Hexham,
Northumberland NE48 1DD
Telephone: +44(0)1434 240382
enquiries@thepheasantinn.com
www.thepheasantinn.com

Nestling in unspoilt countryside, this 400-year-old former farmhouse, just a mile from Kielder Water, has all the trappings of a traditional Northumberland pub. All areas of this well-maintained building are spotlessly clean, the décor cottagey and entirely appropriate to the style of the building and area; indeed, the Pheasant wears its comfortable look well. Polished wood tables and chairs add to the country feel of the low-ceilinged dining room, and there's a pretty garden courtyard.

The menu delivers sound, traditional country cooking, with Northumberland lamb, beef and game coming from a local butcher and fresh fish from North Shields quay. Typically, start with smoked salmon with salad garnish and brown bread, or farmhouse paté and toast, move on to confit of duck breast with port-and-raspberry sauce or homemade steak-and-kidney pie, and round off with rhubarb-and-ginger crème brulée or a plate of farmhouse cheeses. There are homemade bar meals and hearty Sunday roasts and excellent accommodation in eight light and prettily decorated en-suite rooms.

Rooms: **8. Double/twin room from £75, single from £40, family from £85.**

Prices: Main course dinner from £9.25, main course lunch from £6.75. House wine £9.95.

Last orders: Bar: afternoon 15.00; evening 23.00. Food: lunch 15.00; dinner 21.00.

Closed: Monday, Tuesdays and from November to March.

Food: Traditional pub food.

Real ale: Black Sheep Best, Timothy Taylor Landlord, Greene King Old Speckled Hen, Wylam Gold Tankard.

Other points: Smoking area. Children welcome. Garden. Car park. Wheelchair access.

Directions: Follow signs to Kielder Water from the B6320 at Bellingham, 17 miles north of Hexham. (Map 12)

See pub walk on page 484

MEMBER ENTRY
171

Langley-on-Tyne

Langley Castle Hotel

Langley-on-Tyne, Hexham,
Northumberland NE47 5LU
Telephone: +44(0)1434 688888
manager@langleycastle.com
www.langleycastle.com

Country-house hotel

*'A fantastically romantic setting.
You can't fail to be won over by
the drama of it all.'*

Rooms: 19. Double room from £119, single
from £99.50. Family-room supplement £20.
Prices: Set lunch £18.95 and dinner £32.95
Restaurant main course from £19.95. Bar main
course from £7.95. House wine £14.75.
Last orders: Food: lunch 14.00; dinner 21.00.
Closed: Never.
Food: Modern British.
Other points: Smoking area. Children welcome.
Garden. Car park. Licence for civil weddings.
Directions: M6. Exit on to the A69 at Carlisle
towards Heydon Bridge. The hotel is situated
between Newcastle and Carlisle, two miles
south of Haydon Bridge on the A686.
(Map 12)

Langley Castle is one of the few medieval
fortified-castle hotels in England. It was built
in 1350 during the reign of Edward III and its
castellated towers, mullioned windows and
seven-foot thick stone walls, coupled with
a tasteful makeover, create a fantastically
romantic setting. You can't fail to be won
over by the drama of it all, especially as
the medieval feel has been captured in the
huge public rooms. Bedrooms have been
lavishly decorated and each comes with a
canopied or four-poster bed and a luxurious
bathroom.

The exposed stone and arched doorways
in the restaurant form the backdrop for
classic Anglo-French cooking. The set-price
table d'hôte menus use quality ingredients
sourced within 10 miles of the hotel. The
choices are exquisite, with ham hock and
vegetable terrine to start, then rack of lamb
on mushroom risotto with red-wine jus, or
whole Dover sole with nut-brown butter, and
dark-chocolate and rum mousse with crème
anglaise to finish. The wine list offers a good
choice of Old and New World wines (10 by
the glass).

Longframlington

The Anglers Arms

Country inn

'Cosy up with a pint of Timothy Taylor Landlord and a good old-fashioned bar meal.'

Weldon Bridge, Longframlington,
Morpeth, Northumberland NE65 8AX
Telephone: +44(0)1665 570271
johnyoung@anglersarms.fsnet.co.uk
www.anglersarms.com

Set in an idyllic rural spot beside the old stone bridge over the River Coquet, this grand, 18th-century coaching inn is perfectly located for fishing and walking in the Cheviot Hills and exploring Northumberland's famous coast and castles. Bar and lounges are spacious and handsomely appointed, with wood panelling, log fires, antique ornaments and some fine old prints.

Cosy up with a pint of Timothy Taylor Landlord and a good old-fashioned bar meal, perhaps cod and chips, steak-and-ale pie or the generous farmhouse mixed grill, prepared from quality local ingredients. For quite a different dining experience, book into The Carriage restaurant, where fine foods are served in a refurbished Pullman carriage. Starters take in scallop-and-bacon salad and garlic king prawns, while mains may include cod-and-crab fish cakes with lemon-and-herb hollandaise, or Border rack of lamb with red-wine sauce. Puddings are the hard-to-resist variety, such as hot chocolate fudge cake. Refurbished bedrooms have quality en-suite bathrooms and lovely rural views. The inn has fishing rights on the Coquet.

Rooms: 5. Double room from £60, single from £40, family from £90.
Prices: Restaurant main course from £14.95. Bar main course from £7.95.
House wine £12.50.
Last orders: Food: 21.30.
Closed: Rarely.
Food: Traditional British.
Real ale: Timothy Taylor Landlord.
Other points: Smoking area. Children welcome. Dogs welcome in overnight. Garden. Car park. Licence for civil weddings. Wheelchair access to the restaurant/pub.
Directions: From the A1, take the A697 to Wooler and Coldstream, carry on to Weldon Bridge and follow signposts. (Map 12)

...for recipe ideas

Otterburn

Otterburn Tower

Hotel

Otterburn, Northumberland NE19 1NS
Telephone: +44(0)1830 520620
info@otterburntower.com
www.otterburntower.com

'A relaxing stay for guests in its effortlessly luxurious surroundings.'

Rooms: 18. Double room from £65 per person, single from £80. Children £30 each.
Prices: Set dinner £25. Restaurant main course from £13.95. Bar snacks from £6. House wine £12.50.
Last orders: Food: lunch 17.00; dinner 21.30.
Closed: Never.
Food: Modern British.
Other points: Smoking area. Children welcome. Dogs welcome overnight. Garden. Car park. Licence for civil weddings. Wheelchair access. Directions: A1, Newcastle airport exit. Take the A696 until you reach Otterburn. (Map 12)

Standing in 32 acres of grounds in the beautiful Redesdale Valley close to the Scottish Borders, Otterburn Tower has seen some turbulent times. It used to protect armies, but now all the action is on providing a relaxing stay for guests in its effortlessly luxurious surroundings. The historic building has an evocative atmosphere created by its thick walls, large fireplaces and oak panelling. The comfortable bedrooms come with their quota of period features, notably the Library Room with its log fire and four-poster bed.

This remote part of Northumberland is rich in fine food products, used superbly in the Tower's menu. The farms provide beef, lamb and game, and the kitchen garden provides vegetables and herbs, while local ingredients, from River Rede salmon to Longwitton Farm beef, make for an exquisite dinner. They excel with their marinated Longwitton lamb and tender beef dishes. There is much else besides to tempt, from local game, free-range chicken and pork to Northumbrian cheeses, such as Brinkburn and Cheviot. Even the mineral water comes from the Tower's own well. After dinner, retire to the elegant bar.

Hotel

'You'll find a cosy and welcoming bar with good local beers.'

The Battlesteads Hotel

Wark, Hexham,
Northumberland NE48 3LS
Telephone: +44 (0)1434 230209
info@battlesteads.com
www.battlesteads.com

Originally built as a farmstead in 1747, the stone-built Battlesteads Hotel stands on the edge of Wark in the heart of Hadrian's Wall country. Enthusiastic owners Richard and Dee Slade, who created the legendary Magnesia Bank pub in North Shields, took over early in 2006 and are steadily rejuvenating the fortunes of this country inn. The 14 en-suite bedrooms have been comfortably modernised and freshly decorated; four rooms are specifically designed for disabled guests.

You'll find a cosy and welcoming bar, with warm winter log fires, and good local beers from Black Sheep, Wylam and Durham breweries on handpump. Menus and chalkboard specials reveal a commitment to sourcing produce locally, notably lamb and Angus beef from their own stock at nearby Belsay Barns Farm, and fish and seafood landed at North Shields. A speciality is their delicious cured-beef recipe, using prime beef, juniper berries, peppercorns and herbs. Alternatively, try the homemade beefburger, lamb shoulder with rosemary-and-redcurrant sauce, or cod in beer batter. Sunday carvery roast lunches are popular – booking is advisable.

Rooms: 14. Double/twin room from £80, single from £45. Family room from £120.
Prices: Set lunch £7.50 (two courses). Set dinner £12.50 (two courses). Restaurant main course from £8.50. Bar main course from £8.50. House wine £11.95.
Last orders: Bar: 23.00 (seasonal variations).
Food: lunch 15.00 (Sunday 16.00); dinner: 22.00.
Closed: Never.
Food: Modern British.
Real ale: Theakston Ales, Black Sheep Ales, Wylam Bitter, Durham Light Ale.
Other points: No-smoking area. Dogs welcome in the bar. Garden. Children welcome. Car park. Wheelchair access to some bedrooms.
Directions: Exit 44/M6. Take the A69 towards Hexham, then the A6079 to Chollerford, then the A6430 signposted for Bellingham, and Wark is halfway along the road. (Map 12)

...for events

MEMBER
175
ENTRY

Warkworth

Warkworth House Hotel

Hotel

16 Bridge Street, Warkworth,
Northumberland NE65 0XB
Telephone: +44(0)1665 711276
stay@warkworthhousehotel.co.uk
www.warkworthhousehotel.co.uk

'Check out the magnificent stairway originally made for Brandenberg House in London.'

Rooms: 15. Double/twin room from £79, single from £49, family from £95.
Prices: Set lunch £15.95 (Sunday only) and dinner from £24.95. Restaurant main course from £8.50. Bar snack from £6.50. House wine £11.95.
Last orders: Bar: afternoon 14.00; evening 23.00. Food: lunch 14.00; dinner 21.30. Open all day for food in summer.
Closed: Never.
Food: Modern British.
Real ale: Greene King Old Speckled Hen. One guest beer.
Other points: Smoking area. Children welcome. Dogs welcome in the bar. Car park. Wheelchair access.
Directions: From the A1, north of Newcastle, take the B6345 towards Amble and Felton. Follow the signs for Warkworth Castle. The hotel is on the main street. (Map 12)

Traditional and relaxing, this smart hotel is a fine example of a provincial former coaching inn. Warkworth village is enclosed by a loop of the River Coquet and has a magnificent castle as a centrepiece; the hotel is near the old stone bridge. Enjoy a morning coffee as you sink into a comfortable leather sofa in the lounge, or a pre-lunch or dinner drink in the bar, remembering on your way in to check out the magnificent stairway originally made for Brandenberg House in London.

The individually designed bedrooms are spacious. Two on the ground floor are suited to those with mobility difficulties. Dinner is served in the dining room, overlooking the courtyard. The kitchen team takes great pride in the menus, preparing everything from breads to puddings. Start with smoked salmon, caper and dill tian and move on to oven-roasted North Sea cod with fennel and roasted peppers. Finish with a traditional Queen of Puddings, or apple tarte Tatin. You can also eat in the bar. As with its sister establishment, The Brackenrigg Inn, wines are well chosen, with a good selection by the glass.

Village pub

'A cracking free house offering well-kept ales and first-class wines.'

The Bottle & Glass

High Street, Harby, Newark,
Nottinghamshire NG23 7EB
Telephone: +44(0)1522 703438
info@jocastas.co.uk
www.bottleandglass.co.uk

Refurbished in a sophisticated, relaxed and unpretentious style, the Bottle & Glass is an impressive 16th-century building set in a pretty village close to Lincoln. Both bar areas are cosy with brick fireplaces, while the separate dining area is light and airy with a modern feel. Landlord Steve Horbury has injected new life into the place, and it is now a cracking free house offering well-kept ales, first-class wines, friendly service and well-cooked and presented food.

Dishes are certainly a cut above your normal pub grub, with starters of Whitby potted crab with prawn mayonnaise or warm Roquefort soufflé with rocket-and-walnut salad. Mains are just as good, with lamb noisettes in creamy rosemary, saffron and cider sauce, or belly pork with black pudding, sweet-onion mash and a pork jus. All produce is local, with meats being sourced from named local farms. The selection of puddings covers indulgent whims, from baked pavlova roulade with raspberries to dark-chocolate parfait, or you could try the excellent local cheeses. There are great breads and traditional homecooked lunchtime dishes, too.

Prices: Restaurant main course from £9.50. Bar snack from £5.50. House wine £10.50.
Last orders: Bar: afternoon 14.00; evening 23.00.
Food: lunch 14.00; dinner 21.30 (Friday and Saturday 22.00). No food Monday.
Closed: Monday lunch.
Food: Modern British.
Other points: No smoking. Children welcome. Garden. Car park. Licence for civil weddings. Wheelchair access.
Directions: Lincoln exit/A1. From Newark, follow the signs for Collingham. Go through to Besthorpe, turn right and follow the signs for Harby. (Map 8)

See pub walk on page 486

...for competitions

Newark-on-Trent

The Curio Café

Café

57/59 Castle Gate,
Newark-on-Trent, Nottingham,
Nottinghamshire NG24 1BE
Telephone: +44(0)1636 700716
info@thecuriocafe.com
www.thecuriocafe.com

'Every effort is made to use the best regional produce, from vegetables to game.'

Prices: Restaurant main course from £8.95.
Bar snacks from £4.95. House wine £10.50.
Last orders: Food: lunch 16.30 (Sunday 16.00);
dinner 21.30.
Closed: Sunday to Tuesday evening.
Food: Modern British.
Other points: No smoking. Children welcome.
Garden. Wheelchair access.
**Directions: Follow signs from the A1 to Newark
Castle. The Curio Cafe is 200 yards from the
gates of the castle, on Castle Gate. (Map 8)**

A magnificent Grade II-listed building, this former 'beer house' and cycle-repair shop has a double identity. Behind the 16th-century façade lie the two modern dining rooms of The Curio Café, while upstairs a warren of small rooms showcases an array of antiques and collectables, plus there's a shop and exhibitions. By day, the downstairs and adjoining patio is a bustling café serving delicious light meals, sandwiches, cakes and top-notch Williamson's teas and fair-trade coffee. In the evening, chef-proprietor John Partridge cuts free to present his eclectic mix of seasonally inspired dishes.

Every effort is made to use the best regional produce, from vegetables to game. Smoked-salmon and crayfish tartare, and Spanish Teruel ham with fresh fig, rocket and balsamic reduction are typical starters, while the main courses include lamb shoulder braised in aubergine, rosemary and red-capsicum sauce or whole sea bass baked Basque style. The short wine list majors in good-value New World wines. Hearty eaters not tempted by the puddings will find a savoury treat in the baked Camembert.

www.routiers.co.uk

Nottingham

Saagar Tandoori Restaurant

Indian restaurant

'One of the town's top foodie destinations.'

473 Mansfield Road,
Sherwood, Nottingham,
Nottinghamshire NG5 2DR
Telephone: +44(0)115 962 2014

In Urdu, 'saagar' means ocean, and its name reflects the far-reaching Indian influences on its menu. Its upmarket menu encompasses Punjabi, Balti and Kashmiri dishes, and much more besides, and without stinting on quality. The charismatic Mr Khizer has owned the restaurant for over 20 years and the food and atmosphere attract a discerning crowd. Dining, though, is a relaxed affair in elegant surroundings. Indecisive diners should plunder the five set menus, which are ensembles of well-matched dishes, while vegetarians can opt for the two vegetable thali specials.

Prices: Restaurant main course from £10.30.
House wine from £12 a litre.
Last orders: Food: lunch 14.00; dinner 24.00.
Closed: Rarely.
Food: Traditional Indian.
Other points: No smoking. Children over 7 welcome. Car Park. Private room.
Directions: Exit 26/M1. Follow the ring road to Sherwood. Saagar Tandoori is on Mansfield Road, opposite the County Library. (Map 8)

The selection of individual dishes is immense, from the list of two dozen starters to the popular favourite mains of korma, bhona and Bangalore dishes to a mouth-tingling array of specials. There is something for all tastes, from the gentle green masala, Kashmiri and begum bahar dishes with yogurt, cream, nuts and herbs to the more fiery and challenging house specialities, such as chilli chicken tikka masala and dilkush dishes. Prices look dear at first, but mains include rice, poppadums and chutney. It's best to book, as the restaurant is one of the town's top foodie destinations.

...for special offers

MEMBER ENTRY
179

Tuxford

Mussel and Crab

Sibthorpe Hill, Tuxford, Newark,
Nottinghamshire NG22 0PJ
Telephone: +44(0)1777 870491
musselandcrab1@hotmail.com
www.musselandcrab.com

Country pub

'Has built a huge reputation on serving the freshest fish and seafood.'

Prices: **Main course from £11. House wine £10.50.**
Last orders: **Bar: afternoon 14.30 (Sunday 14.45); evening 22.00 (Sunday 21.30). Food: lunch 14.30 (Sunday 14.45); dinner 22.00 (Sunday 21.00).**
Closed: **Rarely.**
Food: **Modern British.**
Real ale: **Tetley's Cask.**
Other points: **Smoking area. Children welcome. Dogs welcome in the bar. Garden. Car park. Wheelchair access.**
Directions: **From Exit A57/A1 (Markham Moor), take the B1164 to Ollerton/Tuxford; the pub is 800 yards along on the right. (Map 8)**

Bruce and Allison Elliott-Bateman have certainly brought a genuine taste of the sea to land-locked Nottinghamshire. This popular and lively country pub has built a huge reputation on serving the freshest fish and seafood, whether native or exotic, with much of it delivered daily from Brixham. Choose from starters of steamed mussels in white wine, garlic, leeks and cream or fresh oysters with a wedge of lemon. Main courses might be Cromer crab with thermidor sauce or a grilled Torbay sole served on the bone with lemon juice and parsley. Meat eaters will not be disappointed with the huge mixed grill or game from local shoots.

The stylishly refurbished interior offers eating areas, a couple of bars with welcoming log fires, up to 22 different specials chalkboards, and has everything on the wine list on display. There are two distinct restaurant areas, one a sheer, vibrant Mediterranean, with terracotta and ochre hues, the other offering the period surroundings of a traditional oak-beamed dining room. Gents, look out for the live goldfish in the plastic cistern above the urinals in the 'buoys' room.

MEMBER
180
ENTRY

Banbury

The George & Dragon

Village inn

'An interesting range of sound country cooking.'

Silver Street, Chacombe, Banbury,
Oxfordshire OX17 2JR
Telephone: +44(0)1295 711500
thegeorgeanddragon@msn.com

Just minutes from the M40, the mellow sandstone George & Dragon dates from the 17th century, and stands tucked away close to the church in this pretty conservation village. The flower-festooned façade is a picture in summer. Popular locally for a welcoming atmosphere, the traditional, rustic interior – replete with exposed stone walls, worn flagstones, low beams, roaring log fires, and a well built into the bar counter forms a backdrop to an interesting range of sound country cooking.

Printed and daily chalkboard menus take in decent sandwiches and jacket potatoes (try the prawn-and-lime dressing), various salads such as smoked duck or roast chicken, and ham, egg and chips for lunch. At dinner, follow potted prawns or game terrine with ham hock with a creamy caper sauce, lambs' liver and bacon, steak-and-kidney pie, or rib-eye steak. There's a choice of roasts on the good-value set Sunday lunch menu. Expect Everards ales on handpump, plus a short global list of wines, with five offered by the glass. Overnight accommodation is in two clean and tidy en-suite rooms.

Rooms: **2. Double/single room from £60, single from £50.**
Prices: Restaurant main course from £8.
Bar main course from £8. House wine £11.
Last orders: Bar: 23.00. Food: lunch 14.30 (Sunday 15.00); dinner 21.30. No food Sunday evening.
Closed: **Rarely.**
Food: Traditional British.
Real ale: Everards Tiger, Everards Beacon. One guest beer.
Other points: Smoking area. Children welcome. Dogs welcome in the bar and overnight. Garden. Car park. Private dining room.
Directions: Exit 11/M40. Take the A461 signposted for Daventry. Chacombe is the next road on the right. Bear left in the village to the pub. (Map 8)

...for the latest news

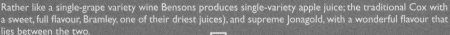

Bensons Apple Juice,
Sherborne, Gloucestershire, 01451 844134

Rather like a single-grape variety wine Bensons produces single-variety apple juice; the traditional Cox with a sweet, full flavour, Bramley, one of their driest juices), and supreme Jonagold, with a wonderful flavour that lies between the two.

Haynes, Hanson & Clark Wine Merchants,
Stow-on-the-Wold, 01451 870808
A thriving, independent wine merchant that sources wine direct from growers, ensuring excellent value and allocations of the finest-quality wines. Best known for burgundy domaines, as well as extensive Bordeaux listings, great Loire domaines, and Spain's finest syrah – the Finca Sandoval.

Visit the Farmers' Market

Nearby Stow-on-the-Wold holds a farmers' market in the main square on the second Thursday of every month, from 9am to 2pm.

W J Castle & Jesse Smith Butchers,
Burford, 01993 822113
Traditional butchers selling Hereford and Buccleuch beef alongside Gloucester Old Spot pork and locally farmed lamb. Cheese, olives, handmade sausages, and roast meats are also available from laden deli-counters.

Fifield House Farm,
Fifield
The Orr-Ewings use as much local, free-range and organic produce as possible and this includes their own Aberdeen Angus beef, which is reared on the family farm a few miles from The Kings Head. Although not organic, it is entirely grass-fed – no additives – and is hung for 21 days to enhance its unique flavour.

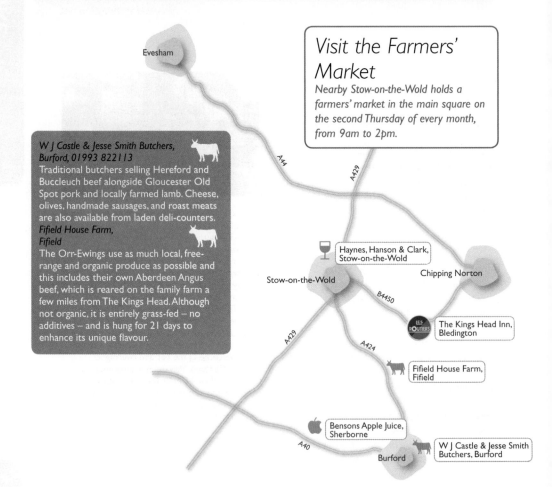

Evesham

A44

A429

Haynes, Hanson & Clark,
Stow-on-the-Wold

Chipping Norton

Stow-on-the-Wold

B4450

The Kings Head Inn,
Bledington

A429

A424

Fifield House Farm,
Fifield

Bensons Apple Juice,
Sherborne

A40

Burford

W J Castle & Jesse Smith
Butchers, Burford

Bledington

The Kings Head Inn

Village inn

'The Kings Head is surely the quintessential Cotswold pub.'

The Green, Bledington, Kingham,
Oxfordshire OX7 6XQ
Telephone: +44(0)1608 658365
kingshead@orr-ewing.com
www.kingsheadinn.net

The Kings Head is surely the quintessential, Cotswold pub. Built of mellow local stone in the 15th century, it stands in a gloriously unspoilt village, facing the green with its brook and border-patrolling ducks. Inside, the original bar is charming, full of low beams, ancient settles and flagstone floors, and a huge log fire burns in the inglenook, while the separate dining area is an informal setting for some imaginative pub food.

Archie and Nicola Orr-Ewing are passionate about local, free-range and organic ingredients, notably Angus beef from the family farm in nearby Fifield, and fresh Cornish fish. Start, perhaps, with sautéed tiger prawns with lime-and-garlic butter, then opt for steak, ale and root vegetable pie, or chargrilled venison with sage-and-mustard butter. Finish with rhubarb-and-ginger flan, or regional cheeses. Lighter lunchtime choices include roast beef and horseradish sandwiches. There are tip-top local ales on handpump and an interesting global wine list. Beautifully refurbished en-suite bedrooms are split between the inn and the converted barn.

Rooms: 12. Double/twin room from £70.
Prices: Main course from £8.95. House wine £11.95.
Last orders: Bar: afternoon 14.00; evening 23.00.
Food: lunch 14.00; dinner 21.00 (Friday and Saturday 21.30).
Closed: Rarely.
Food: Traditional/modern British.
Real ale: Hook Norton Best Bitter. Three guest beers.
Other points: Smoking area. Children welcome. Dogs welcome in the bar. Garden. Car park. Wheelchair access.
Directions: On the B4450 between Chipping Norton and Stow-on-the-Wold. (Map 8)

Henley-on-Thames

The Cherry Tree Inn

Stoke Row, Henley-on-Thames,
Oxfordshire RG9 5QA
Telephone: +44(0)1491 680430
info@thecherrytreeinn.com
www.thecherrytreeinn.com

Country inn

'Original features, such as worn flagstones, low beams and open fireplaces, remain and blend in beautifully.'

Rooms: **4. Double from £65.**
Prices: **Restaurant main course from £8.95. Bar/snack from £5.50. House wine £12.95.**
Last orders: **Bar: 23.00. Food: lunch 15.00 (Saturday and Sunday 16.00); dinner 22.00.**
Closed: **Rarely.**
Food: **Modern European.**
Real ale: **Brakspear Ales.**
Other points: **No smoking. Children welcome. Garden. Car park. Wheelchair access.**
Directions: **Exit 6/M40 towards Watlington. Then take the B480 towards Nettlebed and then the B481 towards Reading. Turn right at Highmoor, and Stoke Row is one mile away. (Map 5)**
See pub walk on page 488

Pull off the M40 to find this collection of 400-year-old brick-and-flint farm cottages deep in the rolling Chilterns countryside – you won't be disappointed! Paul Gilchrist and chef Richard Coates have worked wonders in bringing this old pub bang up to date. Bar and dining areas have been elegantly refurbished – think relaxing, earthy tones to the décor, subdued lighting and modern furnishings, yet original features such as worn flagstones, low beams and open fireplaces remain and blend in beautifully.

Equally stylish and modern is the cooking. With an emphasis on simplicity and fresh, seasonal ingredients, daily menus may take in starters of smoked haddock and parsley fish cakes with hollandaise, and mains such as roast belly pork with smoked black pudding, caramelised apples and cider jus, or grilled squid and chorizo salad with roast peppers and chilli-oil dressing. Choose from good puddings or local cheese to finish. Brakspear ales, select wines (11 by the glass), and wonderful accommodation in four impeccable bedrooms housed in a refurbished barn complete the picture.

www.routiers.co.uk

Boze Down Vineyard,

Whitchurch-on-Thames, 0118 984 4031, www.bozedown.com

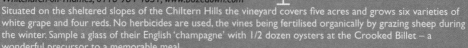

Situated on the sheltered slopes of the Chiltern Hills the vineyard covers five acres and grows six varieties of white grape and four reds. No herbicides are used, the vines being fertilised organically by grazing sheep during the winter. Sample a glass of their English 'champagne' with 1/2 dozen oysters at the Crooked Billet – a wonderful precursor to a memorable meal.

Wysipig, Ellis Hill Farm, Arborfield,

0118 976 2221, www.wysipig.com

Wysipig simply translates as What You See is PIG – just pork, raised with care and very tasty. The Coombes' herd are traditional Large Black and Saddleback pigs, reared outdoors or in cottager's sties on this family-run Berkshire farm. Call by between Wednesday and Saturday for bacon and ham, or half pigs, jointed for the freezer.

Brookleas Fish Farm,

East Hendred, 01235 820500

The Fish Farm was established in 1979 on the beautiful site of an old mill on the East Hendred Brook at Ludbridge. From the farm shop you can purchase fresh trout, locally caught crayfish, oak-smoked trout and smoked-trout pâté.

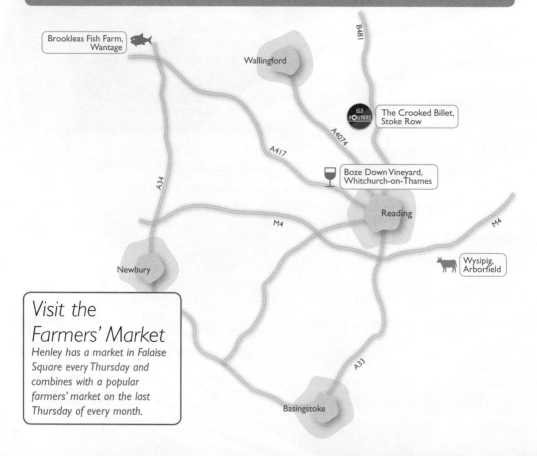

Visit the Farmers' Market

Henley has a market in Falaise Square every Thursday and combines with a popular farmers' market on the last Thursday of every month.

Stoke Row

The Crooked Billet

Country pub

'Expect an enthusiast's wine list, and quality live jazz on Sundays.'

Newlands Lane, Stoke Row,
Henley-on-Thames,
Oxfordshire RG9 5PU
Telephone: +44(0)1491 681048
www.thecrookedbillet.co.uk

Built in 1642, and once the haunt of highwayman Dick Turpin, Paul Clerehugh's well-hidden little gem remains largely unchanged, with masses of rustic appeal. It is a quaint village local that has upgraded itself to pub-restaurant status, and is well worth seeking out. It has the feel of a great winter pub, with small intimate rooms with low, heavy-beamed ceilings, rustic furnishings, and the roar of burning logs in the inglenook fireplace. There is no bar; pints of Brakspear are drawn direct from the cask in the cellar.

The lengthy, cosmopolitan and adventurous menu has plenty of interest, and the food is unpretentious with a rustic, homely quality that doesn't lose sight of its surroundings. From the à la carte or the set lunch menu choose, perhaps, bouillabaisse, followed by confit of organic saddleback pork with bean-and-pulse casserole, rack of Ipsden lamb with rosemary jus, or smoked haddock served with scallops and mustard sauce. For pudding, try the white-chocolate raspberry cheesecake, or a plate of local cheeses. Expect an enthusiast's wine list, and quality live jazz on Sundays. Booking is essential.

Prices: **Set lunch £14.95. House wine £12.**
Last orders: **Food: lunch 14.30; dinner 22.00.**
Closed: **Rarely.**
Food: **Modern British.**
Real ale: **Brakspear Bitter.**
Other points: **Smoking throughout. Car park.**
Directions: **Exit 8/9/M4 and follow the signs for Henley, then the A4130 to Nettlebed. Turn left and follow the signs to Stoke Row. (Map 5)**

Thame

The Birdcage

Town-centre pub

4 Cornmarket, Thame,
Oxfordshire OX9 3DX
Telephone: +44(0)1844 260381
birdcagepub@hotmail.com
www.twokiwisltd.co.uk

'Listed by English Heritage and oozing history.'

Prices: **Restaurant main course from £9.50. Bar main course from £4.95. House wine £10.50.**
Last orders: **Bar: 23.00 (Wednesday and Thursday 24.00, Friday and Saturday 01.00).**
Food: **lunch 14.30 (15.30 Sunday); dinner: 22.30.**
Closed: **Rarely.**
Food: **Traditional British.**
Other points: **Smoking area. Wheelchair access.**
Directions: **Exit 6 or 8/M40. Take the A418 to Thame and The Birdcage is on the main thoroughfare. (Map 5)**

Thame's oldest pub dates from around 1300, and it's a quaint, black-and-white beamed-and-timbered place, listed by English Heritage and oozing history. In medieval times it was used to detain petty thieves and criminals, even lepers on the upper floors, and during the Napoleonic Wars it housed French prisoners. Sympathetic refurbishment in the rambling, wooden-floored bars has revealed thick elm beams from beneath modern plaster, and the two oak-framed windows are of historic importance.

The drinks menu is impressive. Quaff real ale or quality Belgian beers – Leffe, Hoegaarden, Blanc – or choose one of 50 wines available by the glass. Food ranges from traditional roast-beef and horseradish sandwiches and lasagne to exotic sausages (pheasant, steak au poivre, pork, port and stilton), all served with mash and gravy, and more imaginative meals, served in the new dining room. In the latter, tuck into fish cakes with chilli sauce, followed by braised lamb shank with parsnip purée and red-wine jus, and apple tarte Tatin.

Clipsham

The Olive Branch

Country inn

'Good-quality innovative and traditional food using first-class local produce.'

Main Street, Clipsham, Oakham,
Rutland LE15 7SH
Telephone: +44(0)1780 410355
info@theolivebranchpub.com
www.theolivebranchpub.com

With a host of industry gongs to its name, including a Michelin star, the Olive Branch is very much a foodie hang-out. Yet, despite the serious approach to both food and wine, it retains all of its pub qualities – space for just having a drink and a casual, relaxed style. Its success is down to a philosophy of offering good-quality, innovative and traditional food using first-class local produce.

Chalkboards list lunchtime sandwiches and the very reasonable set lunch. Otherwise, grab a menu and a table anywhere in the rambling bar and dining areas, which sport log fires, soft lamplight and plain wooden tables. Kick off a memorable meal with roasted scallops, black-pudding mash and red-wine sauce, move on to roast lamb with saffron-and-garlic mash, and finish with caramelised lemon tart. Wine is obviously a passion, with chalkboards detailing house specials, classics and up-and-coming producers. This unpretentious old stone pub is now even more attractive to foodies and A1 travellers, as five smart en-suite bedrooms have recently been created in Beech Cottage opposite. Don't miss the pub shop.

Rooms: 6, 4 en-suite, 1 with shower only. Double room from £80. Family room available.
Prices: Set lunch £17.50. Restaurant main course from £9.50. Bar main course from £7.25. House wine £12.95.
Last orders: Bar: afternoon 15.00 (Saturday and Sunday open all day); evening 24.00. Food: lunch 14.00 (Sunday 15.00); dinner 21.30 (Sunday 21.00).
Closed: Rarely.
Food: Modern pub food.
Real ale: Grainstore Olive Oil. Two guest beers change weekly.
Other points: Smoking area in bar. Children welcome. Dogs welcome in the bar. Garden. Car park. Wheelchair access. Private dining room for 12-20 guests.
Directions: Two miles off the A1 at the B668 junction north of Stamford. (Map 8)

...for recipe ideas

Church Stretton

Mynd House

Ludlow Road, Little Stretton,
Church Stretton, Shropshire SY6 6RB
Telephone: +44(0)1694 722212
info@myndhouse.co.uk
www.myndhouse.co.uk

Bed and breakfast

'One of the most comfortable, colourful and gastronomically exciting bed and breakfasts in the area.'

Rooms: **8. Double/twin room from £75, single from £45. Family room from £110.**
Prices: **Set dinner £21.**
Closed: **Mid-November to mid-February. Group bookings taken only for New Year.**
Food: **Malaysian/Modern British.**
Other points: **No smoking. Children welcome. Car park.**
Directions: **Exit 7/M54. One and a half miles south of Church Stretton on the A49. Take the B5477 to Little Stretton, go through the village and pass Ragleth Inn. Mynd House is on the left. (Map 9)**

This former red-brick Edwardian family home hides an exotically styled interior, devised in the main by owner Theresa, who hails from Malaysia. She and her husband Nigel have spared no effort in making this one of the most comfortable, colourful and gastronomically exciting bed and breakfasts in the area. Views to the Long Mynd are the backdrop to a most pleasant stay and the comfortable beds deserve a special mention. En-suite bedrooms are vibrant and airy, while downstairs you can relax in the south-facing living room with its leather armchairs and sofas.

Make time for a drink in the bar before heading to the dining room for an exciting and fun menu of British and Malay favourites. For the less adventurous, there are good starters of chicken-and-bacon salad or veggie tart, while those looking for something spicy, can tuck into spicy prawns or rojak, a popular Indonesian vegetable-and-fruit salad with a sweet tamarind sauce. This dual theme continues into the mains, offering nasi goreng istimewa or pan-fried pork escalopes. Nigel's well-planned wine list offers plenty of options to deal with the range of dishes.

Cucurbita pepo
'Green Acorn'

Home produce at Lower Buckton
The Chesshire's home-reared rare-breed Berkshire pigs and old-English bantams free-range in the yard, while the kitchen garden provides vegetables, salads, herbs and fruit throughout the seasons.

Monkland Dairy
Monkland, Leominster, 01568 720307, www.mousetrapcheese.co.uk
Monkland Dairy is a specialist in handmade cheeses, including the Little Hereford Cheese, made to the original Herefordshire recipe. You can visit the dairy, or buy them from the Mousetrap Cheese Shops in Hereford, Leominster and Ludlow. Take a tour or visit the coffee shop while here.

Organic Smokehouse
Clunbury Hall, Clunbury, 01588 660206, www.organicsmokehouse.com
A traditional smokehouse where smoking is carried out without any mechanical intervention. It uses the 'draft method', with air-dried, naturally fallen Shropshire oak. This gives greater flavour to smoked salmon, butter, cheeses and olive oil.

Bacheldre Watermill
Churchstoke, Montgomery, Powys, 01588 620489, www.bacheldremill.co.uk
Carolyn Chesshire bakes superb cakes and biscuits using the quality stone-ground flour milled with traditional grinding stones by artisan millers at Bacheldre Mill. They produce both an organic and a traditional flour range, the latter milled from local wheat grown at Bacheldre Farm.

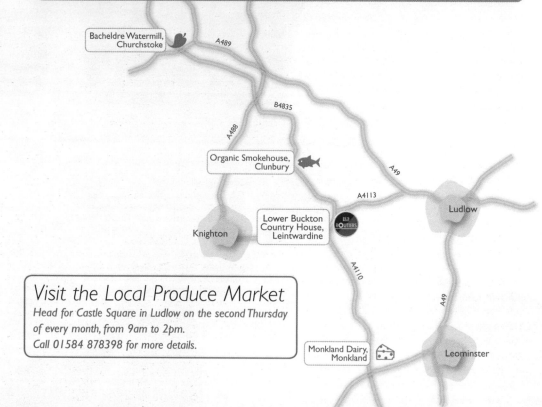

Bacheldre Watermill, Churchstoke

A489

B4835

A488

Organic Smokehouse, Clunbury

A49

A4113

Ludlow

LES ROUTIERS

Knighton

Lower Buckton Country House, Leintwardine

A4110

A49

Visit the Local Produce Market
Head for Castle Square in Ludlow on the second Thursday of every month, from 9am to 2pm.
Call 01584 878398 for more details.

Monkland Dairy, Monkland

Leominster

Bed and breakfast

Lower Buckton Country House

Buckton, Leintwardine, near Ludlow,
Shropshire SY7 0JU
Telephone: +44(0)1547 540532
carolyn@lowerbuckton.co.uk
www.lowerbuckton.co.uk

'There is a total commitment to local foods in season, with everything sourced within a 12-mile radius.'

The tiny hamlet of Buckton straddles the Herefordshire/Shropshire border where England meets Wales and is only 10 miles from the gastronomic epicentre of Ludlow. Although no longer a working farm, owners Carolyn and Henry Chesshire do keep free-range, rare-breed Berkshire pigs for the table and promote Lower Buckton as country-house accommodation with private dining. The three bedrooms sleep six, but arrangements with a neighbour means that house parties of 12 can be accommodated. The house itself is decorated in country-house fashion with Victorian and Georgian furniture.

The wonderful dining room, with its long table and sideboard crammed with silver, is the perfect setting for the set-menu dinners, where diners bring their own wine. There is a total commitment to local foods in season, with everything sourced within a 12-mile radius. The kitchen garden provides homegrown vegetables, herbs and fruits. A typical six-course dinner may include baked shoulder of lamb with rosemary, garlic and garden tomatoes and Lower Buckton apple spiced crumble, finishing with local cheeses.

Rooms: **3. Double/twin room from £80, single from £50. Dinner, bed and breakfast from £65 per person.**
Prices: **Set dinner £25. BYO wine.**
Closed: **Never.**
Food: **Traditional/modern British.**
Other points: **No smoking. Children, dogs and horses welcome by prior arrangement. Private dinners and house parties. Car park. Credit cards not accepted.**
Directions: **One mile from Leintwardine on the A4113 Knighton road. Turn off at Walford crossroads and take the lane to Buckton and Adleymoor. Lower Buckton is the second on the left in the hamlet. (Map 5)**

Shrewsbury

The Inn at Grinshill

Country inn

High Street, Grinshill, Shrewsbury,
Shropshire SY4 3BL
Telephone: +44(0)1939 220410
sales@theinnatgrinshill.co.uk
www.theinnatgrinshill.co.uk

'Six fabulous bedrooms, all with stylish furnishings and wired broadband access.'

Since taking over in 2002, Kevin and Victoria Brazier have turned this 18th-century country inn into a classy pub/restaurant with rooms. Extensively renovated by the couple, The Inn at Grinshill now boasts six fabulous bedrooms, all of which have been finished to a high standard with stylish furnishings and wired broadband access. Downstairs, The Elephant & Castle Bar has a welcoming hearth, bar meals and a good choice of real ales on tap.

The contemporary restaurant menu showcases plenty of local produce, including meat from Shrewsbury Market and sausages and bacon from Wenlock Edge Farm. Chef Jeremy Stone's cooking has an international flavour – seared king scallops arriving with green-mango slaw, and cumin-seasoned pan-roasted chicken breast served with soused red onions and burrito sauce – but there are more traditional steaks from the grill and old favourites such as beer-battered cod, chips and mushy peas. Desserts such as hot chocolate fondant or summer pudding vie for attention alongside a cheeseboard of British truckles.

Rooms: 6. Double/twin room from £100, single from £50. Family room from £115.
Prices: Set lunch and dinner £9.95. Restaurant main course from £8.95. Bar main course from £8.95. House wine £13.
Last orders: Bar: afternoon 15.00; evening 23.00.
Food: lunch 14.30 (Saturday and Sunday 15.00); dinner 21.30 (no food Sunday evening).
Closed: Sunday evening and bank holiday evenings.
Food: Modern British.
Real ale: Hanby Drawwell Bitter, Ruddles County Ale, Theakston Best.
Other points: Smoking area. Children welcome. Dogs welcome in the bar. Garden. Car park. Wheelchair access.
Directions: M54. A49 towards Whitchurch. Pass Hadnall and take the third left to Grinshill. The inn is half a mile along on the left. (Map 9)

Shrewsbury

The White Horse Inn

Country pub

'As a refuelling stop, it's hard to beat.'

Castle Pulverbatch, Shrewsbury,
Shropshire SY5 8DS
Telephone: +44(0)1743 718247
steve@whitehorsepulverbatch.co.uk
www.whitehorsepulverbatch.co.uk

Smack on the Shropshire Way and the Marches Way in beautiful countryside, just north of the Long Mynd and east of the Stiperstones, The White Horse is a welcome pitstop for weary walkers. Step inside and you'll find a cracking bar, replete with flagstones, rustic stools and benches around low wooden tables, and a roaring woodburning stove to ease away the winter chill. Beyond lies the homely and carpeted dining room.

As a refuelling stop, it's hard to beat, as Steve and Debbie Bruce offer tip-top ales from Woods, Salopian and Weetwood microbreweries on tap, alongside a chalkboard listing 11 wines by the glass, and some hearty country cooking. Meat is sourced from local farms, black pudding and sausages are made at Wenlock Edge Farm, and venison comes from nearby Lyth Hill. This equates to a wonderful beef, Guinness and mushroom pie, sausages with caramelised-onion mash and rich gravy, and lamb's liver casseroled in red wine and served with black-pudding mash. Light bites include homemade burgers and local cheese ploughman's.

Prices: Restaurant main course from £7.50. Bar main course from £5.75. House wine £10.50.
Last orders: Bar: afternoon 14.30; evening 23.00. Food: lunch 14.30; dinner 21.30.
Closed: Monday, except bank holiday Mondays.
Food: Traditional and Modern British.
Other points: No-smoking area. Children welcome. Dogs welcome in the bar. Garden and Patio. Car park. Wheelchair access (not WC).
Directions: M54. Take the A5 towards Shrewsbury and either the A49 to Craven Arms or the A488 to Bishop's Castle. Pulverbatch is signposted off these two main roads.
(Map 9)

...for events

Telford

The Hundred House Hotel

Country inn

'Herbs and dried flowers from the inn's wonderfully luxuriant gardens adorn beams and tables.'

Bridgnorth Road, Norton, Shifnal,
Telford, Shropshire TF11 9EE
Telephone: +44(0)1952 730353/
0845 644 6100
reservations@hundredhouse.co.uk
www.hundredhouse.co.uk

This mellow, creeper-clad, red-brick inn is a jumble of ages and styles. The main building is of Georgian origin and has quarry-tiled floors, exposed brickwork, huge fireplaces and some beautifully restored fine oak panelling. Herbs and dried flowers from the inn's wonderfully luxuriant gardens adorn beams and tables – diners are invited to pick the fresh herbs for garnish. The personality of the inn gains from the inimitable input from the Phillips family since 1986.

This enthusiasm for freshness and quality extends to the excellent food prepared by Stuart Phillips, who sources local produce and cooks both a brasserie-style and full restaurant menu. Expect such dishes as venison with braised red cabbage and red-wine sauce, rack of Shropshire lamb with rosemary jus, and lighter dishes such as Greek salad and steak-and-kidney pie. Delicious homemade puddings include dark chocolate mousse with orange anglaise. You'll also find five real ales and a well-chosen list of wines; 12 by the glass. Both the names and colour schemes of the 10 enchanting bedrooms look to the garden for inspiration.

Rooms: 10. Double room from £99, single from £75, family from £125.
Prices: Restaurant main course from £10. Bar main course from £7.95. House wine £12.50.
Last orders: Bar: afternoon 15.00; evening 23.00. Food: lunch 14.30; dinner 22.00 (Sunday 21.00).
Closed: Rarely.
Food: Modern British.
Real ale: Phillips Heritage Bitter, Phillips Heritage Mild, Bateman's XB Bitter, Everards Tiger Best Bitter, Highgate & Walsall Saddlers Strong Ale. One guest beer.
Other points: Smoking area. Children welcome. Garden. Car park. Wheelchair access to the restaurant/pub.
Directions: Exit4/M54. On the A442, midway between Bridgnorth and Telford. (Map 8)

MEMBER 191 ENTRY

Exford

Exmoor White Horse Inn

Country inn

Exford, Exmoor National Park,
Somerset TA24 7PY
Telephone: +44(0)1643 831229
peter@exmoor-whitehorse.co.uk
www.exmoor-whitehorse.co.uk

'Look out for the inn's specialities, namely venison, pheasant and partridge.'

Rooms: 28. Double/twin room from £90, single from £45.
Prices: Set dinner £30 (three courses). Main course from £12. Bar snack menu from £6. House wine £10.95.
Last orders: Bar: 23.00. Food: lunch 14.30; dinner 21.30.
Closed: Never.
Food: Traditional British.
Real ale: Greene King Old Speckled Hen, Fulller's London Pride, Exmoor Ale, Exmoor Gold, Exmoor Fox. Two guest beers.
Other points: No smoking in the restaurant/bedrooms. Children welcome. Dogs welcome. Garden. Car park. Wheelchair access.
Directions: On the B3224, midway between Simonsbath and Wheddon Cross (A396), south of Minehead. (Map 4)

A lovely, creeper-clad, 16th-century building, this coaching inn stands opposite the River Exe in the heart of a small village in the Exmoor National Park. Close to Tarr Steps, the picture-postcard villages of Dunster, Selworthy and Porlock, and the dramatic north Somerset/Devon coast, the White Horse has long been a favoured pit-stop on the tourist trail. It is also popular with walkers and as a base for exploring Exmoor.

Downstairs in the comfortable, beamed and carpeted bar, there are country-themed prints adorning the walls, blazing log fires, Exmoor ale on tap, and an extensive menu listing traditional pub meals. Look out for the inn's specialities, namely venison, pheasant and partridge from the surrounding moors, locally caught lobster and fresh fish, and the platter of Somerset cheeses. There is also a Sunday-lunch carvery. The inn offers good-value accommodation in bedrooms that reflect the character of the place. All have a soft, cottagey look that takes in pastel colours and floral fabrics. Activities organised from the inn include Land Rover safari trips across Exmoor.

Shepton Mallet

Thatched Cottage

Town-centre inn

'Expect oodles of space, movie channels, broadband access and impressive slate-floored bathrooms.'

63-67 Charlton Road, Shepton Mallet,
Somerset BA4 5QF
Telephone: +44(0)1749 342058
enquiries@thatchedcottage.info
www.thatchedcottage.info

A smartly refurbished 300-year-old thatched cottage standing on the edge of town on the old Fosse Way. Money has been lavished on the interior, resulting in a cool, comfortable and contemporary open-plan bar that blends the traditional – oak beams, wood-tiled floors and log fires – with stylish, modern décor, squashy sofas, and chunky candles on pale-wood tables. Comfort and style extend upstairs to the eight, tastefully designed bedrooms. Expect oodles of space, movie channels, broadband access and impressive slate-floored bathrooms.

Back in the bar, tuck into Wiltshire ham, egg and chips, slow-cooked lamb shank, smoked salmon and scrambled eggs, or Somerset beef fillet with pepper sauce. An authentic Indian buffet is served on Sunday evenings. Head for the restaurant for a warm orange-and-scallop salad starter, followed by rack of salt-marsh lamb with ratatouille, or chicken, Old Spot bacon and apple risotto, with British cheeses from Longman's Cheese, or bitter-chocolate tart for dessert. Accompany with a pint of Greene King or with one of 16 wines by the glass.

Rooms: **8. Double/twin room from £93, single from £72.95.**
Prices: **Set lunch £12. Restaurant main course from £9.95. Bar snacks from £5. House wine £11.95.**
Last orders: **Bar: 23.00. Food: lunch 14.30; dinner 21.30.**
Closed: **Rarely.**
Food: **Modern European.**
Real ale: **Green King Old Speckled Hen, and Suffolk Summer.**
Other points: **Smoking area. Garden. Car park. Wheelchair access to public areas only.**
Directions: **Exit Wincanton/A303. At the roundabout, turn left on the A371 to Castle Carey. Follow the A371 towards Shepton Mallet and, at the roundabout, take the A37. After one mile, take the first right into Fosse Lane. Continue to the Charlton Road junction and Thatched Cottage is straight ahead. (Map 4)**

...for competitions

J A & E Montgomery Cheeses,
Manor Farm, North Cadbury, 01963 440243
Jamie Montgomery is the third generation to continue to hand make traditional unpasteurised cheeses.
The Camelot showcases their award-winning Montgomery Cheddar (Supreme Champion – British Cheese
Awards 2004), Ogle Shield (Best English Cheese at the same) and Montgomery Butter.

Burrow Hill Cider,
Pass Vale Farm, Burrow Hill, Kingsbury Episcopi, 01460 240782
Burrow Hill Cider is pressed from traditional cider apples (some of which are supplied by the Montgomerys
at Manor Farm). At Burrow Hill they grow 40 different varieties of cider apples. The result is a vintage-quality
cider and you can sample and buy draught cider from the barrel and in bottles, as well as Cox and Russet
apple juices and cider vinegar.

Andrew Barclay Butchers,
45 High Street, Wincanton, 01963 34880
This long-established family butcher supplies The Camelot's meat, including lamb from James Tabor (Home
Farm, Sutton Montis), and Gloucester Old Spot pork from Guy Mason (Sutton Farm, Sutton Montis).

Rowswell Fruit & Vegetables,
Baker's Farm, Barrington, Ilminster, 01460 52381
The Rowswell family have turned 27 acres of their farm into a market garden. Using traditional methods and
no chemicals, they grow and supply quality mixed leaves, carrots, parsnips, butternut squash, tomatoes and
garlic to The Camelot.

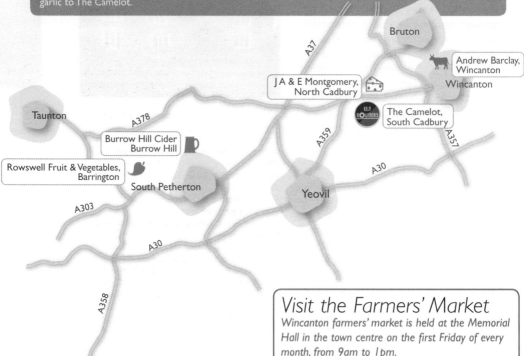

Visit the Farmers' Market

Wincanton farmers' market is held at the Memorial
Hall in the town centre on the first Friday of every
month, from 9am to 1pm.

South Cadbury

The Camelot

Pub and restaurant

'Enjoy a pint of local Butcombe Bitter with a ploughman's to beat all ploughman's.'

Chapel Road, South Cadbury, Yeovil,
Somerset BA22 7EX
Telephone: +44(0)1963 440448
enquiry@thecamelot.co.uk
www.thecamelot.co.uk

Now in the safe hands of renowned Somerset cheesemakers Jamie and Zizi Montgomery, the former Red Lion is firmly established as one of the best 'new' pubs in the region. The friendly bar, with flagstones, wooden tables and brightly coloured cushioned chairs or the relaxing lounge with comfortable leather sofas are ideal places for wining and dining.

Enjoy a pint of local Butcombe Bitter with a ploughman's to beat all ploughman's – it features the owners' award-winning Ogle Shield and Montgomery Cheddar with pickles, mixed salad and an apple – or a 'knife and fork' sandwich or light meal from the bar menu. The kitchen majors on using local produce and the lunch à la carte menu offers an extensive line-up of favourites from home-cooked ham, egg and chips to grilled rib-eye steak with horseradish cream. Dinner may start with deep-fried Somerset brie wrapped in filo pastry and follow with Somerset pork chop with baked apple, cabbage and a Somerset cider and Calvados cream sauce. A lovely beer garden extends the dining-area options in summer.

Prices: Set lunch £13 and dinner £19. Restaurant main course from £7.50. Bar meal from £4.50. House wine £11.
Last orders: Bar: afternoon 14.30; evening 22.00 (open all day Saturday and Sunday). Food: lunch 14.30; dinner 21.30.
Closed: Rarely.
Food: Modern British.
Real ale: Butcombe Bitter. Two guest beers.
Other points: Smoking area. Children welcome. Dogs welcome in the bar. Garden. Wheelchair access. Skittle alley.
Directions: Half a mile south of the A303, between Wincanton and Sparkford. (Map 4)
See pub walk on page 490

Stoke-sub-Hamdon

The Priory House Restaurant

Restaurant

1 High Street, Stoke-sub-Hamdon,
Somerset TA14 6PP
Telephone: +44(0)1935 822826
reservations@
theprioryhouserestaurant.co.uk
www.theprioryhouserestaurant.co.uk

'Hot vanilla soufflé or honey-and-walnut tart with ice cream are fabulously indulgent.'

Prices: **Restaurant main course from £17.50. House wine £15.**
Last orders: **lunch 14.00 (Saturday only); dinner 21.00.**
Closed: **The last week in May, first two weeks of November and all day Sunday and Monday.**
Food: **Modern British fine dining.**
Other points: **No smoking. Garden. Wheelchair access.**
Directions: **Exit 25/M5. Half a mile off the A303 in the centre of Stoke-sub-Hamdon. (Map 4)**

Originally built as a guesthouse for the nearby priory, this attractive restaurant has a lovely bright and airy feel, and is decorated in blues and creams. Diners can be assured of attentive service by proprietor Sonia Brooks, while husband Peter prepares the fine food. His beautifully executed menu focuses on English food with hints of the Mediterranean. Dishes are made using what's best in season from the local area, notably farm meats and cheeses.

A typical menu may list starters of duck-and-herb terrine with beetroot chutney and honeyed-parsnip soup. Main courses could take in local lamb with redcurrant and rosemary jus, loin of wild venison with celeriac rösti and blueberry sauce, or baked sea bass with hollandaise. Desserts of hot vanilla soufflé or honey-and-walnut tart with honey-and-almond ice cream are both fabulously indulgent. Alternatively, sample the cheeseboard, which features local varieties. This small restaurant also offers a remarkable wine list, with 10 by the glass and 13 by the half bottle, or there's potent Somerset cider.

Wedmore

Table 8

Restaurant

'If you don't have room for one of the gorgeous puds, opt for a luscious sorbet.'

Church Street, Wedmore,
Somerset BS28 4AB
Telephone: +44(0)1934 710232
book@table-8.co.uk

Mike and Chrissie McKenzie have worked wonders since arriving at this once-derelict building three years ago. They have restored traditional elements and introduced a Mediterranean feel to create a chic bistro and restaurant. The simple but stylish décor sets off the original features of this traditional Wedmore stone house. In keeping with the individual look, food on the bistro and à la carte menus is not run-of-the-mill either, but an interesting array of dishes using good seasonal, local ingredients.

The bistro menu features modern European dishes with an Italian bent. Start with a pesto-pastry tartlet and move on to free-range chicken baked with herbs, Marsala and mushrooms, or orecchiette Genovese. Wedmore lamb and locally reared beef are used in the mouth-watering and inventive dinner mains, and there is always a good supply of fresh, dayboat-caught Cornish fish – poached halibut served with herb-and-tomato risotto. If you don't have room for one of the gorgeous puds, opt for a luscious sorbet. Much of the wine list focuses on single-estate wines from a top supplier.

Prices: **Set lunch and dinner £13.95 (two courses) and £18.95. Restaurant main course from £15. House wine £11.95.**
Last orders: **Food: lunch 14.00; dinner 21.30**
Closed: **Saturday lunch, Sunday evening and all day Monday.**
Food: **Modern European.**
Other points: **Smoking area. Children welcome.**
Directions: **Exit 22/M5. Take the Weston Road and turn right at The Fox and Goose. Follow the road to the B3139 and turn left to Wedmore and Cheddar for approximately six miles. (Map 4)**

...for special offers

MEMBER
196
ENTRY

Wells

The Crown at Wells and Anton's Bistrot

Town-centre inn

Market Place, Wells, Somerset BA5 2RP
Telephone: +44(0)1749 673457
stay@crownatwells.co.uk
www.crownatwells.co.uk

'Anton's menu offers modern dishes that don't stint on quality.'

Rooms: 15. Double room from £90, single from £60, family from £110.
Prices: Set lunch from £11.95. House wine £11.50.
Last orders: Bar: afternoon 15.00; evening 23.00. Food: lunch 14.30; dinner 21.30 (Sunday 21.00).
Closed: Never.
Food: Mediterranean.
Real ale: Butcombe Bitter, Oakhill Best Bitter, Smiles Best. One guest beer.
Other points: Smoking area. Children welcome. Dogs welcome overnight. Courtyard. Car park. Wheelchair access to the restaurant/pub.
Directions: Follow signs for hotels and deliveries to take you into the Market Place. The Crown is in the centre of the Market Place, with the car park at the rear of the building. (Map 4)

This historic 15th-century inn is situated in the heart of the city, overlooking the Market Place and in sight of the Gothic cathedral and Bishop's Palace. The Crown retains many of its original features. For a traditional pub atmosphere, head for the Penn Bar, where local Oakhill, Butcombe and Smiles ales and popular bar meals are served, or, for a more contemporary dining experience, head to Anton's, a wine-bar-cum-bistro. The dining is casual and informal, and stripped-pine tables and candles by night set a relaxed scene.

Anton's menu offers modern dishes that don't stint on quality. Start with chicken and wild-mushroom pâté with sweet-onion jam before moving on to roast Brixham monkfish wrapped in bacon with lemon-butter sauce. At lunchtime and early evening Sunday to Thursday, you can choose from a specially compiled Les Routiers menu that includes good-value mains of braised pork sausages in cider, sage and onion gravy, and creamy fish pie. Bedrooms are all en suite and decorated in keeping with the traditional inn. Some of the larger front rooms have four-poster beds.

ENGLISH

Local Spinach CLASS 1

£1.35

/BUNCH

Wells

Fountain Inn and Boxer's Restaurant

Town-centre pub

1 St Thomas Street, Wells,
Somerset BA5 2UU
Telephone: +44(0)1749 672317
eat@fountaininn.co.uk
www.fountaininn.co.uk

'Draws locals and visitors in for foaming pints of Butcombe Bitter and freshly prepared food.'

Prices: **Set lunch £9.75. Restaurant main course from £7.25. Bar main course from £3.50. House wine £9.95.**
Last orders: **Food: lunch 14.00 (Sunday 14.30); dinner 22.00 (Sunday 21.30).**
Closed: **Rarely.**
Food: **Modern British.**
Real ale: **Butcombe Bitter, Courage Best Bitter. One guest beer.**
Other points: **Smoking area. Children welcome. Car park. Wheelchair access.**
Directions: **Exit 22/M5. In the city centre, 50 yards from the cathedral. Follow signs for the Horringtons. (Map 4)**

Built to accommodate the builders working on Wells Cathedral, just 500 yards away, this popular 16th-century pub draws locals and visitors in for foaming pints of Butcombe Bitter and freshly prepared food in Boxer's Restaurant. The bar offers the main focal point on entry, along with a welcoming fire, but what hits you is the unpretentious nature of the place. Dark-wood furniture and a floral carpet happily clashing with the terracotta walls offer a no-nonsense bistro atmosphere within a pub setting.

For Adrian and Sarah Lawrence, who have been at the helm for over 20 years, the pub is all about food, and there's a profusion of chalkboards displaying the daily specials, such as grilled sea bass with cumin-roasted vegetables. The printed menu cranks out a lengthy repertoire of familiar and more contemporary dishes: cod in beer batter, and ham, egg and chips for lunch. Evening dishes take in king prawns pan-fried in garlic, lamb shank with redcurrant-and-rosemary sauce, and warm Bakewell tart with almond custard. Portions are honest and robust, and prices are reasonable.

Wincanton

The Old Inn

Country pub

Holton, Wincanton, Somerset BA9 8AR
Telephone: +44(0)1963 32002

'There's a lovely flower-filled terrace for summer sipping.'

Weary A303 travellers should look out for the Holton exit and head for this 17th-century former coaching inn for rest and refreshment – there's a lovely flower-filled terrace for summer sipping. It enjoys a peaceful village setting in good walking country. It is also popular locally for good straightforward pub food, with produce sourced from local suppliers. The character beamed bar, dominated by a large stone fireplace with log-burning stove, boasts ancient flagstones, upholstered wooden settles, large refectory tables and a clutter of bric-a-brac, including polished copper pots, pewter mugs, and an interesting collection of key rings hanging from the beams by the bar counter.

Sup a pint of local Butcombe Bitter or Otter Ale and tuck into a traditional bar meal, perhaps a ploughman's lunch with farmhouse cheddar cheese from Ditcheat, roast beef and horseradish sandwich, lasagne, or rump steak with all the trimmings. From the separate restaurant menu, perhaps choose lamb cutlets with rosemary, or peppered steak flamed in brandy and cream. A local butcher sources the meats from nearby farms.

Prices: **Main course from £7.25. Bar meal from £6.25. House wine £8.95.**
Last orders: **Bar: afternoon 14.00; evening 22.00. Restaurant: lunch 14.00; dinner 22.00.**
Closed: **Restaurant closed Sunday evening, bar meals available from 19.00.**
Real ale: **Butcombe Bitter, Otter Ale.**
Other points: **Smoking area. Dogs welcome in the bar. Garden. Car park. Wheelchair access to the restaurant/pub.**
Directions: **(Map 4)**

...for the latest news

Lower Langford

The Langford Inn & Restaurant

Langford Road, Lower Langford,
North Somerset BS40 5BL
Telephone: +44(0)1934 863059
langfordinn@aol.com

Country pub

'Austere-looking it may be, but a warm welcome awaits.'

Prices: **Restaurant main course from £6.25.
Bar snacks from £4.25. House wine £10.05.**
Last orders: **Bar: 23.00. Food: 21.00 (Friday
and Saturday 21.30, Sunday 20.00).**
Closed: **Never.**
Food: **Traditional British.**
Real ale: **Butcombe Bitter, Brains Rev James.**
Other points: **Smoking area. Children welcome.
Dogs welcome in the bar. Garden. Car park.
Wheelchair access.**
Directions: **Exit 21/M5. Take the A370 to
Congresbury and turn right at the Ship & Castle
traffic lights. Turn left at the mini roundabout
to Lower Langford. Alternatively the inn is five
miles south of Bristol Airport off the A38.**
(Map 4)

New owner Phillip Howells has big improvement plans for this substantial stone coaching inn, built around 1870 and conveniently located off the A38 five miles south of Bristol Airport. Austere-looking it may be, but a warm welcome awaits visitors beyond the heavy wooden front door that leads to the spacious bar and restaurant areas. Original flagstones, warm-toned carpets, polished wooden furnishings and open log fires lend a traditional air and set the scene for sampling pints of local Butcombe beer and some hearty pub food.

Extensive menus list a wide range of familiar dishes. Bar snacks (served until 6pm) take in hot crusty baguettes, filled jacket potatoes and prawns 'on draught' – by the half-pint or pint. The all-day menu offers fisherman's pie, calves' liver and bacon with mash, lasagne, homemade beef-and-ale pie, beer-battered fish and chips, and steaks with all the trimmings, while daily specials focus on fresh fish and a choice of roasts on Sundays. There is a super secluded courtyard and a beer garden for summer sipping.

Restaurant-with-rooms

'It has plenty more to offer besides smart bedrooms and a fine restaurant.'

64 St Edward Street, Leek,
Staffordshire ST13 5DL
Telephone: +44(0)1538 381900

Tasteful refurbishment has transformed this lovely Grade II-listed Georgian town house, built in 1740 to classic, clean lines, and set right in the centre of Leek. It has plenty more to offer besides smart bedrooms and a fine restaurant, as it has a speciality food shop and patisserie. There's also a coffee lounge, serving an all-day menu, plus a vaulted basement wine bar that's good for a simple snack and a glass of wine, or the pretty restaurant. In the kitchen, they cook with regional ingredients to create modern British dishes.

Lunch includes stroganoff of Aberdeenshire beef and escalope of Cornish cod with a Puy-lentil and bacon ragout. For a truly gastronomic experience, try the evening signature menu of four courses. This starts with tian of hot-roasted West Coast salmon, then moves on to pavé of Devon lamb with a creamed leek, apple and baby-spinach suet pudding. The chocolate delight 64 is just as its name suggests, delightful. The wine list opens with two pages of global house wines; prices, even at the finer end, are reasonable. There are three well-appointed bedrooms.

Rooms: **3. Rooms from £65 per night.**
Prices: **Continental breakfast included in room rate, cooked breakfast £5 supplement. Sunday lunch from £15 (two courses). Main course lunch from £7.95. Main course dinner from £12. House wine £12.**
Last orders: **Food: snacks 17.00; lunch 14.00 (15.00 on Sunday); dinner 21.00 (22.00 on Saturday).**
Closed: **Sunday evening.**
Food: **Modern British.**
Other points: **Smoking area. Garden. Licence for civil weddings.**
Directions: **In the centre of Leek. (Map 9)**

...for recipe ideas

MEMBER
201
ENTRY

William Perry Butchers & Game Dealers,
Eccleshall, 01785 850288

Geoff Holland at the Holly Bush sources all his beef, pork and lamb from this traditional village family butcher in nearby Eccleshall. In operation since 1927, it is one of the few butchers' shops in Staffordshire that has its own abattoir where sheep, pigs and cattle from within a 15-mile radius are slaughtered. Perry's handmade sausages are on the Holly Bush menu.

Fowlers of Earlswood, Earlswood, 01564 702329
A selection of cheeses from Fowlers of Earlswood, the oldest cheese-making family in England, are served at the pub. Founded in Derbyshire before 1840, Fowlers has been using traditional skills to handcraft its award-winning cheeses for 13 generations.

Buttercross Farm Foods,
Market Drayton, 01630 656670, www.buttercross.com
Fresh pork and pork products from free range organic pigs reared at Packington Fields Farm near Lichfield are prepared and packaged at Buttercross Farm Foods. The pigs are reared to the highest of welfare standards to maximise flavour, taste and tenderness.

Jolly Jersey Ice Cream, Admaston, Stafford, 01889 881509
Natural ingredients and full-cream milk from Jersey cows grazed by the shores of Blithfield Reservoir are used to make the superb Jolly Jersey ice creams.

Burslem Oatcakes, Burslem, 01782 819718
Fresh baked, hand-poured oakcakes have been made in the traditional manner on cast iron Baxtons for over 600 years.

Halfpenny Green Vineyard,
Bobbington, 01384 221122, www.halfpenny-green-vineyards.co.uk
Vine grower and wine producer offering guided tours and wine tastings.

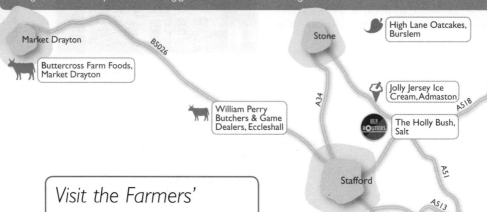

Market Drayton

B5026

Stone

High Lane Oatcakes, Burslem

Buttercross Farm Foods, Market Drayton

A34

Jolly Jersey Ice Cream, Admaston

A518

William Perry Butchers & Game Dealers, Eccleshall

LES ROUTIERS

The Holly Bush, Salt

A51

Stafford

A513

Visit the Farmers' Market

Head for the Market Square in Stafford on the second Saturday of every month between, 9am and 4pm, to sample the atmosphere and produce of Stafford's farmers' market

Halfpenny Green Vineyards, Bobbington

A34

Fowlers of Earlswood

Cannock

Stafford

The Holly Bush

Country pub

'A new wood-fired oven in the garden produces some fantastic pizzas.'

Salt, Stafford, Staffordshire ST18 0BX
Telephone: +44(0)1889 508234
geoff@hollybushinn.co.uk
www.hollybushinn.co.uk

Reputedly Staffordshire's oldest licensed premises, this pretty thatched 14th-century pub – parts of which are thought to reach back to 1190 – maintains its historic charm. The cosy interior, with carved heavy beams, a planked ceiling, exposed brick walls, old oak furnishings, open fires and intimate alcoves characterises the main bar. Landlord Geoff Holland is passionate about using fresh local produce, and sources meat from W M Perry, an Eccleshall butcher with his own abattoir, and game from local shoots.

The recent addition of a commercial smoking oven allows him to smoke his own meat and fish, and a new wood-fired oven in the garden produces some fantastic pizzas. Among the good-value dishes on offer, you will find green-shelled mussels or warm bacon, potato-and-watercress salad for starters, followed by fillet of beef Wellington or marinated Milwich lamb with onion purée for mains. Alternatives include fresh fish from Torbay and prime steaks. Expect good lunchtime sandwiches and daily seafood specials. Round off with a traditional pudding or a selection of Staffordshire cheeses.

Prices: **Main course from £7.25. House wine £8.25.**
Last orders: **Bar: 23.00 (Sunday 22.30). Food: all day until 21.30.**
Closed: **Rarely.**
Food: Traditional/modern British.
Real ale: Adnams, Marston's Pedigree. One guest beer.
Other points: **No smoking. Children welcome. Garden. Car park. Wheelchair access.**
Directions: **Exit 14/M6. Four miles along the A51 Stone to Lichfield road, or half a mile from the A518 Stafford to Uttoxeter road. (Map 9)**

202
MEMBER ENTRY

Barnby

The Swan Inn

Swan Lane, Barnby, Beccles,
Suffolk NR34 7QF
Telephone: +44(0)1502 476646

Country inn

'Up to 80 different fish dishes are on the menu.'

Rooms: 3. Rooms from £40 per person.
Prices: **Set lunch £13 and dinner £18. Restaurant main course from £7.95. Bar main course from £3.95.**
Last orders: **Bar: afternoon 15.30; evening 23.30.**
Food: **lunch 14.00; dinner 21.30.**
Closed: **Rarely.**
Food: **Seafood.**
Real ale: **Adnams, Greene King Abbot Ale, Greene King IPA. One guest beer.**
Other points: **Smoking area. Children welcome. Garden. Car park.**
Directions: **From the A146, turn into Barnby (left from the west) and follow signs to the inn. (Map 10)**

Up to 80 different fish dishes are listed on the printed menu and ever-changing chalkboards at this flower-adorned, pink-washed village local. It must be the most extensive menu of fish and seafood to be found in a Suffolk pub. More importantly, though, the quality and freshness here is first class, thanks to pub owner and Lowestoft fish wholesaler, Don Cole, who supplies the pub with the best of the day's catch landed at Lowestoft dock five miles away.

The choice is mind-boggling, from local sprats traditionally smoked in Don's smokehouse, and smoked-haddock soup, the menu extends to lemon sole in crisp batter, and turbot fillet in prawn-and-brandy sauce. The house speciality, however, is an 18oz Dover sole, simply grilled to preserve flavours and freshness. In addition, expect to find oysters, Cromer crabs, locally caught lobster, deep-fried fresh scampi and monkfish tails in hot garlic butter. All are accompanied with salad, new potatoes or chips and peas, and served throughout the traditional bar and restaurant. Booking is advisable. A self-contained flat is available on a nightly basis.

www.routiers.co.uk

Bury St Edmunds

Wines Bar & Kitchen at the Six Bells

Country pub

'This is hearty food cooked with panache and flair.'

Church Road, Felsham, Bury St Edmunds,
Suffolk IP30 OPJ
Telephone: +44(0)1449 736268

Dating back to the 15th century, this well-preserved pub sits directly opposite the church in the attractive and peaceful village of Felsham. Off the beaten track, but not far from Bury St Edmunds, it is surrounded by beautiful countryside, and is a popular pit-stop for walkers. Husband-and-wife team Julie and David Wine run the lovely pub and restaurant with terrific natural hospitality: David runs the kitchen and Julie takes care of the front of house. It's a formidable team.

Just about everything on the menu is produced on the premises, from the breads and jams to the curry pastes and pesto. David sources quality local ingredients for the dishes on his wide-ranging, internationally influenced menus. Food in the bar may include cottage pie or a turkey-and-aubergine tagine with couscous, with the à la carte selection featuring Thai fishcakes, followed by Normandy chicken, fish pie, beef fillet with pepper sauce, or lobster thermidor. This is hearty food cooked with panache and flair using local butcher meats, seasonal game from Rougham Estate, and vegetables and cheeses sourced from local markets.

Prices: Restaurant main course from £5.95. Bar main course from £5.95. House wine £11.95.
Last orders: Bar: afternoon 15.00 (open all day Saturday and Sunday); evening 23.00. Food: lunch 15.00 (Sunday 15.30); dinner 21.30.
Closed: Monday lunch except bank holidays.
Food: Modern global.
Real ale: Greene King IPA, Greene King Abbot Ale.
Other points: Smoking area. Garden. Children over one welcome. Dogs welcome. Car park.
Directions: A14. Take the A134 for Bradfield St George. At the junction with the green, turn left at the pub on the corner opposite the church. (Map 6)

...for events

Southwold

The Crown

Hotel

High Street, Southwold, Suffolk IP18 6DP
Telephone: +44(0)1502 722275
crown.hotel@adnams.co.uk

'Beautifully refurbished and maintained bedrooms simply underline the thread of quality that runs throughout.'

Rooms: 14, 1 with private bathroom. Double/ twin room from £120.
Prices: Set dinner £29 and £24 (two courses). House wine £13.75.
Last orders: Bar: 23.00. Bar food: lunch 14.00; dinner 21.30. Restaurant food: lunch 14.00; dinner 21.00.
Closed: **Never.**
Food: **Modern British.**
Real ale: **Adnams.**
Other points: **No smoking. Children welcome. Car park. Wheelchair access to the restaurant/pub.**
Directions: Take the A1095 off the A12, 14 miles south of Lowestoft, for Southwold. (Map 10)

From the outside, Adnams flagship inn looks stately, all white paintwork, with a flag flying and a wrought-iron sign hanging over the pavement. Inside, the town's maritime past is echoed in a magnificent ship's binnacle, marine paintings and glazed screen in the Back Bar while, at the front, the Parlour is a buzzing mix of contemporary wine bar, brasserie and English village pub, and the centre of local life.

With Adnams brewery and wine store next door, you'll find prime-condition beers and excellent wines (20 by the glass), plus modern British menus offering, perhaps, crab spring roll with Mersea oyster and seared scallop, as a precursor to crisp bass with pickled cucumber and sauce vierge. The restaurant menu, offering two or three courses, adds a further dimension, perhaps offering pot-roast Dingley Dell pork belly, black-pudding mash and apple compote, venison with garlic, and white-chocolate fondant with confit oranges. Imaginatively selected wines and beautifully refurbished and maintained en-suite bedrooms simply underline the thread of quality that runs throughout.

205

www.routiers.co.uk

Stradbroke

The Ivy House

Village pub

'The Ivy House is picture-postcard pretty.'

Wilby Road, Stradbroke, Suffolk IP21 5JN
Telephone: +44(0)1379 384634
stensethhome@aol.com
www.ivyhousestradbroke.co.uk

Having made a huge success of The Queens Head in Brandeston, an Adnams tenancy, Suzanne and Egil Stenseth decided to buy their own, and headed north a few miles to Stradbroke and this 16th-century thatched pub. Pink-washed and flower-adorned in summer, the Ivy House is picture-postcard pretty. The Stenseths' plan to gently refurbish the traditionally furnished and unpretentious bar and dining room. Beams abound and log fires blaze in winter.

Suzanne has a good local reputation for offering honest, freshly cooked pub food on weekly-changing menus. She sources local seasonal produce and cooks an eclectic range of dishes that draw inspiration from around the globe. Typically, you'll find classic dishes such as steak-and-kidney pudding and oxtail braised in ale, alongside roast cod with tagliatelle, gremolata and vine tomatoes, or roast belly pork with Spanish chorizo sauce. Puddings take in dark chocolate and orange marmalade tart, and apple-and-plum crumble. Wines are supplied by Adnams and offer good value, while tip-top beers come from Woodforde's, Buffy's and Adnams.

Prices: Restaurant main course from £9.95. Bar main course from £9.95. House wine £9.95.
Last orders: Bar: afternoon 14.30; evening 23.00. Food: lunch 14.00; dinner 20.45.
Closed: Rarely.
Food: Modern British and Asian.
Real ale: Adnams, Buffy's Ales, Fuller's London Pride.
Other points: No smoking. Garden. Children over 10 welcome.
Directions: A140. Follow the signposts to Stradbroke. (Map 10)

...for competitions

Chiddingfold

The Swan Inn

Village inn

Petworth Road, Chiddingfold,
Guildford, Surrey GU8 4TY
Telephone: +44(0)1428 682073
the-swan-inn@btconnect.com
www.theswaninn.biz

'Modern, chic, Manhattan-style rooms with plasma screens and trendy tiled bathrooms.'

Rooms: 11. Rooms from £65, family room from £120.
Prices: Restaurant main course from £12.95. Bar main course from £8.50. House wine £9.95.
Last orders: Bar: 23.00. Food: lunch 14.30; dinner 22.00.
Closed: Never.
Food: Traditional/modern British.
Other points: Smoking area. Children welcome. Dogs welcome in the bar. Garden. Car park. Wheelchair access to the restaurant/pub.
Directions: A3. From the south, take the Elstead, Milford and Petworth exit and from London take the Guildford exit for Milford and Petworth. (Map 6)

A hip hotel-meets-gastropub concept has breathed new life into this expertly reincarnated 14th-century inn, following a serious fire in 2004. It provides all the charm of the country with modern, chic, Manhattan-style rooms and suites, all of which are superbly appointed with plasma screens, and trendy tiled bathrooms with power showers and posh toiletries. A drink in the welcoming bar is a pleasant precursor to a meal in the rustic-meets-contemporary open-plan bar area or the more formal restaurant.

Chef Darren Tidd, formerly of Cliveden Hotel, offers classic European dishes in the bar – calves' liver and bacon, moules, fishcakes, fresh sardines or a delectable duck confit. The carte may list seared-scallop and asparagus salad with chilli-oil dressing, beef fillet with pepper sauce, and pork medallions with blackberry sauce. Desserts include homemade ice creams as well as lemon-and-lime tart with mixed berries. The comprehensive wine list includes 10 choices by the glass. There is a lovely terraced area with plants in tubs, heaters and upmarket benches, and brollies for summer alfresco dining.

Chilworth

The Percy Arms

Country pub

'The attraction is the unique 'butcher's counter' where you can choose your own steak.'

75 Dorking Road, Chilworth,
Guildford, Surrey GU4 8NP
Telephone: +44(0)1483 561765
info.percy@tmp.uk.com
www.tailormadepub.co.uk

Set back from the road in upmarket Chilworth, with scenic views over rolling Surrey countryside from its huge rear garden, this 18th-century, tile-hung building operates as a smart pub-restaurant. Owned by Tailor Made Pubs, who also manage The Sun Inn at Rake and The Inn on the Hill in Haslemere (see entries), it has been revamped in contemporary style, with stripped wooden floors, leather chairs and open fires throughout the spacious bar and dining areas. The latter leads out on to a decked terrace kitted out with heaters and smart teak tables and chairs.

The attraction, other than Greene King ales, a choice of wines by the glass, and a family-friendly atmosphere, is the 'butcher's counter' from where you can choose your own cut and size of steak, which is then cooked how you want it. You can order burgers in the same way. Menus are extensive, ranging from salads, barbecue dishes and Sunday carvery lunches to a list of main courses that include lamb shank roasted with rosemary and red wine, and chef's sausage of the week, served with mash and gravy.

Prices: Restaurant main course from £9.95. Bar main course from £9.95. House wine £9.95.
Last orders: Bar: 23.00. Food: lunch 15.00; dinner 22.00 (Sunday 21.00).
Closed: Rarely.
Food: Modern British.
Real ale: Greene King IPA, Greene King Abbot Ale, Black Country Fireside.
Other points: Smoking area outside. Children welcome. Garden. Car park. Wheelchair access.
Directions: A3. Take the Guildford exit, follow the A281 out of Guildford, then follow signs for Chilworth. (Map 6)

...for special offers

MEMBER ENTRY

Cobham

La Capanna

48 High Street, Cobham,
Surrey KT11 3EF
Telephone: +44(0)1932 862121
reservations@lacapanna.co.uk
www.lacapanna.co.uk

Italian restaurant

'Take time out to enjoy an aperitif in the comfortable bar while you choose from the menu.'

Prices: **Restaurant main course from £9.
Set Sunday lunch £22.95. House wine £14.**
Last orders: **Food: lunch 14.30; dinner: 23.00.**
Closed: **27-28 December and 1 January.**
Food: **Italian.**
Other points: **Smoking area. Children welcome.
Dogs welcome in the bar. Garden. Car park.
Wheelchair access (not WC).**
Directions: **Exit the M25 on to the A3 towards
London. Leave the A3 at the next exit and
follow the signs to Cobham. Take the A245 to
the far side of Cobham. (Map 6)**

This traditional Italian restaurant is set in an unusual building: behind its 17th-century cottage façade is a rebuilt 16th-century farmhouse. Take time out to enjoy an aperitif in the comfortable bar while you choose from the menu, before dining in the main restaurant with its abundance of beams and brickwork. In summer, you can dine in the bright and airy conservatory, which leads through to the Italian patio garden, overlooking the River Mole.

La Capanna's new menu offers an excellent choice of dishes, with house specialities, including an antipasto selection, and more individual choices such as spaghetti with mussels, clams, chilli and garlic; roast organic salmon with scallops, roast fennel and tarragon sauce; and aged Irish beef fillet with calvo Nero and mushroom sauce, as well as a range of pasta dishes. The carte lists more traditional dishes, perhaps Parma ham, mango and melon, and calves' liver with fresh sage. Italian puddings are chosen from the trolley. La Capanna looks to its homeland for top wines and offers the best of Tuscany, Umbria, Veneto and Piedmont.

www.routiers.co.uk

The Pride of the Valley Hotel

Inn and restaurant

'It's worth seeking out for its lovely country garden.'

Jumps Road, Churt, Farnham,
Surrey GU10 2LE
Telephone: +44(0)1428 605799
reservations@prideofthevalleyhotel.com
www.prideofthevalleyhotel.com

Charming, traditional and dating back to 1868, this grand-looking inn can be found tucked away down winding country lanes deep in rolling Surrey countryside. It's worth seeking out for its lovely country garden, the cosy and relaxing interior, and the good choice of food offered in both the bar and bistro. Bedrooms are spacious yet comfortable, and decorated with different themes, from Moroccan to Far Eastern, with smart en-suite facilities.

The dining options are also extensive, with a wide choice of dishes, from fish pie, beef in Guinness, local game, and sirloin steak with all the trimmings to bar snacks such as cottage pie, filled baguettes, ploughman's lunches and daily specials. You can eat in the bar, where comfy sofas, scrubbed pine tables and real fires create a warm, friendly ambience, or in the baronial-style, oak-panelled restaurant. There are also stunning walks from the inn – an excellent prelude to a delicious Sunday lunch and a pint of local Hog's Back ale. The pub was frequented by former prime minister David Lloyd George, and there's an interesting sculpture park opposite.

Rooms: 15. Double/twin room from £125, single from £75. Family room from £100.
Prices: Restaurant main course from £12. Bar main course from £3. House wine £12.95.
Last orders: Bar: 23.00. Food: lunch 14.15 (Saturday 14.30, Sunday 15.00); dinner 21.15 (Friday and Saturday 21.30, Sunday 21.00). Bar food until 22.00.
Closed: **Never.**
Food: Traditional British.
Real ale: Hog's Back TEA.
Other points: Smoking area. Children welcome. Garden. Wheelchair access to the pub.
Directions: Exit 4/M3. Four miles from Farnham and two miles from the A3 Hindhead exit. (Map 5)

Gatwick

Latchetts Cottage

Bed and breakfast

Norwood Hill, near Horley,
Surrey RH6 OET
Telephone: +44(0)1293 862831
davidjlees@tiscali.co.uk
www.latchettscottage.co.uk

'Early arrivals taking tea in the cottage-style garden will find it hard to believe that Gatwick is a short drive away.'

Rooms: **3, not en-suite. Double/twin room from £50, single from £30.**
Closed: **Never.**
Other points: **No smoking. Garden. Children over five welcome. Car park. Credit cards not accepted.**
Directions: **Exit 9/M23. Take the A23 for Redhill, then the A217 to Reigate. After the Tesco roundabout, turn right at the second roundabout, then fork left to Norwood Hill. After 1 1/4 miles, turn left into Collendean Lane and at the crossroads by the Fox pub, go straight over. Latchetts is 200 yards along on the left. (Map 6)**

Set in a rural hamlet, with serene country views extending to the North Downs, David Lees's spotlessly maintained farmhouse offers a peaceful night's stopover for guests jetting in and out of nearby Gatwick Airport. David can provide holiday parking (£20 a week) and free courtesy transport to the airport after 7.30am. Early arrivals taking tea in the cottage-style garden will find it hard to believe that Gatwick is a short drive away down country lanes.

Formerly two early 19th-century farmworker's cottages, sympathetically extended by David in recent years, the accommodation comprises three small, yet comfortable rooms, each kitted out in old pine and enjoying garden and country views. Facilities include TVs, beverage trays, hairdryers and bathrobes; rooms share a bathroom and a separate shower room with WC. Guests are welcome to use the lounge, and a hearty breakfast is served in the dining room, with most items sourced locally, including fresh fruits and honey. The local pub for evening meals is just a short stroll along the lane.

Town-centre inn

Haslemere
The Inn on the Hill

SURREY

Lower Street, Haslemere,
Surrey GU27 2PD
Telephone: +44(0)1428 642006
info.hill@tmp.uk.com
www.tailormadepub.co.uk

'The garden is ideal for a family picnic – hampers and blankets are available at the bar.'

Money has been lavished by Tailor Made Pubs on this imposing Victorian building opposite Haslemere's railway station. Expect a chic, contemporary, open-plan interior, with a soothing cream-and-red decor, slate or stripped wood floors, deep leather sofas and easy chairs in a relaxing chill out area, and chunky oak furnishings. The cool, elegant feel extends upstairs to the eight refurbished bedrooms, each equipped with darkwood furniture, flat-screen televisions, broadband access, and smart en-suite bathrooms.

The style of food revolves around the company's popular 'butcher's counter' approach, whereby diners can select choice cuts of steak or freshly made burgers prior to cooking. We sampled a beautifully cooked rib-eye steak, served with rocket and red onion. Menus offer a huge range of dishes, from pastrami-and-mustard sandwiches and salad Niçoise to chicken supreme and grilled salmon. To the rear there's a decked terrace and a two-tiered garden, which is ideal for a family picnic – hampers and blankets are available at the bar. It's also worth noting that the pub opens at 7am for breakfast.

Rooms: 8. Double/twin room from £80, single from £75.
Prices: Restaurant main course from £9.95. House wine £11.95.
Last orders: Bar: 23.00. Food: 22.00 (Sunday 21.00).
Closed: Rarely.
Food: Modern British.
Real ale: Greene King IPA, Greene King Abbot Ale.
Other points: Smoking area. Children welcome. Garden. Wheelchair access to the restaurant/pub.
Directions: A3. Opposite Haslemere train station. (Map 5)

212

...for recipe ideas

Thames Ditton

The Crown

Town-centre pub

Summer Road, Thames Ditton,
Surrey KT7 OQQ
Telephone: +44(0)208 398 2376

'An impressive choice of wines and a modern menu that trawls the globe for inspiration.'

Prices: **Set lunch £15.95. Set dinner £21.95. Restaurant main course from £10. Bar main course from £7. House wine £12.50.**
Last orders: **Lunch 14.45 (Saturday and Sunday 15.30); dinner 21.30 (Saturday and Sunday 22.00). No food Sunday evening.**
Closed: **Rarely.**
Food: **Modern global.**
Real ale: **Timothy Taylor Best Bitter, St Peter's Best.**
Other points: **No-smoking area. Dogs welcome in the bar. Garden. Children welcome. Car park.**
Directions: **Exit 10/M25. Take the A3 towards London, exit on to the A244 towards Esher and follow signs to Hampton Court. Turn right at the last turning before Hampton Bridge.**
(Map 6)

The Crown may not have the sought-after Thameside setting enjoyed by some of its neighbouring pubs, but this fine brick-and-timber building is worth seeking out for its relaxing atmosphere and its short, imaginative menu. Refurbished three years ago and self-styled as a bar and restaurant, the pub draws an appreciative crowd for pints of Timothy Taylor Landlord, an impressive choice of wines (16 by the glass), and a modern menu that trawls the globe for inspiration.

Nibble on flatbread and dips, share a platter of antipasti at the bar, or look to the daily menu for something more substantial and adventurous. Tuck into starters of griddled squid with risotto Nero or Wensleydale cheese, bacon and potato soup, followed by whole roast chicken with lentils, olives and caramelised onion jus, or Malaysian fish balls and tiger prawns with coconut broth and noodles. The décor is stylish gastropub, with sofas fronting a log fire, magazines to peruse in the bar and a dining area decked out with rustic wooden furnishings.

www.routiers.co.uk

Deli and restaurant

Coriander Restaurant & Deli

4/5 Hove Manor Parade, Hove Street,
Hove, East Sussex BN3 2DF
Telephone: +44(0)1273 730850
coriander.brighton@hotmail.co.uk
www.corianderbrighton.com

'A bustling deli by day and popular restaurant by night.'

EAST SUSSEX

An impressive 90 per cent of the dishes at this neighbourhood gem are organic. A bustling deli by day and popular restaurant by night, Coriander enables foodies to do a one-stop shop, as the well-stocked deli sells vegetables, groceries, and spices ground to order, as well as all the classic French and Italian offerings. At lunchtime, enjoy a plate of charcuterie and, in the evening, treat your taste buds to a quite different carte experience in the restaurant next door.

Prices: **Set lunch £15.20 and dinner £25.30. Restaurant main course from £12.20. House wine £13.25.**
Last orders: **Food: lunch 16.00; dinner 20.30.**
Closed: **Sunday and Monday evening.**
Food: **North African with Latin influences.**
Real ale: **St Peter's Best.**
Other points: **No smoking. Children welcome. Wheelchair access.**
Directions: **In the centre of Hove, on Hove Street (A2023). (Map 6)**

An eclectic menu has been created by chef-patrons South African David Smale and his half-German, half-Russian wife, Katrin, for their modern restaurant with a bohemian air. North African and Latin influences make for interesting combinations. Start with fish cakes with crab-and-prawn relish. Mains take in grilled portobello mushroom, aubergine and scamorza, and Welsh lamb with wild-garlic mashed potatoes. Puddings such as saffron-and-rosewater crème brulée, and Baileys and banoffi croissant pudding hold their own for originality. The extensive wine list is mainly organic, and there's a fun range of beers.

...for events

Lewes

The Rainbow Inn

Country pub

Resting Oak Hill, Cooksbridge, Lewes,
East Sussex BN8 4SS
Telephone: +44(0)1273 400334

'The warmly decorated dining areas sport an eclectic mix of furnishings and a relaxed atmosphere.'

Prices: **Set lunch £10.95 (two courses).
Restaurant main course from £8.95. Bar main
course from £3.95. House wine £13.20.**
Last orders: **Bar: afternoon 15.00; evening 23.00.
Food: lunch 14.30; dinner 22.00.**
Closed: **Rarely.**
Food: **Traditional English/modern European.**
Real ale: **Harvey's.**
Other points: **Smoking area. Children welcome.
Dogs welcome in the bar. Garden. Car park.
Private dining. Barbecue area. Wheelchair
access.**
Directions: **M23/A23/A27. Take the exit for
Eastbourne and Lewes. Situated on the A275
between Lewes and Haywards Heath on the
edge of Cooksbridge village at the Barcombe
fork. (Map 6)**

Occupying an attractive corner site on the A275 just north of Lewes, this brick-and-flint, 17th-century pub makes a great summer dining venue. Choose between the rustic benches on the flower-filled front patio and the sun-trap enclosed rear terrace, replete with smart benches and brollies, barbecue and distant South Downs views. Inside, beyond the small rustic bar, where you'll find a cracking pint of local Harvey's ale, the warmly decorated dining areas sport an eclectic mix of furnishings and a relaxed atmosphere.

Fresh local produce is sourced for modern, daily-changing menus and chalkboard specials, the latter listing fresh Newhaven fish, lamb from local farms and game in season. The printed menu may offer prawn-and-chicken ravioli with crispy leeks and saffron cream, followed by roast cod with a parmesan crust and chervil-butter sauce, and rhubarb crème brûlée. The short, carefully selected global list of wines complements the menu. The two upstairs private dining rooms ooze charm and character and are perfect for intimate dinner parties. A good pit-stop en route to Plumpton Races.

Rye

Jeake's House Hotel

Bed and breakfast

'The breakfasts are legendary and can be enjoyed by non-residents.'

Mermaid Street, Rye,
East Sussex TN31 7ET
Telephone: +44(0)1797 222828
stay@jeakeshouse.com
www.jeakeshouse.com

Built by merchant Samuel Jeake as a storehouse, 17th-century Jeake's House is, like the medieval cobbled street on which it stands, steeped in history. Owner Jenny Hadfield has decorated each room individually using fresh flowers and deft personal touches to create an opulent feel that mixes bold floral prints and striking colours with beams, standing timbers and many period pieces. An open fire (as well as Jenny's two cats) may greet you, as you come down to breakfast in the galleried hall.

The breakfasts are legendary and can be enjoyed by non-residents. Tuck into award-winning sausages, natural oak-smoked kippers and haddock from Rye Harbour, devilled kidneys, scrambled free-range egg with smoked salmon, and bread and croissants from the local baker. An honesty bar operates in the library. Bedrooms are splendid, with brass or mahogany beds or four-posters, drapes, cushions and sparkling bathrooms. If you really want to spoil yourself, stay in the Aiken Suite. The private car park is a real boon, as parking in Rye can be difficult.

Rooms: 11. Double room from £44 per person.
Prices: Full breakfast menu £9.50 (charge for non-residents). House wine from the bar £12.
Closed: Rarely.
Other points: Smoking area. Children over 8 welcome. Dogs welcome. Car park.
Directions: Exit 10/M20 and follow signs for Brenzett, then directions for Hastings and Rye. Parking in Rye is restricted, but Jeake's House has its own private car park. (Map 6)

...for competitions

Rye

Oaklands

Bed and breakfast

Udimore Road, Rye,
East Sussex TN31 6AB
Telephone: +44(0)1797 229734
info@oaklands-rye.co.uk
www.oaklands-rye.co.uk

'Unwind in the grounds, join in a game of croquet or have your own barbecue.'

Rooms: 3. Double/twin room from £70. Single supplement from £12.
Closed: Rarely.
Food: Homemade afternoon teas.
Other points: No smoking. Garden. Children welcome. Car park. Croquet.
Directions: Exit 10/M20. Follow the signs for Brenzett, then Hastings and Rye. From Rye, take the B2089 to Broad Oak and Battle. Oaklands is on the right, just past the fire beacon, approximately one mile from Rye, after the Parish of Udimore sign. (Map 6)

In an elevated position within an 'Area of Outstanding Beauty', this imposing Edwardian house offers the best of both worlds. As well as being an ideal retreat for those who want to get away from it all, this tranquil place, which is set in extensive and secluded grounds, is also close enough for sampling the historic towns of Rye and Battle. Use the house as a base for exploring the area all year round, or, in summer, simply unwind in the grounds, join in a game of croquet or even have your own barbecue.

All three of the comfortably furnished bedrooms make the most of the all-round views. They have a shower, TV, small fridge, hospitality tray and hairdryer, and reception is happy to provide emergency supplies of toiletries. After a hearty traditional or continental breakfast in the elegant dining room or on the terrace, head to the medieval, Tudor and Georgian buildings of Rye, or Rye Harbour Nature Reserve, which are just over a mile away. While dinner is not served at Oaklands, they do prepare packed lunches and picnics on request.

www.routiers.co.uk

The Anglesey Arms at Halnaker

Country pub

'Come for mouth-watering Sunday roasts, lunchtime pub classics or renowned 21-day hung steaks.'

Stane Street, Halnaker, Chichester,
West Sussex PO18 ONQ
Telephone: +44(0)1243 773474
angleseyarms@aol.com
www.angleseyarms.co.uk

Part of the Goodwood Estate, famous for its horse racing, Roger and Jools Jackson's welcoming country pub has built up a formidable reputation for its quality food. An unpretentious Georgian brick-built pub with stripped pine, flagstones, beams and panelling, and crackling log fires, The Anglesey Arms draws race-goers, walkers from the South Downs and locals for well-kept pints of Adnams bitter and interesting menus that utilise top-notch local and organic produce.

Come for mouth-watering Sunday roasts or lunchtime pub classics, or book an evening table and tuck into one of their renowned 21-day hung steaks. Local fishermen supply rope-grown mussels, crab, lobster and fish listed on the daily-changing chalkboard. Game comes from the Goodwood Estate and vegetables from the Organic Farm Shop in Chichester. The arrival of head chef Steve Taylor has raised the standard further. A starter of pan-seared scallops with organic cauliflower purée could be followed by noisettes of organic lamb. The garden, with petanque pitch, is the setting for the popular 'Moules and Boules' evenings in summer.

Prices: Restaurant main course from £9.95. Bar main from £4.95. House wine £12.
Last orders: Bar: afternoon 15.00 (Saturday and Sunday 17.00); evening 23.00. Food: lunch 14.30; dinner 21.30.
Closed: Rarely.
Food: Traditional British/modern European.
Real ale: Caledonian Deuchar's IPA, Youngs Bitter, Adnams Best, Hop Back Summer Lightning.
Other points: Smoking area. Children welcome. Dogs welcome in the bar. Garden. Car park. Wheelchair access.
Directions: On the A285 Chichester to Petworth road. From the A27, take the Boxgrove exit at Tangmere and turn right at the A285. (Map 5)

...for special offers

MEMBER
218
ENTRY

Country inn

'Classy modern British food draws the discerning.'

Pook Lane, East Lavant, Chichester,
West Sussex PO18 0AX
Telephone: +44(0)1243 527434
nickroyaloak@aol.com
www.thesussexpub.co.uk

Set in beautiful Goodwood country, just two miles from the cathedral city of Chichester, this 200-year-old, flint-built gastropub-with-rooms comprises an open-plan bar and dining area with log fires, leather sofas, church candles on scrubbed tables, and Sussex ales straight from the cask. Classy modern British food draws the discerning, the main menu and daily chalkboard additions featuring quality fish and meats from London markets.

Typically, begin with fresh lobster and tiger-prawn cocktail or chargrilled calves' liver with warm potato, pancetta and apple salad, followed by duo of monkfish and king scallops with jasmine rice, or lamb cutlets and sautéed kidneys. Lunchtime brings sandwiches, home-cooked ham, eggs and bubble-and-squeak, and there are good homemade puddings, such as apple tarte Tatin with pistachio clotted cream. Decent wines include some interesting French classics. Six stylish bedrooms feature pastel décor, smart, contemporary furnishings, high-spec CD players, plasma-screen TVs with Sky, quality tiled bathrooms that boast power showers and newly installed free wireless broadband facilities in every room.

Rooms: **6. Double/twin room from £70.**
Prices: **Restaurant main course from £11. House wine £11.50.**
Last orders: **Bar: 23.00. Food: lunch 14.30; dinner 21.30.**
Closed: **Rarely.**
Food: **Traditional English/Mediterranean.**
Real ale: **Badger Best, Badger Sussex Bitter, Ballards.**
Other points: **Smoking area. Garden and terrace. Car park. Wheelchair access to the restaurant/pub (not WC).**
Directions: **The village is signposted off the A286 Midhurst road, one mile north of Chichester. (Map 5)**

Chichester

The Ship Inn

Country inn

The Street, Itchenor, Chichester,
West Sussex PO20 7AH
Telephone: +44(0)1243 512284
www.theshipinn.biz

'Nicely nautical interiors and excellent seafood to boot.'

Rooms: **1 family apartment (double room, twin room, lounge with sofa bed) from £40 per person per night.**
Prices: **Restaurant main course from £6.95. Bar snacks from £4.50. House wine £12.**
Last orders: **Bar: 23.00. Food: lunch 14.30; dinner 21.15 (Sunday 21.00).**
Closed: **Afternoons of 25-26 December and 1 January.**
Food: **Traditional British/French.**
Real ale: **King Horsham Best Bitter, Itchen Valley Godfathers, Ballards Best.**
Other points: **Smoking area. Dogs welcome. Patio. Car park. Wheelchair access to the restaurant/pub. Function room.**
Directions: **Six miles south of Chichester on the A286 towards West Wittering. Turn right at the sign for Itchenor and the Ship is 1 1/2 miles along on the left. (Map 5)**
See pub walk on page 492

Built on the site of the original 18th-century inn, the exterior of this 1930s reincarnation belies its nicely nautical interiors, and the excellent seafood, to boot. Just 150 yards away from Chichester Harbour, it's decked out in ship décor; with old wood panelling and portholes, wonderfully scrubbed tables and a weather station. Apart from the appealing atmosphere – cosy fires in winter and a relaxed buzz in summer – the good local fish is the big draw.

At lunch, you can simply have a roast ham and tomato baguette or fish soup to start, with mains of beer-battered cod or steak-and-ale pie. At dinner, dishes step up a gear to include pan-fried scallops wrapped in pancetta with coral sauce, followed by lamb shank with red-wine and rosemary gravy, or one of the daily fish specials, perhaps local plaice with prawn, mushroom and lemon butter, or whole sea bass with lime, ginger, chilli and soy sauce. Add in four locally brewed ales, notably Ballards Best, decent wines, plus excellent walks and boat trips nearby, and this becomes a day-trip destination in itself.

www.routiers.co.uk

Fontwell

Denmans Garden

Café

'A lovely place to enjoy morning teas and lunches.'

Denmans Lane, Fontwell,
West Sussex BN18 0SU
Telephone: +44(0)1243 542808
denmans@denmans-garden.co.uk
www.denmans-garden.co.uk

The Garden Café is a lovely place to enjoy morning teas and lunches after exploring the inspiring four-acre gardens that surround it. Owned and designed by respected writer and landscape designer John Brookes, the relaxing room is tastefully decked out with garden-style furniture covered with check tablecloths, and lush potted palms add a distinctly Mediterranean feel. An all-weather cover to the original terrace – with tables and umbrellas for alfresco dining in summer – enables the fully licensed café to open all year round.

The menu takes in morning coffee, lunches and cream teas. Choices range from homemade quiches, paninis and sandwiches to salmon-and-dill lasagne, steak-and-kidney pudding and the popular higgidy pie, which comes with a choice of fillings. There is an admission charge to see the gardens, but you can head straight to the café for which there is no admission charge. Within the café is a charming gift shop selling an array of souvenirs, chutneys and jams, while in the plant-sales area, there are more than 1,500 varieties of perennials, shrubs and herbs.

Prices: Main course from £4.50. House wine £8.99.
Last orders: Food: Lunch 16.45.
Closed: Rarely.
Food: Modern British.
Other points: No smoking. Children welcome. Garden. Car park. Wheelchair access.
Directions: A27. Five miles from both Chichester and Arundel. (Map 6)

...for the latest news

221
MEMBER ENTRY

Henfield

The Gallops Restaurant

Restaurant

Wheatsheaf Road, Woodmancote,
near Henfield, West Sussex BN5 9BD
Telephone: +44(0)1273 492077
info@the-gallops.co.uk
www.the-gallops.co.uk

'The menu is a tantalising parade of dishes made using well-sourced ingredients.'

Prices: **Restaurant main course from £12.95.
House wine £11.95.**
Last orders: Bar: afternoon 14.30; evening 21.30.
Closed: All day Monday and Sunday evenings.
Food: Modern European.
Other points: Smoking area. Garden. Car park.
Wheelchair access (not WC).
Directions: Situated on the B2116 between
Henfield and Albourne. The Gallops is close to
the A23 at Hickstead. (Map 6)

Once renowned as one of the first purveyors of chicken in the basket, The Wheatsheaf pub has been transformed into a sophisticated and modern restaurant under the stewardship of Richard Holmes and Cara Bexton. Before you enter the elegant restaurant with its tables set with crisp tablecloths and sparkling glasses, there's a seating area furnished with comfortable sofas, which is the perfect place for an aperitif. As well as a range of lighter lunch options, such as smoked-haddock and chive fishcakes or salad Niçoise, the main menu is a tantalising parade of dishes made using well-sourced ingredients.

Start with devilled kidneys cooked in brandy, shallots and cream or marinated seafood cocktail, then choose from the mains, which take in confit duck leg, braised belly pork with celeriac purée, black pudding and caramelised apple, or maybe a seared fillet of brill. The dessert menu is the sort that's hard to resist and tempts with light rhubarb mousse or a warm pear-and-almond Bakewell tart. A broad range of sensibly priced wines from around the world offers many by the glass and half bottle.

www.routiers.co.uk

Country pub

'Wine drinkers have a mind-boggling choice of 35 wines by the glass.'

London Road, Rake,
West Sussex GU33 7PQ
Telephone: +44(0)1730 892115
info.sun@tmp.uk.com
www.tailormadepub.co.uk

Tailor Made Pubs, a select pub group that owns The Percy Arms near Guildford and The Inn on the Hill at Haslemere (see entries), have injected a new lease of life into this attractive country pub, which dates from the 1700s. The traditional interior has been spruced up and, from the conservatory-style dining area, you can access a raised and heated decked terrace – perfect for summer alfresco dining. On tap there are tip-top Greene King ales, while wine drinkers have a mind-boggling choice of 35 wines by the glass.

Food follows the tried-and-tested and hugely successful formula that operates at the sister pubs. The unique 'butcher's counter' draws diners from far and wide, keen to select their own burger or cut of steak prior to cooking. Menus are wide-ranging to suit all tastes, from lunchtime sandwiches, salads and side orders, to starters of moules marinières and beef carpaccio, and mains dishes such as peppered tuna, Cajun cod, beef stroganoff, lamb steaks cooked in shallots and red wine, or seafood pasta.

Prices: **Restaurant main course from £9.95. House wine £11.95.**
Last orders: **Bar: afternoon 15.00; evening 23.00. Food: lunch 14.45; dinner 21.45 (Sunday 20.45).**
Closed: **Rarely.**
Food: **Modern British.**
Real ale: **Greene King IPA, Greene King Abbot Ale.**
Other points: **Smoking area. Garden. Children welcome. Car park. Wheelchair access.**
Directions: **A3. Between Liphook and Liss. (Map 5)**

...for recipe ideas

Petworth

The Halfway Bridge Inn

Country inn

Halfway Bridge, Petworth,
West Sussex GU28 9BP
Telephone: +44(0)1798 861281
hwb@thesussexpub.co.uk
www.thesussexpub.co.uk

'You'll find a warren of charming little rooms decorated with a relaxed, contemporary feel.'

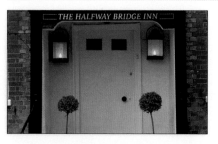

THE HALFWAY BRIDGE INN

Rooms: **6.** Double/twin room from £100, single from £65, family/suite from £120.
Prices: **Restaurant main course from £8.75. Bar main course from £4.95. House wine £12.50.**
Last orders: **Bar: 23.00. Food: lunch 14.30; dinner 21.30 (Sunday 20.30).**
Food: **Modern British.**
Real ale: **Skinner's Betty Stogs, Ringwood Best Bitter, Badger Best.**
Other points: **Smoking area. Children welcome. Dogs welcome in the bar. Garden. Car park. Wheelchair access. Disabled bedroom suite.**
Directions: **A3. Take the A272 from Midhurst to Petworth. Continue past the left turn to Lodsworth. The inn is just after, on the left. (Map 6)**

On the A272, midway between Petworth and Midhurst, the mellow, red-brick Halfway Bridge was originally built as a coaching inn in 1740. Nick and Lisa Sutherland, owners of The Royal Oak, Chichester (see entry), worked their magic on the place in 2005 and have since leased it to Paul Carter. Although spruced up with style and panache, it's not a clone of the Oak, and you'll find a warren of charming little rooms decorated with a relaxed, contemporary feel. A272 travellers, local diners and the polo set are drawn here for first-class modern pub food, local ales, and decent wines.

Snack in the bar on a poached-salmon open sandwich or smoked-chicken Caesar salad, or look to the menu and chalkboard in the dining area for scallops with tomato salsa, belly pork, bubble-and-squeak and red-wine sauce, or fresh fish from Billingsgate Market. In a converted barn a short amble away from the pub are six stunning en-suite rooms. All have been given the Sutherland treatment – exposed beams, quality fabrics, four-poster beds, plasma TVs, hi-fi systems and luxury bathrooms. A super Sussex base.

Country pub

Royal Oak

The Street, Poynings,
West Sussex BN45 7AQ
Telephone: +44(0)1273 857389
mail@royaloakpoynings.biz
www.royaloakpoynings.biz

'There's a fabulous summer garden with barbecue facilities, serene rural views, and all-day food.'

Originally a small hotel, there has been a Royal Oak on this site since the 1880s. Set in a pretty village below the South Downs, a fabulous summer garden with barbecue facilities, serene rural views, and all-day food are the major attractions at this cream-painted country pub. Add hop-adorned beams, roaring winter log fires and local Harvey's bitter on tap and you have a cracking destination pub for food and drink.

Head chef David Wharton's food successfully blends traditional favourites with more ambitious modern dishes. Ingredients are carefully sourced – smoked fish arrives daily from the local smokery, beef and lamb are reared at Poynings Farm, sausages are handmade in neighbouring Henfield, and fruit and vegetables come from a farm within walking distance of the pub. So, expect locally smoked salmon and gravadlax with lemon-and-lime dressing, almond-and-herb crusted fillet of cod with steamed asparagus, alongside a 'Best of British' menu that includes home-roasted gammon with fried eggs and chips, and deep-fried whole tail scampi. There's also a good range of sandwiches.

Prices: Restaurant main course from £9. Bar snacks from £3. House wine £12.
Last orders: Bar: 23.00. Food: 21.30.
Closed: Rarely.
Food: Modern/traditional British.
Real ale: Harvey Sussex Best Bitter.
Other points: No smoking. Children welcome. Dogs welcome in the bar. Garden with barbecue facilities. Car park. Marquee available. Wheelchair access.
Directions: M23. From the A23, follow the A281 towards Henfield, then the signs to Poynings village. (Map 6)

...for events

Shipley

The Countryman Inn

Country pub

Countryman Lane, Shipley,
West Sussex RH 13 8PZ
Telephone: +44(0)1403 741 383
countrymaninn@btopenworld.com
www.countrymanshipley.co.uk

'You will never be stuck for choice or go home unsatisfied.'

Prices: **Set lunch £15 and dinner £22.**
Restaurant main course from £9.50. Bar main course from £4.50. House wine £11.95.
Last orders: **Bar: afternoon 14.30; evening 21.30.**
Food: **lunch 14.30; dinner 21.30.**
Closed: **Rarely.**
Food: **Traditional British.**
Real ale: **Horsham, Bass, Harvey's.**
One guest beer.
Other points: **No smoking. Dogs welcome in the bar. Garden. Car park.**
Directions: **One mile south of the A272.**
Situated outside the village at the junction of Smithers Hill and Countryman Lane. (Map 6)

Just a 10-minute drive away from Horsham, The Countryman offers all you'd expect of a traditional, cosy inn tucked away down a country lane. The Vaughan family have run the pub for 20 years, and have maintained its old-fashioned charm – the impressive inglenook fireplace remains a centrepiece – while ensuring their menus have moved with the times. You can eat informally in the comfortably seated bars or the main restaurant area, which can seat 50. This, too, has a log fire and beams, plus lovely views on to the gardens.

Alongside the good-value, hearty country dishes such as liver-and-bacon casserole, braised oxtail, Auntie Betty's lamb stew, and steak-and-kidney pudding, you'll find scallop-and-bacon skewers with garlic butter, duck-leg cassoulet, lamb tagine and monkfish thermidor. They source locally grown vegetables, game from Knepp Estate, local farm-reared meats, and homegrown herbs. Add in calorie-bursting desserts, and you will never be stuck for choice or go home unsatisfied. They serve local ales from Horsham and Harvey's breweries and 14 wines by the glass.

Riverside brasserie

'Long windows make the most of the view of the ancient bridge and river.'

The Bridge

55 High Street, Bidford-on-Avon, Alcester, Warwickshire B50 5BG
Telephone: +44(0)1789 773700
www.thebridgeatbidford.com

An old saddler's shop on the banks of the Avon, turned into a relaxing and stylish brasserie by chef Rosemary Willmott and partner Patrick Marshall in 2005. Long windows make the most of the view of the ancient bridge and river. Inside, the decor is plain and simple. Upstairs there is a bar and lounge area with brick-red walls, comfortable sofas and coffee tables.

Firmly wedged into the brasserie tradition, the menus here draw on North European as well as Mediterranean traditions, with starters including confit duck leg with Puy lentils and lime-pickle dressing, or chicken and duck-liver pâté with dill pickle. Mains are split into Char Grill and Stove & Oven sections. From the former is beef fillet with béarnaise sauce and garlic chips or veal chop with Roquefort butter, and there's Greek lamb stew, chicken baked with avocado, garlic and cream, or fish and chips from the latter. Accompanying vegetables are unusual and creative. The short but effective dessert menu includes chocolate mousse cake. The wine list has a majority of Old World wines, six served by the glass.

Prices: Restaurant main course from £7.75. House wine £12.95.
Last orders: Bar: 24.00. Food: lunch 14.30 (Sunday 15.00); dinner 21.30 (no food Sunday evening).
Closed: Never.
Food: Modern British.
Other points: Smoking area. Children welcome. Garden. Car park. Wheelchair access.
Directions: M40. Follow signs to Stratford and Evesham for approximately six miles. (Map 8)

...for competitions

Coventry

Turmeric Gold

166 Medieval Spon Street, Coventry,
Warwickshire CV1 1BB
Telephone: +44(0)2476 226603
info@turmericgold.co.uk
www.turmericgold.co.uk

Indian restaurant

'A vibrant place in many senses, serving spicy Indian food with a modern twist.'

Prices: **Set lunch from £7.50 to £8.50 and dinner from £15 to £20. Restaurant main course from £10. House wine £9.95.**
Last orders: **Food: lunch 14.00; dinner 23.30.**
Closed: **Sunday lunch.**
Food: **Modern Indian.**
Other points: **No smoking. Garden. Car park. Large private room.**
Directions: **Situated off the city ring road at exit 9, going towards Upper Well Street. Turn right at the second traffic lights on to Corporation Street. At the top of the street, turn right at the roundabout on to Medieval Spon Street. Turmeric Gold is opposite Bonds night spot. (Map 8)**

Tumeric Gold is set on a medieval street and none of the building's original charm and features have been lost to modernisation. Exposed brick, beams and timber framework are enhanced by the beautiful eastern colours and oriental antiques within the revamped interior. There is even a special private lounging area, which is covered in silk and can be draped over for privacy, under which you can eat and drink like a Maharaja. It's a vibrant place in many senses, serving spicy Indian food with a modern twist in an exotically coloured setting.

The upstairs dining room has a particularly romantic feel, with lots of hidden features and private dining areas. The menu has the popular line-up of baltis and tandoori dishes and a wide choice of specials such as chicken jalfrazi, chicken moglai, lamb khatta massala, duck and fish specials. A good choice of breads, vegetarian sides and excellent-value set menus complete the offering. What distinguishes the cooking, however, are the fresh-tasting flavours and lightness of touch to the dishes. A shining light on Coventry's less-than-attractive Inner Ring.

Knowle

Café Saffron

Indian restaurant

'The kitchen pays much attention to detail, preparation, and the look of the dishes.'

1679 High Street, Knowle, Solihull, Warwickshire B98 0RL
Telephone: +44(0)1564 772190

This evening-only Indian in well-heeled Knowle is a cut above your average curry house. Just one mile from exit 5 of the M42, it is easy to find, thanks not only to a prominent High Street location, but to its bright outside lights. Inside, the minimalist contemporary décor, with modern prints and warm orange-plastered walls, is a refreshing change from that of the more traditional curry house. The owners have also set high standards with their menu, as the kitchen pays much attention to detail, preparation, and the look of the dishes.

Good-quality meat and poultry are sourced from local butchers, and many herbs and spices are imported directly from Calcutta and then freshly ground on site. All the favourite recipes from India, Pakistan and Bangladesh are here. Start with a classic chicken shashlick or prawn pathia puri, for example, and move on to tandoori grills, and curries such as bhuna, korma, dopiaza, passanda, jalfrezi and rogan josh. The wide menu provides a comforting, something-for-everyone choice, but look to the list of specialities for a more varied selection.

Prices: **Main course from £8. House wine £7.95.**
Last orders: **Food: 23.30.**
Closed: **Lunch.**
Food: **Indian.**
Other points: **Children welcome. Car park.**
Directions: **Exit5/M42. Two miles south-east of Solihull. (Map 8)**

...for special offers

Stratford-upon-Avon

The Mary Arden Inn

Country inn

The Green, Wilmcote,
Stratford-upon-Avon,
Warwickshire CV37 9XJ
Telephone: +44(0)1789 267030
info@mary-arden.co.uk
http://mary-arden.co.uk

'The inn has 12 newly refurbished bedrooms with spa baths and CD systems.'

Rooms: 11. Double/twin room from £70, single from £55. Family room from £100.
Prices: Restaurant main course from £12.50. House wine £10.
Last orders: Bar: 23.00. Food: lunch 14.30 (Friday to Sunday food served all day); dinner 21.30 (Sunday 21.00).
Closed: **Never.**
Food: Traditional and Modern British.
Real ale: Greene King IPA, Greene King Abbot Ale.
Other points: Smoking area. Children welcome. Dogs welcome in the bar. Garden. Car park.
Directions: Exit 15/M40. Three miles from the centre of Stratford. Follow the brown tourist-information signs for Mary Arden's House in Wilmcote. The Mary Arden Inn is in the village at the T-junction. (Map 8)

Set in the heart of Shakespearian England, you approach this Warwickshire inn along Featherbed Lane and past Mary Arden's House. A 14th-century timbered cottage that was home to Shakespeare's mother, the house is a major attraction. Running through the picturesque village of Wilmcote is the Stratford-upon-Avon canal and many of the barge and narrow-boat users frequent The Mary Arden Inn. The olde-worlde bar has exposed timbers and a glass panel in the floor exposing a secret tunnel to the church.

The restaurant is more contemporary, with a menu that suits all. Lunch is more informal, with salads, grills, sandwiches and dishes such as fig and goat's cheese gratin. For dinner, start with Caesar salad and follow with seared sea bass, fennel broth and crayfish or cannon of lamb with red-pepper mash and red-wine jus. Puddings are of the pavlova or sticky toffee variety and cheeses are local. Wash all of it down with real ales from the Greene King stable or one of the wines off the well-balanced list. The inn also has 12 newly refurbished bedrooms with spa baths and CD systems.

San Carlo

Italian restaurant

'Look out for excellent lobster Thermidor, crevettes in garlic butter, and spaghetti shellfish.'

4 Temple Street, Birmingham B2 5BN
Telephone: +44(0)121 633 0251
www.sancarlo.co.uk

This popular restaurant was the first in what is now a chain with three other branches in Bristol, Leicester and Manchester. It is located in a narrow street off the city centre and has a lively and friendly buzz. Its modern Mediterranean look has a façade of marble and glass, which leads into a spacious light and bright dining area with mirrored walls, white ceramic floor tiles and potted plants creating a fresh and airy contemporary look.

Classic flavoursome dishes are the order of the day, and prices are very fair for cooking that's above the norm for a city-centre eaterie majoring in pizzas and pasta. There's plenty to tempt in the way of soups, salads and risottos, as well as trattoria classic mains, such as bisteca Diana, petto di pollo lucullo, and fegata di vitello. Chalkboard specials extend an already wide choice, offering some very good fresh fish dishes; look out for excellent lobster Thermidor, crevettes in garlic butter, and spaghetti shellfish. There's a list of well-priced Italian wines, with a good selection (10) by the glass, but with French and New World wines also making a splash.

Prices: **Main course from £11. House wine £12.95.**
Last orders: **Food: 23.00.**
Closed: **Rarely.**
Food: **Italian.**
Other points: **Smoking area. Children welcome.**
Directions: **In the centre of the city. (Map 8)**

...for the latest news

Brinkworth

The Three Crowns

The Street, Brinkworth, Swindon,
Wiltshire SN15 5AF
Telephone: +44(0)1666 510366
www.threecrowns.co.uk

Country pub

'Few people leave dissatisfied: portions are not for the faint-hearted, and food quality is well above average.'

Prices: **Main course from £14.95. Bar snacks from £6.95. House wine from £12.95.**
Last orders: Bar: **afternoon 15.00 (Saturday 16.00, Sunday 17.00); evening 23.00 (Sunday 22.30). Food: lunch 14.00; dinner 21.30.**
Closed: **Rarely.**
Food: **Modern British/traditional French.**
Real ale: **Archers Best, Greene King IPA, Castle Eden, Fuller's London Pride, Wadworth 6X. One guest beer.**
Other points: **Smoking area. Children welcome. Dogs welcome in the bar. Garden. Car park. Wheelchair access.**
Directions: **Exit 16/M4. Take the A3102 towards Wootton Bassett, then follow the B4042 Malmesbury road for five miles. (Map 4)**

Set back from the road, close to the church and green, and just five minutes from the M4, Anthony and Allyson Windle's 200-year-old stone pub is a bustling dining destination, drawing a discerning clientele in search of the unusual and often adventurous dishes available here. The traditional pubby bar, with its real fires, brasses, dark wood, soft lighting and two remarkable tables created from huge 18th-century bellows, is the spot for lunchtime snacks, namely enormous ploughman's and filled double-decker rolls.

A comprehensive list of main courses is displayed on a huge chalkboard that dominates one wall of the pine-furnished conservatory dining extension. Few people leave dissatisfied: portions are not for the faint-hearted, and food quality is well above average. The ambitious dishes make good use of local produce, including locally farmed veal, venison and free-range poultry. Typically, tuck into griddled wild boar, lamb-and-mint pie, whole lobster, or even marinated slices of kangaroo, venison and ostrich. Round off with a sticky toffee pudding or a plate of cheese from an impressive cheeseboard selection.

www.routiers.co.uk

Chippenham

Revolutions Café Bar and Restaurant

Restaurant and café bar

66 New Road, Chippenham,
Wiltshire SN15 1ES
Telephone: +44(0)1249 447500
sanddwebb@aol.com

'Revolutions is certainly a revelation in this Wiltshire market town.'

Contemporary in style, this town-centre brasserie-style restaurant is classically good looking and serves excellent seasonal food. Sandie and Doug Webb are passionate about buying produce from local suppliers, so much so that menus credit their beef (Home Farm) and organic egg producers (Church Farm). Despite using top-notch ingredients, you can eat very well here at very reasonable prices. Lunch dishes produce a magnificent Niçoise salad, salmon fishcakes, hearty beef pie topped with tarragon pastry crust, a classic steak sandwich with mustard mayonnaise, and a good choice of filled jacket potatoes.

The set evening menu offers a selection of imaginative starters, such as sweet-pepper and chilli-tomato soup or duck breast with mango salsa. The mains include a strong line-up of steaks, plus other meat and vegetarian meals, perhaps lamb shank with red-wine and rosemary jus, while for pudding there could be warm pecan pie with custard. Drinks on offer include an excellent wine list with minimal mark-ups, and a selection of lagers, beers and spirits. Revolutions is certainly a revelation in this Wiltshire market town.

Prices: **Set brunch/lunch from £3.25. Set dinner £16.95 (two courses 14.95). House wine from £8.95.**
Last orders: **Food: Tuesday-Thursday 21.00, Friday and Saturday 21.00, Monday 14.00.**
Closed: **All day Sunday and Monday evening.**
Food: **Modern British.**
Other points: **Smoking area. Children welcome. Wheelchair access.**
Directions: **Exit 17/M4. Take the dual carriageway towards Chippenham and follow signs to the town centre. Turn left through the railway arches. Revolutions is just before the first crossing on the right. (Map 4)**

...for recipe ideas

Malmesbury

The Horse and Groom

Country inn

The Street, Charlton, Malmesbury,
Wiltshire SN16 9DL
Telephone: +44(0)1666 823904
info@horseandgroominn.com
www.horseandgroominn.com

'Food is clearly the selling point here, with a bar menu featuring old-fashioned favourites.'

Rooms: **3. Double/twin room from £49.95.**
Prices: **Restaurant main course from £7.95. Bar main course from £7.95. House wine £12.95.**
Last orders: **Bar: 23.00. Food: 21.00.**
Closed: **Never.**
Food: **Modern British.**
Real ale: **Three guest beers.**
Other points: **Smoking area. Children welcome. Dogs welcome. Garden. Car park. Wheelchair access to the restaurant/pub (not WC).**
Directions: **Exit 17/M4. Take the A429 to Malmesbury signposted Cirencester. At the second roundabout take the B4040 to Cricklade and Charlton. The Horse and Groom is on the left-hand side as you leave Charlton. (Map 4)**

The solidly elegant Cotswold stone house fronted by a tree-sheltered lawn stands in its own paddock well back from the B4040, and just a few miles from Malmesbury. Its history as a coaching inn dates back to the 17th century and this fine building was taken over by the expanding Merchant Inns group in April 2006. A typical roadside inn with a porched entrance, the new owners may have fitted carpet on the stone floors, but old pine tables and window seats retain the country-pub feel. Both bars are laid for dining, but a selection of good local real ales and a rack of newspapers attract drinkers.

As with its sister establishment, The Carnarvon Arms near Newbury, Berkshire (see entry), food is clearly the selling point here, with a bar menu featuring old-fashioned favourites such as steak and oyster-mushroom pie or well-made sandwiches such as mature Cheddar and apple chutney. The restaurant menu boasts more à la carte choices of lemon sole fillet with prawn-and-scallion risotto, calves' liver with bacon, buttered spinach and onion gravy, and chocolate cake with black cherries and mascarpone.

Swindon

The Sun Inn

Country pub

'The interior retains much of the building's original charm and character.'

The Street, Lydiard Millicent, Swindon,
Wiltshire SN5 3LU
Telephone: +44(0)1793 770425
thesuninnlm@yahoo.co.uk
www.cotswoldinns.co.uk

Close to the village pond and the beautiful parish church, The Sun Inn lies tucked away in a pretty conservation village that goes back at least as far as the Domesday Book. The Georgian stately home Lydiard House is nearby. The refurbished interior of this late 18th-century inn sports tiled and wooden floors, open fires and exposed timbers, and retains much of the building's original charm and character.

The food is freshly prepared from local produce, with meat supplied by Harts' specialist butchers in Cricklade, smoked fish from Severn and Wye Smokery, and first-class vegetables from Mise en Place in Cirencester. Well-presented lunch dishes may include warm ciabatta, pasta with tomato and chorizo, or liver and bacon with mash and onion gravy. Evening additions and daily dishes may feature lime-and-chilli seasoned squid, hake with wild-mushroom risotto, roast pork tenderloin stuffed with apricots, wrapped in bacon and served with a cider jus, and deep-fried cod with pesto butter. There is a short global list of wines, with eight offered by the glass.

Prices: Restaurant main course from £8.95. Lunch menu from £4.50. Bar snacks from £2.50. Wine from £9.95.
Last orders: Bar: afternoon 15.00; evening 23.00 (all day Sunday during the summer). Food: lunch 14.30 (Sunday 15.00); dinner 21.30 (Sunday 21.00).
Closed: Rarely.
Food: Traditional/modern British and European.
Real ale: Wadworth 6X, Flowers Original, Archers Best, Wickwar. Two guest beers.
Other points: Smoking area. Children welcome. Garden. Car park. Wheelchair access.
Directions: Exit 16/M4. Situated in the village of Lydiard Millicent, about three miles to the west of Swindon. (Map 4)

...for events

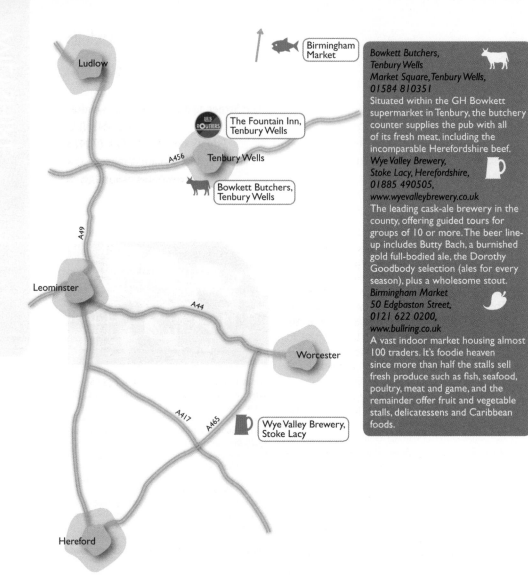

Birmingham Market

Bowkett Butchers,
Tenbury Wells
Market Square, Tenbury Wells,
01584 810351
Situated within the GH Bowkett
supermarket in Tenbury, the butchery
counter supplies the pub with all
of its fresh meat, including the
incomparable Herefordshire beef.

Wye Valley Brewery,
Stoke Lacy, Herefordshire,
01885 490505,
www.wyevalleybrewery.co.uk
The leading cask-ale brewery in the
county, offering guided tours for
groups of 10 or more. The beer line-
up includes Butty Bach, a burnished
gold full-bodied ale, the Dorothy
Goodbody selection (ales for every
season), plus a wholesome stout.

Birmingham Market
50 Edgbaston Street,
0121 622 0200,
www.bullring.co.uk
A vast indoor market housing almost
100 traders. It's foodie heaven
since more than half the stalls sell
fresh produce such as fish, seafood,
poultry, meat and game, and the
remainder offer fruit and vegetable
stalls, delicatessens and Caribbean
foods.

The Fountain Inn,
Tenbury Wells

A456

Tenbury Wells

Bowkett Butchers,
Tenbury Wells

Ludlow

A49

Leominster

A44

Worcester

A417 A465

Wye Valley Brewery,
Stoke Lacy

Hereford

Visit the Farmers' Market
The post-office car park in Tenbury Wells is the location for the town's farmers' market, on the fourth
Saturday of the month, from 9am to 2pm.

Tenbury Wells

The Fountain Inn

Country inn

'Diners come from miles around to see Dancer the leopard shark.'

Oldwood, St Michaels, Tenbury Wells,
Worcestershire WR15 8TB
Telephone: +44 (0)1584 810701
enquiries@fountain-hotel.co.uk
www.fountain-hotel.co.uk

There aren't many pubs, if any, in Britain that can boast of having a 1,000-gallon aquarium complete with a leopard shark, but then the Fountain Inn is no ordinary pub. The real draws in this striking, black-and-white 17th-century inn are the smart, wood-beamed bar and the nautically styled restaurant serving fresh food using quality local ingredients. Seafood is, of course, big business, with fish bought direct from Birmingham market, but other produce is sourced more locally, notably Herefordshire beef from Bowkett's butchers in Tenbury.

Chef Paul Smith also has the pick of the pub's organic herb-and-vegetable garden. Diners come from miles around to see Dancer the leopard shark and tuck into homemade soup, terrine of the day or smoked haddock and wild-mushroom risotto, or mains of pan-fried duck with honey, ginger and soy sauce, chicken Creole and fine Herefordshire steaks, as well as the many daily fish and seasonal game options. There are smart en-suite rooms, and The Oldwood Suite is ideal for wedding functions. Beer lovers will appreciate the award-winning Fountain Ale.

Rooms: 11. Double/twin room from £49.95. Disabled suite available.
Prices: Main course from £6.95. Sunday lunch £9.95. House wine £9.95.
Last orders: Bar: 23.00. Food: 21.00 (later for bookings).
Closed: Never.
Food: Traditional British with European influences.
Real ale: Five guest beers.
Other points: Smoking area. Children welcome. Garden. Car park. Shark aquarium. Wheelchair access.
Directions: Exit 5/M5. One mile from Tenbury Wells on the A4112 Leominster road. (Map 8)

Bridlington

Georgian Tea Rooms

56 High Street, Old Town, Bridlington,
East Yorkshire YO16 4QA
Telephone: +44(0)1262 608600
gadandy@aol.com

Traditional tea shop

'There's a fantastic patio and garden dominated by a central fountain.'

Prices: **Main course from £4.25.
House wine £8.99.**
Last orders: **Food: 17.00 (Sunday 15.00).**
Closed: **Closed for two weeks over Christmas and New Year.**
Food: **Traditional English.**
Other points: **Smoking area. Children welcome. Garden.**
Directions: **In Bridlington's old town. (Map 10)**

A grand, Grade II-listed building on a splendid Georgian high street, these traditional tea rooms are part of the historic quarter of Bridlington, tucked a mile inland from the better-known bustling seaside resort. Brother and sister David and Diane Davison's tea rooms are on the ground floor, forming part of a three-floored antiques emporium packed with collectables, crafts, jewellery and curios.

The spacious rooms have a welcoming glow, with walls painted in striking yellows and greens and highly polished wooden tables. There's a separate room for smokers, plus a fantastic patio and garden dominated by a central fountain. Order at the counter and start the day with a full English breakfast or scrambled eggs with smoked salmon. The menu then moves on to snacks of filled jacket potatoes, salads, toasted sandwiches, as well as teashop stalwarts of toasted teacakes, homemade scones and other irresistible cakes and pastries. The beverages selection is wide and includes flavoured milks and coffees. The tearooms also cater for private functions.

www.routiers.co.uk

Bridlington

Marton Grange

Country-house hotel

Flamborough Road, Sewerby-cum-Marton,
Bridlington, East Yorkshire YO15 1DU
Telephone: +44(0)1262 602034
martongrange@talk21.com
www.marton-grange.co.uk

*'A lovely place to enjoy a drink
and the beautiful surroundings.'*

Formerly a Georgian farmhouse, this Grade II-listed building has been immaculately restored into a smart and comfortable hotel. Proprietor Stuart Nelson has transformed the house, keeping its Georgian elegance but bringing a fresh, cheery, contemporary feel to the rooms. Downstairs, two fine dining rooms look out on to the south-facing, well-tended grounds. The terrace that leads out from french windows is a lovely place to enjoy a drink and the beautiful surroundings. Breakast is served in two interconnecting drawing rooms that are sunny in look and feel.

There are two choices of bedrooms: large, premier, en-suite rooms in the older part of the house, or classic rooms in the newer extension. The full English breakfasts are quite an event, and come with their own freshly laid eggs, with all the other ingredients coming from local suppliers. Explorers should head to nearby Flamborough Head, an outstanding stretch of coastline that is famed for its colonies of nesting seabirds.

Rooms: 11. Double room from £32 per person, single from £40.
Closed: December, January and February.
Food: Traditional British.
Other points: No smoking. Dogs welcome. Garden. Car park. Wheelchair access.
Directions: Exit 37/M62. Take the B1255 Bridlington to Flamborough road; Marton Grange is on the left, the last driveway off the lay-by. (Map 10)

Driffield

The Wold Cottage

Bed and breakfast

Wold Newton, Driffield,
East Yorkshire YO25 3HL
Telephone: +44(0)1262 470696
katrina@woldcottage.com
www.woldcottage.com

*'What sets Wold Cottage apart
is dedication to providing guests
with unbeatable service.'*

Rooms: **5. Double/twin room from £90, single
from £45. Family room from £100. Two self-
catering cottages.**
Prices: **Set dinner £18.50.**
Closed: **Never.**
Food: **Traditional English.**
Other points: **No smoking. Garden. Children
welcome. Car park. Wheelchair access
overnight.**
Directions: **B1249. Follow the signs to Wold
Newton. At the pond, turn right, go round the
double bend and Wold Cottage is the first on
the right. Go past the bungalow. (Map 10)**

On the edge of the well-presented village
of Wold Newton is Wold Cottage, the
home and farm of third-generation farmers
Derek and Katrina Gray. This fine Georgian
house is built of local brick and stands
in spacious grounds. Inside, the sense of
spaciousness continues: ceilings are high and
the public rooms benefit from long windows
overlooking the mature gardens. Three good-
sized bedrooms in the main house are
complemented by further rooms across the
yard in converted outbuildings.

What sets Wold Cottage apart is Katrina's
dedication to providing guests with
unbeatable service. Evening meals and
breakfasts showcase for local producers, be
they farmers, bakers or cereal growers. Local
lamb, for example, may be served with own-
grown new potatoes, broccoli and green
beans, and followed with fresh strawberry
meringue. The Grays' passion for all things
local extends to the beer, which they brew
themselves at the Wold Top Brewery. Sample
Wold Top Bitter or Falling Stone Bitter over
dinner at the cottage or at the family's pub,
The Falling Stone, in nearby Thwing.

Mr Moo's Ice Cream Parlour & Coffee Shop

Café and ice cream parlour

Southfield House Farm, Hornsea Road,
Skipsea, Driffield,
East Yorkshire YO25 8SY
Telephone: +44(0)1262 469829
info@mrmoos.co.uk
www.mrmoos.co.uk

'Enjoy a fabulous range of ice creams that are made on the premises.'

Mr Moo's serves real ice cream made on a working farm. Judith and Stephen Foreman decided that rather than sell all their milk from their Friesian dairy herd to the wholesaler, they would develop their own outlet. So they set up a café-cum-ice cream parlour on their farm, where you can enjoy a fabulous range of ice creams that are made on the premises. The glass-fronted counter lets you see the selection and be tempted. Flavours and creaminess make for a palate-pleasing experience for all.

They have made sure that all the favourites are there, from several ways with vanilla through to the more unusual white chocowlatte, ginger moo and blackberry slammer. But there is more than ice cream and the range of delicious desserts. The café prepares homemade soups and daily specials – you'll find local line-caught fish, crabs and game are often on the menu. Judith also bakes superb cakes, using local free-range eggs. With such wholesome produce on offer, it's no wonder Mr Moo's is becoming so popular – the Foremans have created a sheltered patio and are extending to add extra space.

Prices: **Light lunches from £3.25.**
Last orders: **Food: 13.45.**
Closed: **Rarely.**
Food: **Sandwiches, home-baking, speciality tea and coffee, homemade ice cream.**
Other points: **No smoking. Dogs welcome. Garden. Children welcome. Car park. Wheelchair access. Farm walk to beach. Caravan site.**
Directions: **M62. Half a mile south of Skipsea on the left-hand side of the B1242. (Map 10)**

...for special offers

MEMBER
240
ENTRY

Bedale

The Buck Inn

Village inn

'An impressive selection of malt whiskies.'

Thornton Watlass, near Bedale, Ripon,
North Yorkshire HG4 4AH
Telephone: +44(0)1677 422461

Next to the village-green cricket pitch in a beautiful Bedale village, this is a traditional, well-run, friendly institution that has been in the experienced hands of Michael and Margaret Fox for 20 years. The timeless lounge, with upholstered wall benches, glowing coal fires, several mounted fox masks and a fine mahogany bar counter is comfortably old-fashioned; adjacent to it is the dining room, which overlooks the sheltered rear garden.

At lunchtime, simple, good-value dishes range from Masham rarebit (Wensleydale cheese with local ale topped with bacon) to steak-and-kidney pie and braised lamb shank. Using locally sourced produce, equally traditional and well-prepared evening additions may include goat's cheese-and-tomato tartlet to start, followed by baked cod with avocado and tiger prawns, or the generous Buck mixed grill. At the bar you'll find local Black Sheep and Theakston ales on tap, and an impressive selection of malt whiskies. Cottagey bedrooms – five en-suite – provide a comfortable night's sleep and a useful base from which to explore beautiful Bedale.

Rooms: 7, 2 with shared bathrooms. Double room from £70, single from £50, family from £85.
Prices: Set Sunday lunch £12.50. Restaurant main course from £9.50. House wine £9.95.
Last orders: Bar: 23.00. Food: lunch 14.00; dinner 21.15.
Closed: Rarely.
Food: Traditional British.
Real ale: Black Sheep Best, Theakston Best, John Smith's Cask. Two guest beers.
Other points: Smoking area. Children welcome. Dogs welcome overnight, not in the bar. Garden. Car park.
Directions: From Bedale, follow the B6268 towards Masham. After two miles, turn right at the signed crossroads. (Map 12)

MEMBER
241
ENTRY

Burnsall

The Red Lion Hotel

Country inn

By the Bridge, Burnsall, Skipton,
North Yorkshire BD23 6BU
Telephone: +44(0)1756 720204
info@redlion.co.uk
www.redlion.co.uk

'Cosy and rambling, with lovely gardens.'

Rooms: 15 plus 3 riverside cottages. Room from £62.50 per person.
Prices: Set lunch £22.95 and dinner £32.95. Restaurant main course from £12.50. Bar main course from £3.95. House wine £12.50.
Last orders: Bar: 21.30. Food: lunch 14.30; dinner 21.30.
Closed: Never.
Food: Modern British.
Real ale: Theakston Ales, Timothy Taylor Best Bitter, Timothy Taylor Landlord. Four guest beers.
Other points: Smoking areas. Children welcome. Dogs welcome. Garden. Car park. Licence for civil weddings/partnerships. Wheelchair access to the restaurant. Residents' lounge. Conference facilities.
Directions: A65. From Leeds to Ilkley, turn towards Bolton Abbey just through the town. (Map 9)

Traditional charm and hospitality abound at this stone-built 16th-century inn, which stands beside an ancient bridge in this pretty Dales village. Cosy and rambling, with lovely gardens running down to the River Wharfe, stylish en-suite bedrooms and riverside holiday cottages, it has long been a favoured base for exploring the Dales. In the rustic, oak-floored bar, with its roaring fires, relaxing sofas and hand-pulled pints of Theakston and Timothy Taylor ales, you can tuck into some hearty home-cooked food.

Local ingredients play a big part on seasonal menus, for example, game from nearby estates, beef from the owner's son-in-law's farm, and lamb from the Daggett family's farm across the river. These translate into daily specials of pheasant, partridge and venison terrine with Cumberland sauce, and rack of lamb with redcurrant jus. Light lunch options include decent sandwiches and Yorkshire cheese ploughman's lunches, while dinner in the restaurant could feature confit duck leg with black pudding and caramelised onion, followed by calves' liver with garlic sauce, with banana sticky toffee pudding to finish.

Fadmoor

The Plough Inn

ᴗᴗ

Country pub

'An excellent pit-stop for hungry moorland walkers to rest and refuel.'

Main Street, Fadmoor, Kirkbymoorside,
North Yorkshire YO62 7HY
Telephone: +44(0)1751 431515

A stylishly refurbished old stone pub that provides an excellent pit-stop for hungry moorland walkers to rest and refuel with pints of Black Sheep and some hearty pub food. The Plough stands by the green in tranquil Fadmoor, high up on the edge of the North Yorkshire Moors, with views across the Vale of Pickering to the distant Wolds. Inside, there's a snug little bar replete with black-tiled floor, simple wall benches and a wood-burning old range. Rambling dining rooms and imaginative menus draw discerning local diners to this moorland oasis.

Neil Nicholson sources meat from local farms and butchers, fresh vegetables from Kirkbymoorside, and fish is delivered direct from Hartlepool. Dinner may begin with pork terrine with fruit chutney, followed by venison steak with port jus, or an excellent fish option, such as baked halibut with tiger prawns and a lemon-and-thyme cream sauce, or cod-and-pancetta fishcakes with sweet-chilli and ginger dip. There are good-value two-course lunch and early-bird menus (not Saturday evening or Sunday lunch). Arrive early or book ahead.

Prices: Set lunch £12.95 (two courses). Set early-bird dinner £14.50. Main course from £9.50. House wine from £11.95.
Last orders: **Bar: afternoon 14.30; evening 23.00. Food: lunch 13.45; dinner 20.45.**
Closed: **Rarely.**
Food: **Traditional/modern pub food.**
Real ale: **Black Sheep Best, Tetley's Cask. One guest beer.**
Other points: **Smoking area. Children welcome. Car park.**
Directions: **Head north from Kirkbymoorside (off the A170) for 1 1/2 miles, turn left and then fork left to Fadmoor. (Map 12)**

...for the latest news

Filey

The Downcliffe House Hotel

Seaside hotel

The Beach, Filey,
North Yorkshire YO14 9LA
Telephone: +44(0)1723 513310
info@downcliffehouse.co.uk
www.downcliffehouse.co.uk

'This elegant hotel is right on the beach and most of its rooms have fabulous views.'

Rooms: 12. Double room from £96, single from £48, family from £144.
Prices: Set dinner £20. Main course from £10. House wine £10.
Last orders: Food: lunch 14.00; dinner 20.00.
Closed: January.
Food: Seafood/British.
Other points: No smoking. Children welcome. Dogs welcome overnight. Car park.
Directions: Leave the A165 taking the A1039 and follow to the centre of Filey. Drive through the centre and down Cargate Hill, and turn right along the seafront. (Map 10)

Only a few minutes from the larger resorts of Scarborough and Bridlington, this elegant hotel is right on the beach and most of its rooms have fabulous views of Filey's six miles of golden sands. Nick and Caroline Hunt continue to provide a homely welcome in stylish surroundings. Public areas are smart; in winter, a real fire roars in the bar and the restaurant. All the bedrooms are en-suite, some have four-poster beds, and all are decorated in the Victorian style that runs through the house. Most rooms boast sea views as well as every conceivable extra, including radios, TVs and good toiletries.

True to its location, the menu includes fresh fish, but also acknowledges the farms that surround Filey. The strongly modern British menu may offer prawn cocktail or pan-fried king scallops to start, followed by medallions of beef with mushroom sauce or a selection of succulent prawns, smoked salmon and crab. A suitably indulgent finish would be lemon meringue pie. The wine list offers much under £15, plus a number of treats. A liqueur coffee is a fitting end to a meal at this traditional seaside-town hotel.

www.routiers.co.uk

Harome

The Star Inn

Country inn

'Accommodation is absolutely first-class, as is the extensive wine list.'

High Steet, Harome, Helmsley,
North Yorkshire YO62 5JE
Telephone: +44(0)1439 770397
www.thestaratharome.co.uk

Andrew and Jacqui Pern have transformed a neglected village local into a national culinary institution. The original 14th-century thatched building has low-beamed ceilings, wonky walls, hand-carved oak furniture, and a winter log fire in a very civilised bar. Booking is essential in the separate, beautifully decorated dining room. Andrew's culinary talent delivers outstanding pub food, and his kitchen also provides top-class goodies to their food shop-cum-deli across the lane.

The cooking makes full use of homegrown herbs and seasonal produce comes from a select network of local suppliers, including the Perns' own butchers shop in the village. Weekly-changing menus, enhanced by daily specials, may list pressed Middle White pork terrine with Burrow Hill cider, crackling salad and Yorkshire relish for starters, followed by Harome 'Fidget Pie' with boiled bacon and braised peas, or loin of hare with a little hot pot, parsnip purée, nettles and Black Trumpet mushrooms, with steamed ginger savarin and warm rhubarb compote to finish. Bedrooms in the converted barn opposite are absolutely first-class, as is the extensive wine list.

Rooms: 11. Double/twin room from £130.
Prices: Set lunch £20 and dinner £30. Main course from £14. House wine £13.
Last orders: Bar: 23.00. Food: lunch 14.00; dinner 21.30; Sunday lunch 18.00.
Closed: Monday.
Food: Modern British.
Real ale: Black Sheep Best, John Smith's Cask, Theakstons, Cropton Brewery. Beers. Two guest beers.
Other points: Smoking area. Children welcome. Garden. Car park. Licence for civil weddings/ partnerships.
Directions: The Star is 2 1/2 miles south-east off the A170 between Helmsley and Kirkbymoorside. (Map 12)

...for recipe ideas

MEMBER ENTRY

Radfords Butchers,
18 Coach Road, Sleights, South Whitby,
01947 810229

This traditional family butchers is renowned for its steak pies and pork pies. The lamb and beef stock are from special breeds and from a local farm supplier. In season, they have plentiful supplies of game from local estates.

Alliance Fish,
West Pier, Scarborough,
01723 350400

Ocean's Pantry on the harbour is run by Alliance Fish on the harbour and is one of the best wet-fish shops in the north.

Ryeburn Ice Cream,
Church Farm, Helmsley,
01439 770331, www.ryeburn.com

Former farmer David Otterburn started making ice cream to use up milk that was surplus to their quota. Thirteen years ago, the family closed the farm and decided to open a tearoom and ice-cream parlour. Since 1995, David has won more than 50 awards for his Ryeburn ice cream comes in 46 different flavours.

Waind & Son Butchers,
2 Piercy End, Kirkbymoorside,
01751 431245

You'll find an excellent range of homemade sausages at this traditional butchers, which has been a family business for 150 years.

Visit the Farmers' Market

Malton farmers' market is held on the last Saturday of each month – apart from during the months of August and December – in sheep sheds that flank the Market Square.

Whitby

Radfords Butchers,
South Whitby

A169

A171

Alliance Fish,
Scarborough

Scarborough

A170

A165

Waind & Son Butchers,
Kirkbymoorside

Ryeburn
Ice Cream,
Helmsley

Kirkbymoorside   A170

Pickering

Helmsley

  The Pheasant,
Harome

B1257

Helmsley

Pheasant Hotel

Hotel

'An easy place to relax and slow the pace.'

Harome, Helmsley,
North Yorkshire YO62 5JG
Telephone: +44(0)1439 771241

Overlooking a duck pond in a pretty Yorkshire village, the location and look of this country hotel is quintessentially English. Two former cottages and the village blacksmith's shop have been merged for the best of both worlds – country pub meets hotel. The flagstoned and beamed bar has a relaxed, country-pub feel, while the traditional restaurant and lounge are smartly comfortable. The light, spacious and well-equipped bedrooms have tip-top bathrooms and complement the restful atmosphere of the hotel, and all overlook the pond.

With its open lounge fire and peaceful village position, you will find this an easy place to relax and slow the pace. The restaurant, partly set in a conservatory, serves a daily-changing set-dinner menu of traditional British food, such as game soup, salmon en croute with herb-and-prawn sauce, or local beef braised in red wine, and poached pear with raspberry coulis to finish. There's also a good-value list of wines that favours France. The small heated swimming pool in one of the courtyard buildings is great for a few leisurely lengths before a hearty breakfast or dinner.

Rooms: 12. Double room from £150, single from £75 dinner, bed and breakfast.
Prices: Set dinner £23.50. House wine £9.60.
Last orders: Food: lunch 14.00; dinner 20.30.
Closed: December, January and February. (Open for lunch January and February except Mondays).
Food: Traditional English.
Other points: No smoking. Dogs welcome overnight. Garden. Car park. Indoor heated swimming pool. Wheelchair access.
Directions: Take the A170 from Helmsley towards Scarborough. After a quarter of a mile, turn right for Harome. The hotel is opposite the church. (Map 12)

Lastingham

Lastingham Grange

Country-house hotel

Lastingham, Kirkbymoorside, York,
North Yorkshire YO62 6TH
Telephone: +44(0)1751 417345
reservations@lastinghamgrange.com
www.lastinghamgrange.com

'The Grange has a timeless elegance.'

Rooms: 12. Double room from £189, single from £99, dinner, bed & breakfast.
Prices: Set lunch £18.75 (four courses) and dinner £37.50 (five courses). Main course from £12.50. House wine £8.75.
Last orders: Food: lunch 13.45; dinner 20.30 (Sunday 20.00).
Closed: December to the beginning of March.
Food: Traditional English.
Real ale: Theakston Ales.
Other points: Smoking area. Children welcome. Dogs welcome overnight. Garden. Car park. Wheelchair access to the restaurant/pub.
Directions: From Pickering, take the A170 towards Kirkbymoorside for five miles. Turn right towards Appleton-le-Moors and Lastingham for two miles and turn right by the church. After 75 yards, turn left up the no-through road for 400 yards. (Map 12)

Set in a peaceful rural backwater in the heart of the National Park, the Grange has a timeless elegance. Built of stone and set around a central courtyard in 10 acres of well-kept gardens, this former farmhouse, dating from the 16th century, is well maintained. The Wood family has lived here for 51 years and they make visitors feel very much at home. The public areas and bedrooms are spacious and furnished in soft colours with antiques. Bedrooms and en-suite bathrooms are pristine and comfortable.

Local produce features prominently on the menu; all meat comes from S Waind & Sons in Kirkbymoorside, fish from Whitby, and ice cream and cheeses from Wensleydale. Pâtés, puddings and chutneys are all homemade and honey comes from their own hives. Lunches include smoked salmon with egg mayonnaise, followed by baked fillet of salmon in a leek-and-cider sauce or honey and lemon-glazed roast chicken. Set dinners are a more grand affair and could start with smoked trout with lime vinaigrette and move on to beef-and-venison goulash, baked skate wing, or ragout of kidneys in red wine.

Hotel

'The place to luxuriate in the finer things of life.'

Hazlewood Castle Hotel

Paradise Lane, Hazlewood, Tadcaster,
North Yorkshire LS24 9NJ
Telephone: +44 (0)1937 535317
info@hazlewood-castle.co.uk
www.hazlewood-castle.co.uk

Mentioned in the Domesday Book, this fascinating 950-year-old former castle and monastery is the place to luxuriate in the finer things of life. You arrive through mature parkland and the grandness continues inside. Bedrooms in the castle or the courtyard wing are sumptuously appointed. Food is another source of indulgence. Sophisticated modern dishes, carefully prepared by Valerie Hamelin, are served in the newly named Restaurant Anise, a continental-style, all-day eaterie. The room is beautifully designed with tall french windows opening on to a terrace overlooking the lawns.

From the lunch menu you could choose moules marinières, butternut-squash risotto with fresh sage, salad Niçoise, or chicken tagine with apricot couscous. The excellent-value fixed-price dinner menu lists more extras, such as confit duck leg with orange sauce, rib-eye steak with frites and pepper sauce, and salmon fillet grilled with Anise spices and served with sauce vierge. Puddings include lemon-cream tart with Chantilly cream and rich chocolate torte with crème anglaise.

Rooms: 21. Double room from £155, suite from £225.
Prices: À la carte lunch and dinner £21 (two courses) and £25. House wine £14.95.
Last orders: 21.00.
Closed: Never.
Food: Modern French/Continental.
Other points: No smoking. Children welcome. Garden. Car park. Licence for civil weddings/ partnerships. Wheelchair access.
Directions: At the A64 junction with the A1M, take the A64 towards York, then the first left (A659) towards Tadcaster and follow the brown tourist-information signs to Hazlewood Castle Hotel. (Map 9)

...for events

Leyburn

The Friar's Head at Akebar

Country pub

Akebar Park, Leyburn, Wensleydale,
North Yorkshire DL8 5LY
Telephone: +44(0)1677 450201/450591
info@akebarpark.com
www.akebarpark.com

'Sit at massive, candlelit, stone tables and tuck into some good modern pub food.'

Prices: **Restaurant main course from £8.
Bar main course from £7. House wine £11.50.**
Last orders: **Food: lunch 14.00; dinner 21.30
(Saturday 22.00).**
Closed: **Three days in February – telephone
to confirm.**
Food: **Modern British.**
Real ale: **John Smith's, Theakston, Black Sheep.**
Other points: **Smoking area. Garden. Children
welcome until 19.30 (must be dining with an
adult). Car park. Wheelchair access to the
restaurant/pub.**
Directions: **From the A1 at Leeming Bar, take
the A684 and travel westward towards Bedale.
Continue on the A684 for seven miles, and the
entrance to Akebar Park is signed on the left.
(Map 12)**

Situated in Lower Wensleydale, Akebar Park was a grange farm for Jervaulx Abbey and is still a working farm. It has been transformed by Joyce and Colin Ellwood into a popular leisure facility, namely an 18-hole golf course, a caravan park and The Friar's Head, a country inn created from old farm workers' cottages. Roaring log fires warm the character bar, where old stone and heavy timbers create a traditional pub atmosphere.

The fabulous conservatory-style garden room is festooned with magnificent vines and plants and enjoys great country views. Here you can sit at massive, candlelit, stone tables and tuck into some good modern pub food, washed down with Yorkshire beer and decent wines. Meat is sourced from local family butchers, local shoots provide the seasonal game, local growers supply seasonal fruit and vegetables and many of the herbs are grown in the pub's garden. Begin with a warm salad of black pudding and crispy bacon and move on to traditional Lancashire hotpot with pickled red cabbage. Round off with pear-and-chocolate almond cream tart. Work it off with an invigorating local walk.

Leyburn

The Sandpiper Inn

Village inn

'Some of the best pub food in the Dales.'

Market Place, Leyburn, Wensleydale,
North Yorkshire DL8 5AT
Telephone: +44(0)1969 622206
hsandpiper99@aol.com
www.sandpiperinn.co.uk

Jonathan Harrison is cooking some of the best pub food in the Dales at his 17th-century stone cottage, just off the pretty market square in sleepy Leyburn. The comfortably spruced-up bar has an unspoilt and traditional atmosphere, with a wood-burning stove, cushioned wall benches and low dark beams, while the simple, yet stylish dining area, with its sage-green walls and rustic tables on a wooden floor, hints at Jonathan's modern approach to pub dining.

Listed on a twice-daily-changing chalkboard, light lunchtime options might include fishcakes with herb sauce, cottage pie, fish and chips, and prawn-and-rocket sandwiches. However, dinner reveals a repertoire of well-balanced modern British dishes featuring the best local produce available, notably local game and farm meats. Expect, perhaps, Wensleydale lamb with garlic sauce or halibut with lobster sauce, followed by warm Valrhona chocolate tart. If you're in need of a comfortable bed, then look no further than the two smart upstairs bedrooms or the rooms in the tastefully refurbished cottage across the road.

Rooms: 2. Double room from £70, single from £60. Cottage annex (double) £90.
Prices: Main course from £11.50. House wine £11.50.
Last orders: Food: lunch 14.30 (Sunday 14.00); dinner 21.00 (Friday and Saturday 21.30).
Closed: Monday.
Food: Modern British.
Real ale: Copper Dragon Ales, Black Sheep Best, Daleside Ales. One guest beer.
Other points: No smoking. Children welcome. Dogs welcome in the bar. Garden/terrace.
Directions: Just off Market Square in Leyburn. (Map12)
See pub walk on page 494

...for competitions

Marton

The Appletree

Marton, Pickering,
North Yorkshire YO62 6RD
Telephone: +44(0)1751 431457
appletreeinn@supanet.com
www.appletreeinn.co.uk

Country pub

'A cracking village pub.'

Prices: **Main course dinner from £10. House wine £12.**
Last orders: **Bar: afternoon 14.30 (Sunday 15.00); evening 23.00. Food: lunch 14.00 (Sunday 14.30); dinner 21.30.**
Closed: **Monday, Tuesday and two weeks in January.**
Food: **Modern British.**
Real ale: **Changing Yorkshire guest beers.**
Other points: **Smoking area. Children welcome. Car park. Wheelchair access.**
Directions: **From Kirkbymoorside on the A170, head towards Scarborough. The village is signposted to the right. (Map 12)**

Five years on since TJ and Melanie Drew transformed this village local into one of Yorkshire's best gastropubs, they have decided to scale down the operation in order to maintain the quality of the food (TJ) and service (Melanie). Dining space has been reduced to 24 covers and there is courtyard seating, a lounge and a smaller bar area, where you can order sandwiches and sup Yorkshire micro-brewery ales. Changes have been sensitive and retain the character, charm and intimacy of what is still a cracking village pub.

TJ's innovative monthly menus and daily creations make the most of quality local produce, including lamb, beef and pork from surrounding farms and homegrown herbs, fruit and vegetables. Follow excellent homemade breads with truffled mushroom soup, then opt for daube of Marton beef with horseradish cream, or roast halibut with bacon and red-wine jus. Save room for TJ's delicious petit fours with excellent coffee. In addition, expect quality wines, impeccable service from Melanie, and a shop counter laden with homemade goodies.

MEMBER 251 ENTRY

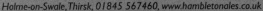

Hambleton Ales,
Holme-on-Swale, Thirsk, 01845 567460, www.hambletonales.co.uk
Nick Stafford's Hambleton Ales is a small family-run business that has flourished since its inception in 1991 on the banks of the River Swale in the heart of the Vale of York. Using malted barley and English hops, traditional ales include the award-winning Hambleton Nightmare, Stallion and Stud, a strongly bitter beer with rich hop and fruit flavours. Take a tour of the brewery and be sure to visit the shop.

The Appletree allotments
Venture to the end of the garden and you will find Melanie and Trajan's other passion – their smallholding that supplies the pub kitchen with the freshest vegetables and herbs. Developed in 2002, it has a polytunnel and neat rows of vegetables and soft fruit, while the adjoining, well-established orchard provides apples, pears, cherries and plums. Soft fruit and other suitable produce usually find their way into the delicious preserves, oils and pickles available from the shop counter in the pub.

Marton meats
Chef-patron TJ sources quality lamb, beef and pork from farms that surround the village. Beef is supplied by Whitethorn Farm, geese at Christmas come from Hall Farm, Riseborough, near Marton, while game is sourced from local shoots.

Shepherd's Purse Cheeses,
Thirsk; tel 01845 587220
The only blue cheese maker in Yorkshire produces four blue-veined cheeses as well as TJ's favourites - Olde York, a fresh ewes milk cheese and Katy's White Lavender, a sheep's cheese marinated in lavender flowers.

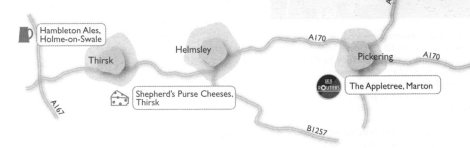

Visit the Farmers' Market
Every Tuesday in summer, a farmers' market is held in the Market Place in Malton. A big farmers' market is held at York's Auction Centre on the first and third Saturday of every month, from 9am to 1pm.

Masham

The Black Sheep Brewery

Wellgarth, Masham,
North Yorkshire HG4 4EN
Telephone: +44(0)1765 680101
sue.dempsey@blacksheep.co.uk
www.blacksheepbrewery.com

Brewery and bistro

'Take a fascinating 'shepherded' tour of the brewhouse.'

Prices: **Lunch main course from £6.95. Evening main course from £8.95. House wine £10.95.**
Last orders: **Bar: 22.50. Lunch 14.30 (Monday, Tuesday and Sunday 17.00); dinner 21.00.**
Closed: **Monday, Tuesday, Wednesday and Sunday evening and 10 days in January.**
Food: **Traditional/modern British.**
Real ale: **Black Sheep Ales.**
Other points: **Smoking area. Children welcome. Garden. Car park. Wheelchair access.**
Directions: **Masham lies midway between Ripon and Leyburn on the A6108. (Map 12)**

Established in 1992 and recently expanded by Paul Theakston, a member of Masham's famous brewing family, Black Sheep not only brews and bottles four award-winning real ales, it has an excellent visitor centre, where you will discover how Black Sheep can brew over 23 million pints a year. You can take a fascinating 'shepherded' tour of the brewhouse, which is laid out in traditional tower fashion, then enjoy a perfect pint and a meal in the spacious, split-level 'baa...r'-cum-bistro, with its wooden floors, bright check-clothed tables, brewery equipment and informal atmosphere.

At lunchtime, tuck into wholemeal sandwiches of Yorkshire ham with wholegrain Riggwelter mustard, say, and haddock in Black Sheep ale batter, or one of the chalkboard specials, perhaps rack of local lamb with rosemary-and-redcurrant sauce. The more imaginative evening menu (Thursday-Saturday) may offer fillet steak with caramelised shallots and bordelaise sauce, with homemade puddings or local Wensleydale cheese to finish. Afterwards, visit the Black Sheep shop. Cakes and set afternoon teas are also available.

Northallerton

Lovesome Hill Farm

Bed and breakfast

'Tranquillity and plenty of walking opportunities.'

Lovesome Hill, Northallerton,
North Yorkshire DL6 2PB
Telephone: +44(0)1609 772311
mail@lovesomehillfarm.co.uk
www.lovesomehillfarm.co.uk

Mary and John Pearson's 165-acre working farm near the market town of Northallerton offers tranquillity and plenty of walking opportunities — it's just 200 yards from Wainright's Coast-to-Coast walk. You can expect a warm welcome and to be well fed, from the moment Mary ushers you into the lounge with a tray of tea and homemade biscuits on arrival. Breakfast is a hearty affair, with eggs from the farm, seasonal fruits, local honey, sausages and bacon, homemade marmalade and preserves.

Dinner is cooked around local supplies, too, perhaps using home-reared meats. Delicious soups, leg of lamb with redcurrant glaze or pork with apricots, served with locally grown vegetables, and raspberry pavlova to finish are some of the dishes you can expect to tuck into. There is one bedroom in the main house; the rest are in a barn conversion, with access to the house. A neat cottage style with floral prints, some canopied beds, and delicate touches distinguish the rooms, which are all en-suite. Gate Cottage sleeps two and offers the flexibility of bed and breakfast or self-catering.

Rooms: 6. Double room from £56, single from £30 to £40, family £86.
Prices: Set dinner £20.
Closed: Rarely.
Food: Traditional English.
Other points: No smoking. Children welcome. Garden. Car park. Wheelchair access.
Directions: Four miles north of Northallerton on the A167 towards Darlington, on the right. (Map 12)

...for special offers

Osmotherley

The Golden Lion

Country inn

6 West End, Osmotherley, Thirsk,
North Yorkshire BL6 3AA
Telephone: +44(0)1609 883526

'Expect a lively and bustling atmosphere.'

Rooms: **3. Twin room from £40 per person.**
Prices: **Restaurant main course from £6.50
to £13.95. House wine from £13.50.**
Last orders: **Bar: afternoon 15.30; evening 23.00.
Food: lunch 16.00; dinner 22.00.**
Closed: **Rarely.**
Food: **Modern pub food.**
Real ale: **Hambleton Bitter, Timothy Taylor
Landlord, John Smith's Cask. One guest beer
on bank holidays.**
Other points: **Smoking area. Children welcome.
Dogs welcome in the bar. Garden.**
Directions: **Off the A19 north of Thirsk.**
(Map 12)

Set on the green overlooking the market cross in beautiful Osmotherley on the flanks of the Cleveland Hills, this wonderful old stone inn is run by affable landlord Christie Connelly. Not only is it a thriving pub that appeals to well-heeled foodies in search of imaginative, good-value cooking, but one that also welcomes walkers hiking the Lyke Wake Walk. Expect a lively and bustling atmosphere in the cosy, wood-panelled bar, with its cushioned pew seating, log fire, and inviting evening candlelight.

Simple, clean and full-flavoured dishes range from fresh mussels in wine, cream and shallots, or a deep bowl of tomato-and-basil soup for a light snack or starter, to warm salads, calves' liver with mash and peas, or sirloin steak with peppered sauce and hand-cut chips. There are good homemade burgers and vegetarian options – goat's cheese and red-pepper terrine, say – and puddings may include fresh strawberry tart and sherry trifle plus decent coffee to finish. Booking is essential at weekends. Three new en-suite bedrooms are available from September 2006 – expect them to be comfortable.

The Bull at Broughton

Country pub

'Honest, freshly prepared food using top-notch local ingredients.'

Broughton, Skipton,
North Yorkshire BD23 3AE
Telephone: +44(0)1756 792065
janeneil@thebullatbroughton.co.uk
www.thebullatbroughton.co.uk

Sleepy Broughton and the rambling, stone-built Bull are part of the Broughton Hall Estate, and the pub's rear terrace overlooks the unspoilt parkland. Sister pub to the highly acclaimed Shibden Mill Inn in West Yorkshire (see entry), it shares the same reputation for honest, freshly prepared food. Using top-notch local ingredients, Neil Butterworth produces robust, full-flavoured dishes on a sound, brasserie-style menu that has proved very popular with local diners.

Bread is baked daily and the sausages, sauces and ice creams are all made on the premises. Dishes range from light meals, such as a classic cassoulet, to smoked haddock, salmon and pollack fishcakes; chargrilled fillet steak with smoked bacon sauce; and an old-fashioned shepherd's pie. Puddings include baked spotted dick and a decent cheeseboard that comes with Swaledale Goat and Dovedale Blue. Wash it all down with a cracking pint of Bull Bitter or one of 12 wines by the glass, all served throughout cosy little rooms, each sporting heavy beams, crackling log fires and a mix of quarry-tiled and wooden floors.

Prices: Restaurant main course from £7.50. Bar main course from £4.20. House wine £10.50.
Last orders: Bar: afternoon 14.30 (Friday 15.00); evening 23.00 (Saturday all day to 23.00, Sunday all day to 19.30). Food: lunch 14.00; dinner 21.00 (Friday and Saturday 21.30, Sunday all day to 18.00).
Food: Modern British.
Real ale: Bull Bitter, Copper Dragon Ales. Two guest beers.
Other points: Smoking area. Children welcome. Dogs welcome. Garden. Wheelchair access (not WC).
Directions: Situated on the A59, three miles from Skipton. (Map 9)

Skipton

Napier's Restaurant

Restaurant-with-rooms

Chapel Hill, Skipton,
North Yorkshire BD23 1NL
Telephone: +44(0)1756 799688
info@accommodation-skipton.co.uk
www.restaurant-skipton.co.uk

'An eclectic menu may draw inspiration from around the globe but features top-notch local produce.'

Rooms: **6. Double/twin room from £75, single from £65. Family room from £90.**
Prices: **Restaurant main course from £9.95. Bar main course from £7.50. House wine £10.95.**
Last orders: **Food: lunch 14.00; dinner 21.30 (Saturday 22.00). Food served all day Sunday.**
Closed: **First two weeks of January.**
Food: **Modern European.**
Other points: **Totally no smoking. Children welcome. Car park. Wheelchair access.**
Directions: **Exit 14/M65. Follow signs for the A56 and A59 to Skipton. Go to the top of the High Street towards the church, take a left at the roundabout, then take the first right. Napier's is set slightly back on Chapel Hill. (Map 9)**

Tucked away off the High Street in the oldest part of Skipton, just a stone's throw from the parish church and castle, Napier's is a distinctive restaurant-with-rooms, offering quality food based around fresh local ingredients, and superior rooms for travellers exploring the Dales. Typically traditional, rather than trend-influenced, the appealing restaurant has a relaxed, French-bistro feel, with well-spaced tables on a tiled floor. Both the compact and grand bedrooms reflect the age of the building, which dates from the 13th century, with ancient oak beams and period furnishings.

An eclectic menu may draw inspiration from around the globe but features top-notch local produce, including well-hung beef, and fresh seafood delivered daily from Fleetwood. Sausages, black pudding, ice creams and bread are made on the premises. A typical meal may start with chargrilled lemongrass king prawns with Vietnamese salad, followed by calves' liver with mustard mash and Burgundy gravy, or rack of Yorkshire lamb with red wine and redcurrant sauce, with apple-and-coconut crumble among the puddings.

Skipton

The Tempest Arms Country Inn

Country inn

'Alongside four cracking Yorkshire beers and 10 wines by the glass, you can order some good pub food from an interesting menu.'

Elslack, Skipton,
North Yorkshire BD23 3AY
Telephone: +44(0)1282 842450
info@tempestarms.co.uk
www.tempestarms.co.uk

Just off the A56 near its junction with the A59 on the edge of the Yorkshire Dales National Park, this fine, 300-year-old stone inn nestles in a verdant hollow with its own stream winding picturesquely round the garden. Although it is now a great deal more than a simple village pub, thanks to a recent extension to the purpose-built block of bedrooms behind, it retains the character, style and atmosphere of a civilised country inn. The interior, with its oak beams, mix of wood and carpeted floors, old wooden settles and real log fires, is comfortable and welcoming.

Alongside four cracking Yorkshire beers and 10 wines by the glass, you can order some good pub food from an interesting menu that serves both the bar and restaurant. Typically, tuck into fish pie, Bolton Abbey rib-eye steak au poivre, pork pie with mushy peas and piccalilli, roast cod loin wrapped in pancetta with langoustine jus, or pan-fried venison with wild-mushroom sauce. Spacious new bedrooms are beautifully furnished with hand-crafted furniture and have superior bathrooms and super views.

Rooms: **21. Double/twin room from £74.95, single from £59.95. Family room from £108.95. Executive suite from £99, single from £74.95.**
Prices: **Restaurant main course from £8.95. Bar main course from £8.95. House wine £10.95.**
Last orders: **Restaurant: lunch 14.30; dinner 21.00 (Friday and Saturday 21.30, Sunday 19.30).**
Closed: **Rarely.**
Food: **Modern British.**
Real ale: **Taylor's Ales, Black Sheep Ales, Theakston Best, Wharfedale Folly Ale, Copper Dragon Ales, Tetley's Bitter.**
Other points: **Smoking area. Children welcome. Dogs welcome overnight. Garden. Car park. Licence for civil weddings. Wheelchair access. Function rooms.**
Directions: **Exit 13/M65. Follow signs to Skipton on the A56 through Thornton-in-Craven, then take the next left. (Map 9)**

...for recipe ideas

MEMBER ENTRY
257

Whitby

The Magpie Café

14/15 Pier Road, Whitby,
North Yorkshire YO21 3PU
Telephone: +44(0)1947 602058
ian@magpiecafe.co.uk
www.magpiecafe.co.uk

Seaside restaurant

'Its quality fish is legendary – halibut, salmon or boxes of lobster are delivered daily, fresh off the boats in the quayside.'

Prices: **Main course from £5.95. House wine £9.95.**
Last orders: **Food: 21.00.**
Closed: **Mid January-early February.**
Food: **Seafood.**
Other points: **No smoking. Children welcome. Wheelchair access.**
Directions: **Directly opposite the fish market on Whitby's harbourside. (Map 12)**

You'd hope to find a good fish restaurant in a fishing port, and The Magpie Café satisfies on all levels. The 18th-century building overlooks the harbour and Abbey ruins and has long been associated with fishing. The Café moved to this site in 1937 and recently expanded into the next-door premises to provide more seating and a takeaway counter. Its quality fish is legendary, so much so that queues have to make way for the daily deliveries of halibut, salmon or boxes of lobster fresh off the boats in the quayside.

Its traditional fish and chips, either haddock or cod, are renowned. There are also plenty of grilled and poached options, and much else to tempt besides. Owner Ian Robson has an extensive repertoire, taking in fish pies and speciality recipes such as seafood chowder and whole Dover sole, served plain or with a garlic or lemon-and-chive butter. The meat dishes, such as own-boiled ham with homemade coleslaw and rib-eye steak with pepper sauce, are equally good and are made using locally sourced ingredients. If you have room, the nursery puds, such as jam roly-poly, won't disappoint.

Restaurant and bar

'Enjoy a drink in the contemporary upstairs bar, which has fantastic harbour views.'

Quayside

7 Pier Road, Whitby,
North Yorkshire YO21 3PU
Telephone: +44(0)1947 602059
carol@fusco123.wanadoo.co.uk
www.fuscowhitby.com

The Fusco family has been producing fish and chips in Whitby since the 1950s and took over the Quayside in 1999. With the fish market on its doorstep, it is in the enviable position of having the pick of the local catch for its traditionally cooked fare. The freshest fish supplies are cooked in the family's special batter and accompanied by its special crinkle-cut chips, and the popularity of this menu continues to grow. Whitby cod, wholetail scampi, a seafood platter and homemade fishcakes are just a few of the piscine favourites on offer, but those looking for meat and vegetarian dishes are well catered for too, with homemade steak pie and cream cheese and broccoli bake.

The three-storey building, once changing facilities for returning fishermen, is open-plan and airy, helped not only by air conditioning but a good eye for décor. The tiled floors are offset with dark green timbered walls, attractive lighting and cast-iron tables. It is claimed Bram Stoker wrote some of his Dracula stories in the first-floor library. Before dining, enjoy a drink in the contemporary upstairs bar, which has fantastic harbour views.

Prices: **Restaurant main course from £6.75. House wine £8.**
Last orders: **Food: 20.00.**
Closed: **December and January, excluding Boxing Day and school holidays.**
Food: **Traditional British.**
Other points: **No smoking. Children welcome. Wheelchair access.**
Directions: **(Map 12)**

...for events

Rishworth

The Old Bore

Oldham Road, Rishworth, Halifax,
West Yorkshire HX6 4QU
Telephone: +44(0)1422 822291
www.oldbore.co.uk

Country pub

'Ambitious modern dishes made from the finest available local produce.'

Prices: **Set lunch £10.95. Restaurant main course from £9.45. Bar main course from £9.45. House wine £11.95.**
Last orders: **Food: lunch 14.15 (Sunday 16.00); dinner: 21.30 (Saturday 22.00, Sunday 20.00).**
Closed: **Monday and the first two weeks of January.**
Real ale: **Old Bore Bitter, Timothy Taylor Landlord, Moorhouses.**
Other points: **Smoking area. Children welcome. Dogs welcome in the bar. Garden. Car park. Wheelchair access.**
Directions: **Exit 22/M62. Take the A58 towards Ripponden. The pub is three miles along on the left after the reservoir. (Map 9)**

A quirky name for a unique pub – Scott Hessel's tucked-away, stone-built dining pub below Rishworth Moor. With valuable experience at Michelin-starred restaurants across Europe, Scott has wowed the local foodies since opening in September 2004. He cooks with flair and imagination, producing ambitious modern dishes made from the finest available local produce – Dexter beef from Pike End Farm in Rishworth, game from Yorkshire estates, and Ryburn lamb.

Expect the likes of Whitby crab and shrimp fishcake with corn velouté and shellfish, saddle of roe deer with pigeon pie, red wine and chocolate, and, for Sunday lunch, roast organic pork loin. To drink, there are five gins, up to five Yorkshire ales and a raft of quality wines. Contrasting the traditional bar area are three very individual dining experiences; one with white cloths and sparkling Riedel glasses, another painted deep red and perfect for winter dining, and a new room kitted out in hunting-lodge style. Add a host of interesting paintings and artefacts, and a landscaped terraced garden and you'll find, like us, that Scott's place is far from boring!

www.routiers.co.uk

Shibden

Shibden Mill Inn

Country inn

'A rather fine place to stay the night.'

Shibden Mill Fold, Shibden, Halifax,
West Yorkshire HX3 7UL
Telephone: +44(0)1422 365840
shibdenmillinn@zoom.co.uk
www.shibdenmillinn.com

The carefully renovated 17th-century corn mill lies hidden in the folds of the wooded Shibden Valley, overlooking the babbling Red Beck. A lovely peaceful spot just minutes from the hustle and bustle of Halifax. While retaining an appealing rustic tone, sympathetic refurbishment has succeeded admirably at the difficult task of creating, simultaneously, a simple pubby brasserie with oak beams, open fires and stone-flagged floors, a restaurant with serious aspirations, and a rather fine place to stay the night. The streamside terrace is floodlit and heated at night.

Simplicity and good local ingredients appear to be the key to the food operation; clear, well-defined flavours are to be seen in a starter of smoked venison, parsnip risotto and chocolate oil, and in Old Spot pork chop with shallot sauce. Own-baked bread deserves a special mention, as does the in-house shop of homemade goodies, the excellent bar food, and the passion for sourcing fresh local produce. Wines are well chosen, with a Connoisseur Collection adding weight. There are 12 bedrooms, all comfortably decorated with style.

Rooms: 12. Double room from £72, single from £68.
Prices: Main course from £10. Main course bar meal from £8. House wine £9.95.
Last orders: Bar: afternoon 15.00; evening 23.00 (all day Saturday and Sunday). Food: lunch 14.00 (all day Sunday); dinner 21.30 (Sunday 19.30).
Closed: Rarely.
Food: Modern British.
Real ale: John Smith's Cask, Theakston Ales, Shibden Mill Inn Bitter. Two guest beers.
Other points: Smoking area. Children welcome. Garden. Car park.
Directions: Exit 26/M62 on the A58; turn right into Kell Lane at Stump Cross Inn (near the A6036 junction), the pub is then signposted. (Map 9)

...for competitions

Channel
Islands

Herm Island

White House Hotel

Herm, via Guernsey, Herm GY1 3HR
Telephone: +44 (0)1481 722159
hotel@herm-island.com
www.herm-island.com

Seaside hotel

'The picturesque White House Hotel is the perfect get-away-from-it-all destination.'

Rooms: 40. Room from £73 per person, half board.
Prices: Set menu £29.75 (including boat fare). Main course lunch from £6. House wine £9.95.
Last orders: Bar: 23.00. Food: lunch 14.00; dinner 21.00.
Closed: From the second week of October to April.
Food: Traditional/modern British and French.
Other points: Smoking area. Children welcome. Garden. No cars on Herm Island. Tennis court. Swimming pool. Croquet lawn.
Directions: Fly or take the boat to Guernsey. There is a regular 20-minute boat service to the island. (Map 4)

Originally the private residence of Prince Blucher, who owned Herm Island, the picturesque White House Hotel is the perfect get-away-from-it-all destination. The only hotel on the car-free island, it sets dazzlingly high standards. Despite the island's peacefulness, there is plenty to do: walking, birdwatching, and exploring. The hotel was created from an old house in 1949 by Peter and Jenny Wood, and is now run by their daughter Penny and son-in-law Adrian.

It has extensive lounges with open fires, a library, games cupboard, solar-heated swimming pool, tennis court and croquet lawn. The best bedrooms have sea views, and all rooms, by popular demand, have no TV or phone. With oyster beds visible from the dining room, local seafood is as fresh as you can get. Local shellfish – lobsters, crabs or scallops – is available as a supplement to the set evening menu. Alternatively, you could opt for sliced smoked goose breast with brandied chilli berries or pan-fried fillet of local sea bass with truffle oil and lime juice. The French-heavy wine list offers a range of well-priced bottles.

www.routiers.co.uk

St Brelade

Chateâu Valeuse

Seaside hotel

'A sun terrace overlooking the garden is the perfect place to enjoy a light lunch.'

Rue de la Valeuse, St Brelade's Bay,
St Brelade, Jersey JE3 8EE
Telephone: +44(0)1534 746281
chatval@itl.net
http://user.super.net.uk/~chatval

Chateâu Valeuse enjoys a peaceful south-facing location, set back from the road and surrounded by impeccably maintained gardens, with the added attraction of stunning views across St Brelade's Bay, one of the most attractive in Jersey. With its large windows and impressive array of balconies, the hotel is more splendid Swiss chalet in style than traditional French pile. Excellent-value bedrooms, many with sea-view balconies, are all comfortably furnished and well maintained, and have pristine bathrooms.

A sun terrace overlooking the garden is the perfect place to enjoy a light lunch or early-evening apéritif, or you can relax in the Tudor Bar, while the more energetic can make the most of the outdoor swimming pool and putting green. In the restaurant, you can choose between the good four-course table d'hôte – perhaps moules marinière, or tiger prawns and mussels in garlic butter, followed by chargrilled pork fillets with tarragon-and-mustard cream or fresh grilled plaice. Choose your pudding from a trolley that is laden with delights.

Rooms: 34. Rooms from £35 per person.
Prices: Sunday lunch £15. Set dinner £21
(four courses). House wine £8.
Last orders: Food: snacks 14.00; dinner 20.45.
Closed: Sunday evening and from November to March for non-residents.
Food: European.
Other points: No smoking. Children over five welcome. Garden. Car park.
Directions: From the airport, take the B4 south towards St Brelade's Bay, then the B6 (La Route de la Baie). Turn left into Rue de la Valeuse; the hotel is on the left. (Map 4)

...for special offers

MEMBER ENTRY

St Martin

Le Frère Restaurant

Restaurant

Rozel Hill, St Martin, Jersey JE3 6AN
Telephone: +44(0)1534 861000
lefrere@jerseymail.co.uk
www.lefrerejersey.com

'With such great views, dining alfresco here is a joy.'

Prices: Set lunch from £15 and dinner from £18.50. Restaurant main course from £15.50. Bar main course from £7. House wine £14.
Last orders: Food: lunch 14.00; dinner: 21.00 (Tuesday to Saturday).
Closed: Monday all day and Sunday night.
Food: Modern British.
Other points: Smoking area in the bar. Children welcome. Garden. Car park. Licence for civil weddings. Wheelchair access.
Directions: (Map 4)

Owner Simon Dufty has created a casually elegant feel to his exciting, new-look restaurant, located on the clifftop at Rozel, with breathtaking sea views towards the French coast. The menu gives more than a nod to the noble cooking of that country. Chef Ludovic Desmoulins uses the amazing seafood and other local ingredients to great effect in the table d'hôte, lunch and carte menus.

From the extensive carte, there are Jersey oysters, moules marinière, crab salad with wasabi mayonnaise, and goat's cheese salad, followed by a middle course of, say, duo of artichoke soup, with mains of Jersey lobster, roast turbot with thyme-and-lemon butter, lamb fillet with rosemary jus, or calves' liver with onion mash. For pudding, try the bitter-lemon tart or the melting chocolate pudding with Jersey cream. There is something for everyone, including a good range of lighter lunchtime and vegetarian dishes, and an excellent, exclusive selection of wines from around the world. With such great views, dining alfresco here is a joy. It is licensed for weddings and has three luxury self-contained suites.

La Sablonnerie

Seaside hotel

Little Sark, Sark GY9 0SD
Telephone: +44 (0)1481 832061

'The hotel sends a horse-drawn barouche to collect you from the tiny harbour.'

As soon as you set foot on Sark, you enter a world of tranquillity and luxury. La Sablonnerie is a magical place and ensures the ultimate get-away-from-it-all experience. A break here is memorable from the start – the hotel sends a horse-drawn barouche to collect you from the tiny harbour to take you to Little Sark at the southernmost tip. The 16th-century farmhouse and cottages that make up La Sablonnerie are delightful and set in extensive grounds.

Owned and run by the Perrée family since 1946, daughter Elizabeth is now at the helm. The heart of the hotel is the low-beamed bar with its granite walls and massive fireplace that has roaring fires in winter. All the traditional charm has been maintained in the public rooms and individually decorated bedrooms. This is a top place to dine, too, as its own farm supplies fresh fruit, vegetables, dairy produce and meat for the restaurant, while locally caught lobsters and oysters are a regular feature on the menu. Dinner may take in roasted scallops with garlic butter, fillet of home-reared beef, and crème brûlée with exotic fruits and berries.

Rooms: 22, 12 en-suite. Rooms from £30 to £60 per person.
Prices: Set lunch £19.80 and dinner £20.80. House wine £7.50.
Last orders: Food: lunch 14.30; dinner 21.30.
Closed: From mid October to Easter.
Food: Modern French.
Other points: Smoking area. Children welcome. Dogs welcome overnight. Garden.
Directions: Fly to Guernsey and take the boat to Sark. (Map 4)

...for the latest news

Scotland

Ballater

The Station Restaurant

Station Square, Ballater,
Aberdeenshire AB35 5RB
Telephone: +44(0)13397 55050

Café and restaurant

'Breakfasts offer real indulgences, either Scottish porridge with honey and cream or the full Scottish monty.'

Prices: **Restaurant main course from £6.**
House wine £12.
Last orders: Food: lunch 17.00; dinner 21.00.
Seasonal variations.
Closed: Rarely.
Food: Scottish.
Other points: No smoking. **Children welcome.**
Car park.
Directions: In central Ballater – the old Royal
Station. (Map 14)

Ballater is well known for its close association with the Royal Family – Balmoral Castle is eight miles away – and no place more so than the small railway station that welcomed visiting royals from the 1860s until its closure in 1966. After major structural restoration, hotelier and railway enthusiast Nigel Franks revamped these refreshment rooms, transforming them into an informal restaurant, but staying true to the spirit of the place. The setting has a period, film-set feel, thanks to the fact that many of the original features, such as stunning wood panelling and a smoked-glass ceiling, are still in place. These are tastefully offset by Lloyd Loom wicker chairs and marble tables.

The food, mainly locally sourced ingredients, puts your average station snacks well and truly into the sidings. Breakfasts offer real indulgences – either Scottish porridge with honey and cream or the full Scottish monty. Later in the day, eat like a king, sampling homemade cakes, scones and caramel shortbread. Lighter dishes of soup, sweetcorn fritters with bacon, roasted tomatoes and rocket, and the daily specials, are a delight.

www.routiers.co.uk

Restaurant

'Sample whiskies from the 45-strong collection.'

Auchmithie, by Arbroath,
Angus DD11 5SQ
Telephone: +44(0)1241 877223

A "but 'n' ben" means a two-roomed cottage in Scots tongue and you'll find Margaret Horn's friendly and cosy little restaurant in two fisherman's cottages that have been knocked into one to form a lounge bar and dining area. If you want to sample the flavours of Scotland, just one meal here would give you a taster of what's so good about the indigenous ingredients. Her menu is unpretentious and she presents her dishes beautifully.

Linger over the menu in the lounge before heading through to dine, where the ambience is just as welcoming. There's a real wood fire at one end and the furniture is rustic country-pine style. Lunch focuses on the excellent local seafood of lobster, crabs, prawns and langoustines, supplemented by game and Aberdeen Angus beef. At dinner, dishes become more lavish, with haddock stuffed with prawns in a creamy cheese sauce or medallions of venison pan fried with red rowan jelly and juniper berries. After dinner, sample whiskies from the 45-strong collection. Margaret also serves a mean home-baked afternoon tea, which is a real treat.

Prices: Lunch à la carte menu from £6.50. Evening à la carte menu from £8.20. High Tea set menu £9.95. House wine £10.
Last orders: Food: lunch 14.30; dinner 21.30. High teas served between 16.00 and 17.30.
Closed: Tuesday.
Food: Traditional Scottish.
Other points: No smoking. Children welcome. Car park.
Directions: From Arbroath head north towards Montrose on the A92. Leaving Arbroath, Auchmithie is signposted on the right, approximately two miles away. The But 'n' Ben is the first gable end on the left at the village entrance. (Map 14)

...for recipe ideas

Cardross

Ardardan Estate Farm Shop & Nursery

Farm shop and café

Cardross, Argyll & Bute G82 5HD
Telephone: +44(0)1389 849188
enquiries@ardardan.co.uk
www.ardardan.co.uk

'A delicious array of Scottish produce.'

Last orders: Tearoom 16.00, shop 17.00.
Closed: Monday, except bank holidays.
Food: Light lunches and home-baking.
Other points: No smoking. Children welcome.
Garden and patio. Car park. Wheelchair access.
Directions: From the M8, go over the Erskine
Bridge. The shop is two miles from Cardross on
the A814 towards Helensburgh. (Map 14)

This nursery and farm shop occupies a beautiful spot on the west coast of Scotland, just 10 miles west of Glasgow, and it's worth visiting for this reason alone, even before you take into consideration the stunning array of produce they sell. It's run by the Montgomery family, who stock the shop with a bountiful selection of fresh produce from their farm's 120 acres, plus homemade cakes and breads and much more besides. Aberdeen Angus beef and grocery lines – from cheeses and smoked and cured meats and fish to preserves and organic ice cream – make up a delicious array of Scottish produce.

By popular demand, the family has opened a tearoom that showcases its homemade soups and light lunches – perhaps chicken and cranberry or Inverawe smoked salmon and cream-cheese sandwiches, or ploughman's platters – as well its wonderful home-baking. After refreshments, head out to the nursery, set in a walled garden with a plant house that stocks a comprehensive array of plants. There are experienced staff on hand to help with garden and planting advice, and they are also specialists on hardy perennials.

Isle of Bute

Russian Tavern at The Port Royal Hotel

Waterside inn

'They excel in real ales, but there's also Russian stout.'

37 Marine Road, Kames Bay,
Port Bannatynne,
Argyll & Bute PA20 0LW
Telephone: +44(0)1700 505073
stay@butehotel.com
www.russiantavern.co.uk

A mere 50 yards from the new marina built in Kames Bay in the old Highland village of Port Bannatyne, this waterfront pub has an interesting history. In World War II, it was used as HQ of the Midget submarines that hunted German destroyers off Norway. The pub has an international influence, thanks to Norwegian-born landlord Dag Crawford and his Russian wife Olga. The stone-built Georgian building overlooks the bay, where fishermen catch the fish and langoustines that feature on the menu.

Dag cooks a Russian-style brasserie menu, based on recipes from the Tsarist kitchen archives in St Petersburg, but using local fish, beef from Orkney and vegetables and salad from his garden. His beef stroganoff is legendary, but gets strong competition from Highland ox steak with blackberry and brandy-sauce latkas. Dinner is remarkably good value, consisting of, say, a plate of smoked sprats, followed by steamed duck with apple sauce and a dessert of Russian chocolate gateau. They excel in real ales, but there's also Russian stout. There are five unpretentious, good-value bedrooms.

Rooms: 5, 3 not en suite. From £25 per person.
Prices: Set lunch and dinner £20. Main course £18. Bar main course from £6.50. House wine £10.50.
Last orders: Bar: 01.00 (Saturday 02.00).
Closed: From 1 to 28 November.
Food: Traditional Russian.
Real ale: Arran Blonde & Dark, Fyne Highlander, Fyne Piper's Gold, Fyne Vital Spark, Kelburn's Cart Blanche.
Other points: No smoking. Children welcome. Car park. Five free yacht moorings. Beach. Golf course at the rear. Wheelchair access.
Directions: Three miles north along the coast road from Rothesay on the Isle of Bute and six miles south on the coast road from the ferry at Colintraive, Argyll. (Map 13)

...for events

Luss

Coach House Coffee Shop

All-day café

Loch Lomond Trading Co Ltd, Luss, Loch Lomond,
Loch Lomond Trossachs National Park,
Argyll & Bute G83 8NN
Telephone: +44(0)1436 860341
enquiries@lochlomondtrading.com
www.lochlomondtrading.com

*'This shop and coffee shop draws
the crowds all day.'*

Prices: **Meals from £6.**
Last orders: **Food: 17.00.**
Closed: **25 December.**
Food: **Modern Scottish.**
Other points: **No smoking. Children welcome.
Garden. Wheelchair access.**
Directions: **From the A82, follow the signs
for Luss. The café is next to the church in the
centre of the village. (Map 14)**

Set in the centre of one of the most visited
villages on the banks of Loch Lomond, this
shop and coffee shop draws the crowds all
day, but manages the high demand efficiently.
Although it looks like an old-style coaching
house, this is, in fact, a new building with
traditional-style exposed beams and a rustic
stone fireplace. It's a friendly stop-off, offering
light refreshments and substantial meals along
the regional-speciality line. Owner Rowena
Ferguson and her excellent staff make you
feel welcome and ensure an ever-revolving
line-up of treats.

The bedrocks of the menu include home-
baked scones and cakes, light lunches of
cullen skink, quiche with coleslaw, salad and
fresh bread, or filled ciabattas. Haggis, neeps
and tatties, and bacon-and-courgette pasta
are the more filling lunch dishes, and they
don't stint on the portions. The choice of
beverages, such as cappuccinos and lattes,
speciality teas and smoothies, is long enough
to require a separate menu, although you
won't find any whisky-liqueur coffees here, as
they don't have a licence. Don't forget to visit
the well-stocked shop.

Rothesay

Brechin's Brasserie

Restaurant

'The brightly coloured lemon-and-blue brasserie is a cheery addition to the Rothesay landscape.'

2 Bridgend Street, Rothesay, Isle of Bute,
Argyll & Bute PA20 0HU
Telephone: +44(0)1700 502922
info@brechins-bute.com
www.brechins-bute.com

Owners Tim and Ann Saul have not looked back since opening this upmarket brasserie in this bustling town. Their brightly coloured lemon-and-blue brasserie is a cheery addition to the Rothesay landscape. Much of the success of their popular menus is down to the quality local ingredients used in the breakfasts, snacks and hot meals available throughout the day. On Fridays and Saturdays, they also offer an evening restaurant menu.

Ann is in charge of the kitchen, while Tim sees to front-of-house. Lattes, cappuccinos and Americanos make great accompaniments for the luscious French pastries and puds, while filled ciabatta, salads and hot dishes, such as seafood pasta, vegetable lasagne and a curry bowl, are ideal for lunch. At dinner, the menu features smoked trout and salmon from Ritchie's of Rothesay, Isle of Bute lamb, and steak and beef from Richard H McIntyre of Rothesay. These ingredients translate into seafood bisque or homemade salmon mousse, followed by peppered rib-eye steak or rack of lamb, with chocolate mousse to finish. The short wine list has classics at reasonable prices.

Prices: **Restaurant evening main course from £7.95. Lunchtime snack from £4.95. House wine £9.95.**

Last orders: **Food: lunch 15.00; dinner 21.00 (Friday and Saturday only).**

Closed: **Sunday and Monday all day and Tuesday to Thursday evening. Open for dinner Thursday during July and August.**

Food: **Scottish/English/European.**

Other points: **No smoking. Children welcome. Wheelchair access.**

Directions: **Take the main road to Wemyss Bay and the Calmac Ferry to Rothesay. The brasserie is situated in the town centre, 400 yards from the ferry terminal and marina. (Map 13)**

...for competitions

Tobermory

Fisherman's Pier Fish and Chip Van

Raraig House, Tobermory,
Argyll & Bute PA75 6PU
Telephone: +44(0)1688 302390
scotshopbiz@aol.com
www.silverswift.co.uk/van.htm

Takeaway

'Fish and chunky-cut chips have never tasted so good.'

Prices: Average price of meal £3.80.
Last orders: 21.00.
Closed: Sunday.
Food: Seafood.
Directions: On the Fisherman's Pier in Tobermory. (Map 13)

Jeanette Gallagher and Jane MacLean's smart black-and-gold takeaway fish-and-chip van on Fisherman's Pier serves stupendously good fish and chips in a superb location overlooking Tobermory Bay. After sightseeing round the island or visiting the nearby Tobermory Distillery, this is the perfect place to stop for lunch or supper. The two friends are into their second decade of trading and have built up a loyal following of regular customers who come from miles around.

Park up at the Clock Tower or by the lobster and prawn creels on the Pier before ordering your meal, which is freshly prepared in no time. Fish comes straight off the boats and into the van, where it is cooked to order. Haddock, for example, is supplied by Taste of Argyll, Oban, while the freshest local scallops are supplied by Grampian Seafood off its fishing vessel Western Belle, which is skippered by Jeanette's son Geoffrey. Come rain or shine, the queues are long, but always good-humoured, and there's plenty of banter from the double act. Fish and chunky-cut chips have never tasted so good.

Tobermory

Highland Cottage

Hotel

'Staying here is a pleasure and a treat.'

Breadalbane Street, Tobermory, Argyll & Bute PA75 6PD
Telephone: +44(0)1688 302030
davidandjo@highlandcottage.co.uk
www.highlandcottage.co.uk

Set on the beautiful island of Mull, there is a feeling of luxury about this Highland accommodation. The cream-painted terrace is distinctive from the entrance – a black-timber canopy over the door with Victorian coach lights either side – and its period charm continues inside. A comfortable lounge in a conservatory is great for relaxing, while dinner is served in the attractive dining room, where the smartly dressed tables are set with cut-glass crystal and linen tablecloths.

Dishes include local specialities and start with, say, Croig crabcakes with chilli-and-caper dressing before moving on to mains of roast West Coast monkfish or loin of lamb with redcurrant-and-rosemary jus. Puddings are the comforting sort and include cranachan with raspberries. David and Jo Currie have a table licence and dispense other drinks on an honesty basis from an oak dresser. The level of accommodation is excellent and the six en-suite rooms have superior beds, hospitality trays, DVD players and white fluffy robes. The Curries have an excellent eye for detail, which, coupled with their hospitality, makes staying here a pleasure and a treat.

Rooms: 6. Double/twin room from £125, single from £100.
Prices: Set dinner £37.50 (five courses). House wine £10.
Last orders: Food: Dinner 21.00.
Closed: November-February.
Food: Modern Scottish/International.
Other points: No smoking. Children over 10 welcome. Dogs welcome. Garden. Car park. Wheelchair access.
Directions: From the main ferry port of Craignure, head for Tobermory (approximately 25 minutes' drive). On approaching Tobermory, at the mini roundabout, go straight across the narrow stone bridge and immediately turn right. Highland Cottage is opposite the Fire Station. (Map 13)

...for special offers

Ballantrae

Balkissock Lodge

Bed and breakfast

Ballantrae, Girvan, South Ayrshire KA26 0LP
Telephone: +44(0)1465 831537
frananden@aol.com
www.balkissocklodge.co.uk

'Fresh country air and peaceful contemplation in comfortable surroundings.'

Rooms: **4. Double room from £29 per person, single from £48, family from £90.**
Prices: **Set dinner £20.**
Last orders: **Dinner served at around 19.00.**
Closed: **Rarely.**
Food: **Modern British.**
Other points: **No smoking. Garden. Car park.**
Directions: **Three miles off the A77 near Ballantrae. On the south side of Ballantrae, take the turn signposted to the campsite. At the T-junction, turn right, bear left at the fork and continue for one mile. The lodge is on the right.** (Map 11)

Balkissock has been a shooting lodge and farm, but it now more than fulfils its remit as an attractive guesthouse. Fresh country air and peaceful contemplation in comfortable surroundings, plus a warm welcome from hospitable hosts Denis and Fran Sweeney, are guaranteed. The lounge is stylishly decorated in cream with comfy sofas, cushions and throws, and a real fire creates a warm glow in winter. The three en-suite bedrooms have been designed to the same high standards. The largest has an adjoining single room and is perfect for families, while the other two are in the converted barn.

Breakfast in the conservatory offers the best of Scottish fare, including porridge, smoked salmon and scrambled eggs. At dinner, the Sweeneys share the cooking, for which they have a real flair. Fran makes the starters and puddings, which may include smoked-haddock and celery soup, and prune-and-chocolate torte, while Denis cooks the mains using local and homegrown ingredients, for example, duck with port-and-berry jus or roast salmon with olive and sun-dried tomato crust. Bring your own wine.

Kinfauns Farm,
Perth and Kinross
Fran fills her cheeseboard with Kinfauns' fabulous cheeses, notably Bishop Kennedy, Howgate, Camembert, and Ayrshire blue cheeses. You can buy these from The Tryst Farm Shop (26 West High Street, Crieff or online at www.the-tryst.co.uk)

Galloway Smokehouse,
Carsluith, Newton Stewart, 01671 820354,
www.gallowaysmokehouse.co.uk
Apart from its popular smoked Scottish salmon, trout, seafood and game are first salted and then gently smoked with whisky-cask sawdust for a gentle, yet distinctive flavour. Both hot- and cold-smoked foods are available at the smokehouse shop.

Ballantrae Fishermen
The fishermen bring in fresh crab and lobster from their day boats, and prepare them at home. You can buy them direct – just head to the harbour and you'll see a signpost directing you to the individual sellers.

Woodlands Farm Shop,
Girvan
Stock up on local goodies, from fresh fruit and vegetables to fabulous local meats, cheeses, heather-scented honey, and preserves.

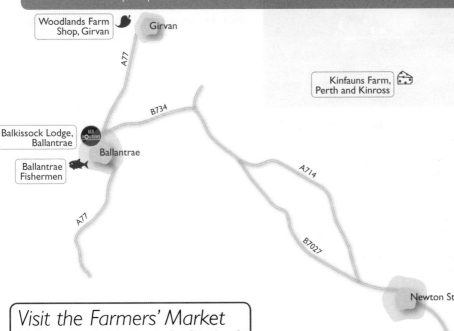

Woodlands Farm Shop, Girvan

Girvan

A77

Kinfauns Farm, Perth and Kinross

B734

Balkissock Lodge, Ballantrae

Ballantrae

Ballantrae Fishermen

A714

A77

B7027

Newton Stewart

Galloway Smokehouse, Newton Stewart

A75

Visit the Farmers' Market
Ayr farmers' market is held on the first Saturday of every month at River Street Ayr. For details, visit www.scottishfarmersmarkets.co.uk

Castle Douglas

Craigadam

Bed and breakfast

Castle Douglas,
Dumfries and Galloway DG7 3HU
Telephone: +44(0)1556 650233
inquiry@craigadam.com
www.craigadam.com

'Dinner is served house-party style around a massive communal table.'

Rooms: 7. Double/twin room from £80, single from £50.
Prices: Set dinner £19. House wine £9.95.
Last orders: Dinner served at 19.00.
Closed: From 24 December to 2 January.
Other points: Smoking area. Children welcome. Dogs welcome. Garden. Car park.
Directions: M74. Leave the motorway on the A75 to Dumfries. Follow signs to Castle Douglas. After nine miles, go through the village of Crocketford and turn right on to the A712. Craigadam is two miles along on the right. (Map 11)

Celia Pickup runs this 300-year-old farmhouse as a charming guesthouse, but with the space, style and service of a country-house hotel, while husband Richard runs the farm along organic lines and organises shooting parties, stalking and fishing in the surrounding 25,000 acres of farmland, woodland and moorland. The dedication they bring to their farm business is extended to the welcome they afford guests, who benefit from the attention to detail in evidence from the dinner table to the bedrooms.

Dinner is served house-party style around a massive communal table in the oak-panelled dining room, which has an honesty bar and snooker table. Locally smoked salmon, estate game, with homegrown vegetables, home-baked bread and regional cheeses, make for a fine meal that may include rack of home-reared lamb with Meaux mustard and medallions of roe venison with blackberries. All seven en-suite bedrooms are decorated in different themes and are beautifully furnished; many have French doors opening on to a gravelled courtyard. There is also a three-bedroom self-catering cottage.

Castle Douglas
Croys

Bed and breakfast

Old Bridge of Urr, Castle Douglas,
Dumfries and Galloway DG7 3EX
Telephone: +44(0)1556 650237
alanwithall@aol.com
www.croys-house.co.uk

'Guests are welcome to wander freely through the magnificent topiary and walled gardens.'

Alan and Pat Withall's rather grand B&B is hidden in 35 acres of glorious parkland, woodland and gardens beside the River Urr. The fine country house dates from the 18th century and guests are welcome to wander freely through the magnificent topiary and walled gardens, and meet the rare-breed animals – belted Galloway cattle, Jacob and Shetland sheep, and Tamworth pigs.

You'll be well looked after from the moment you step through the door, and Pat's memorable dinners, served at a huge oak table, are well worth staying in for. Using farm-reared meats and homegrown fruits and vegetables, a typical meal may include beef in herb-and-juniper sauce, Moroccan lamb with apricots and toasted almonds, and blackcurrants in cinnamon and lemon pastry, with coffee taken by the log fire in the beautifully furnished lounge. Upstairs, the three spacious bedrooms (one en suite) are furnished in equally grand style, featuring antique French beds or four-posters, Victorian period furniture and original architecture.

Rooms: 3, 2 with private bathrooms. Double/twin room from £35 per person.
Prices: Set dinner £17.50.
Last orders: Dinner 20.00.
Closed: Rarely.
Other points: Totally no smoking. Dog kennels available. Garden. Children welcome. Car park.
Directions: From Dumfries, head west along the A75. A couple of miles after Springholm, turn right on to the B794 towards Corsock. After a mile, turn right at the crossroads beside the red telephone box. A short distance up the hill, you will see a white gate on your right; turn in here and follow the driveway to the house. (Map 11)

...for the latest news

Isle of Whithorn

The Steam Packet Inn

Harbourside inn

Harbour Row, Newton Stewart,
Isle of Whithorn,
Dumfries and Galloway DG8 8LL
Telephone: +44(0)1988 500334
steampacketinn@btconnect.com
www.steampacketinn.com

'One of the prettiest natural harbours in this part of Scotland.'

Rooms: 7. Double room from £50, single from £30.
Prices: Main course from £7. Bar snacks from £5. House wine £11.50.
Last orders: Bar: 23.00 (Friday and Saturday 24.00). Food: lunch 14.00; dinner 21.00.
Closed: The bar is closed from 14.30 to 18.00, October to March.
Food: British, with seafood as a speciality.
Real ale: Theakston XB. One guest beer.
Other points: No smoking. Children welcome. Dogs welcome. Garden. Car park. Wheelchair access to the restaurant/pub.
Directions: South of Newton Stewart. Take the A714 and A746 to Whithorn, then the B7004 to the Isle of Whithorn. (Map 11)

The Scoular family has been here for 24 years, constantly modernising and improving this harbourside inn that takes its name from the paddle steamer that plied between the Galloway coast and Liverpool during Victorian times. Large picture windows take in yachts and fishing boats, as well as the comings and goings of local folk and fishermen in what is considered one of the prettiest natural harbours in this part of Scotland. The split bar – one side with a wood-burning stove – serves a good global list of wines and has a relaxed, laid-back atmosphere.

Fish, landed virtually on the doorstep, dictates the menu, served in the beamed, comfortable dining room and conservatory. Chalkboards are scrawled with the daily catch – dishes such as lemon sole with spring-onion and garlic butter, and lobster – and complemented by seasonal game, such as venison with red wine jus, and prime Aberdeen Angus steaks. Bar snacks take in fresh haddock and chips, and filled rolls. En-suite bedrooms are well equipped and the two deluxe rooms overlook the harbour.

Edinburgh

40a Heriot Row

Bed and breakfast

'On a par with a smart, upmarket hotel.'

40a Heriot Row, Edinburgh EH3 6ES
Telephone: +44 (0)131 226 2068
diane@heriotrow.com
www.heriotrow.com

Diane Rae's Georgian garden flat B&B is a real gem and on a par with a smart, upmarket hotel. The attention to detail and style is exemplary throughout, and the accommodation over two light and airy levels is tastefully done. The long, light hallway leads to a large, beautifully furnished drawing room with wall-to-wall bookcases and antiques. This is the ideal place to relax in the evening over a complimentary glass of whisky. One bedroom, a twin, is on this floor – a lovely cosy room with an en-suite shower room. The second bedroom is on the lower-ground floor. Both rooms have tea trays, mineral water and a little decanter of whisky.

The dining room is also on the lower level, making use of the old cellar. It is decorated with painted stone walls, and has huge bookcases, an antique dining table and a traditional sideboard. Here, expect a hearty breakfast of local sausages and bacon, Arbroath smokies, Finnan haddock or oak-smoked kippers. There's a patio filled with exotic plants and across the road is the four-acre private Queen Street Garden, to which guests have access.

Rooms: 2. Double room from £50 per person, single from £60.
Closed: Rarely.
Food: Local Scottish.
Other points: Smoking area. Garden. Children welcome.
Directions: From Princes Street, take a left at Frederick Street and then another left after the gardens. 40a is at the end of the block on the right. (Map 14)

...for recipe ideas

Edinburgh

The Blue Parrot Cantina

Mexican restaurant

49 St Stephen Street, Edinburgh EH3 5AH
Telephone: +44(0)131 225 2941
blueparrot@blueyonder.co.uk

'This is Mexican food at its best.'

Prices: Main course from £8.50. House
wine £10.15.
Last orders: Food: 22.30 (Friday and
Saturday 23.00).
Closed: 24-25 December, 1 January, from
Monday to Friday and on Sundays for lunch
except for August and December.
Food: Modern Mexican.
Other points: No smoking.
Directions: In the centre of Edinburgh.
(Map 14)

In the bustling Stockbridge area of the city,
this small, colourful and exotic restaurant is
as popular as ever. With only nine tables in
the basement, the dining room is intimate and
cosy and absolutely buzzing at weekends. It's
attractively decorated, with dark blue and red
walls, wooden floors, chunky wooden tables
and chairs, and iron wall-candle sconces. This
is Mexican food at its best. And the clientele
obviously think so too, as, by popular demand,
the menu rarely changes.

Fiona Macrae doesn't serve the usual suspects,
such as chilli con carne or tacos, but offers
starters of deep-fried whole chillies stuffed
with cheese and garlic and served with a
sour-cream dip, or seafood ceviche marinated
with lime and orange juice and served
with avocado, chilli and coriander. Mains
include steak fajitas, burritos, enchiladas, and
fresh haddock baked in a lime-and-coriander
tartare sauce. To finish, it's hard to resist the
chocolate fudge cake or pecan pie. Drinks
are a colourful collection of Mexican beers,
margaritas, of course, an impressive range of
tequila, plus New and Old World wines.

MEMBER
279
ENTRY

Britannia Spice

Indian restaurant

'Its contemporary interiors, trendy address and ever-evolving menu put this exotic restaurant in a league of its own.'

150 Commercial Street, Britannia Way,
Leith, Edinburgh EH6 6LB
Telephone: +44(0)131 5552255
info@britanniaspice.co.uk
www.britanniaspice.co.uk

Its contemporary interior, a trendy Leith Docks address and an ever-evolving menu put this exotic restaurant in a league of its own. The Royal Yacht Britannia is docked nearby, hence the name of this restaurant set in an attractive converted whisky bond. Due to its lofty proportions, the nautically themed dining room is open plan, yet offers an intimate feel at the same time, with sunken ceiling spots creating a sense of light and space.

A varied menu explores northern Indian, Bangladeshi, Nepalese, Sri Lankan and Thai cuisines. It is constantly changing, with new dishes added every few weeks. From Nepal comes spicy trout roasted with fried mushrooms, tomatoes, green chilli, mustard seeds and fresh herbs, with its counterpart from Bangladesh of freshwater fish marinated in spices and herbs. Thailand supplies a popular green curry of chicken, or there's chicken kebab with hot spices and a ginger-based sauce with fresh coriander from northern India. There are also various tandoori dishes and a decent selection of vegetarian dishes. A full takeaway menu is also available.

Prices: Main course from £7.95.
Last orders: Food: lunch 14.15; dinner 23.45.
No food Sunday lunch.
Closed: Rarely.
Food: Indian/Bangladeshi/Nepali/
Shri Lankan/Thai.
Other points: No smoking. Children welcome.
Car park. Wheelchair access.
Directions: In Leith, follow signs for the Ocean Terminal or the Royal Yacht Britannia. (Map 14)

...for events

MEMBER
280
ENTRY

Edinburgh

La Garrigue

French restaurant

'A visit here is a holiday for the taste buds.'

31 Jeffrey Street, Edinburgh,
Edinburgh EH1 1DH
Telephone: +44(0)131 557 3032
lagarrigue@btconnect.com
www.lagarrigue.co.uk

Chef-proprietor Jean-Michel Gauffre pays homage to his culinary roots at his exquisite bistro, named after an area of Languedoc. His authentically good and gutsy cooking draws on the area's fine food and wine, and is achieved by sourcing from the French region and using supreme Scottish produce (his wife Karen is Scottish). A visit here is a holiday for the taste buds, with starters of seasonal pear-and-Roquefort salad with walnuts, or rustic Puy lentil soup with smoked ham, followed by, say, a hearty cassoulet with three meats and Toulouse sausage or a more traditional prime Scottish beef with garden vegetables.

An extensive wine list, personally sourced by Jean-Michel, brings together many stunning classics and fine bottles that will appeal to the connoisseur, but also includes interesting examples below the £20 threshold. The three-sectioned restaurant has a cosy atmosphere, and it's not often that you can say the furniture designer – in this case, the talented, late Tim Stead, a graduate of the Glasgow School of Art – also has pieces of his work at the Royal Museum of Scotland. A quality dining experience from start to finish.

Prices: Set lunch £14.50 and dinner £19.50 (two courses). House wine £12.50.
Last orders: Food: lunch 14.30; dinner 20.00.
Closed: Sunday, except during the summer months.
Food: Traditional French/provincial Languedoc.
Other points: No smoking. Wheelchair access (not WC).
Directions: From Waverley station, turn left into Market Street. After 100 yards, turn right into Jeffrey Street. La Garrigue is a further 100 yards along on the right. (Map 14)

Edinburgh

Joppa Turrets Guesthouse

Bed and breakfast

1 Lower Joppa, Joppa,
Edinburgh EH15 2ER
Telephone: +44(0)131 669 5806
stanley@joppaturrets.com
www.joppaturrets.com

'The 'wow' factor is uninterrupted views to the Firth of Forth and the hills of Fife.'

Rooms: 4, 1 with private bathroom. Double/twin room from £58, single from £26.
Closed: Rarely.
Other points: No smoking. Garden. Children over three welcome.
Directions: A1, Milton Road. At the end of Morton Street by the seafront. The guesthouse is the last house on the left, facing the sea. (Map 14)

Stay at the well-positioned Joppa Turrets and you can enjoy a beachside location, but be in the centre of Edinburgh within 20 minutes. The Stanleys' seaside guesthouse is a real find. Facing the sea, all four bedrooms are individually styled in neutral or cheery colours, comfortably furnished and have a colour TV and beverage tray. The 'wow' factor, though, is uninterrupted views to the Firth of Forth and the hills of Fife. You wake up to the sound of waves breaking, but with the bus stop just two minutes' away, you can be exploring the city within the hour.

Apart from a splash of tartan carpet, the Victorian villa is simply furnished to create a relaxing, lost-in-time zone. Breakfast is served in the cosy dining room overlooking the beach, where a large oak table is set family-style for guests. On offer are porridge, local free-range eggs and quality sausages, and toast with local honey or homemade marmalade. There is plenty of reading material for bookworms, and a beautiful old grandfather clock stands in the corner. Felicity and Edward enhance the relaxed atmosphere with their easy-going, charming manner.

Merchants

Restaurant

17 Merchant Street,
Edinburgh EH1 2QD
Telephone: +44(0)131 225 4009
www.merchantsrestaurant.co.uk

'This cheery restaurant is well worth a detour.'

Nestling in a small cul-de-sac off Candlemaker Row, this cheery restaurant is well worth a detour. The attractive setting of stone walls painted blush pink, a low-beamed ceiling, varnished floors, and clever lighting with well-placed mirrors diffusing the light create a warm atmosphere. The wooden floor and bentwood furniture help to retain a rustic/bistro feel. The set lunch and dinner menus change weekly and local and seasonal produce feature prominently in the classic Scottish dishes.

For dinner, you could start with a sauté of king scallops and Spanish black pudding or a more traditional filo-pastry parcel filled with haggis served with creamed neeps and whisky jus. Mains offer some of the best Scottish produce – medallion of Angus beef fillet topped with crumbled stilton and red-wine sauce, or there's pan-seared fillet of sea bass served with soy and spring onion glaze for those wanting something really contemporary. The short wine list opens with well-priced house French wines, and prices remain under £20 throughout for most of its varied international selection.

Prices: Set lunch £12.95 and dinner £24.95.
House wine from £11.95.
Last orders: Food: lunch 14.00; dinner 22.00.
Closed: Saturday lunch, all day Sunday and
2-3 January.
Food: Modern Scottish.
Other points: No smoking. Wheelchair access.
Directions: In Edinburgh old town, just off the
Grassmarket. (Map 14)

...for competitions

283

Edinburgh

Teviotdale House

Bed and breakfast

53 Grange Loan, Edinburgh EH9 2ER
Telephone: +44(0)131 667 4376
eliza@teviotdalehouse.com
www.teviotdalehouse.com

'An excellent base for exploring the city on foot.'

Rooms: 7, 2 not en suite but have private facilities. Double/twin room from £31 per person, single from £41, family from £28 per person.
Closed: Rarely.
Other points: No smoking. Children welcome.
Directions: A720. Leave the city bypass at the Straiton junction and head towards the city centre for 2 miles. Fork left on to Mayfield Road for one mile. Cross the traffic lights at Mayfield church and then take the first left. (Map 14)

Just 10 minutes from the bustle of the city centre, Elizabeth and Willy Thiebaud have created a haven of calm in this charming and friendly hotel. The spacious terraced house provides an excellent base for exploring the city on foot. The bedrooms – five of which are en suite – are individually decorated and show great attention to detail. All have co-ordinated soft furnishings, which provide an attractive finish, a hot-drinks tray, TV, hairdryer, and fluffy towels. The dining room looks out of a picture window on to the back garden and is a lovely place to start the day with a hearty Scottish breakfast.

The couple provide an excellent choice of teas or herbal infusions, porridge, compote of dried fruits 'soaked in a spicy secret', a selection of omelettes, creamed eggs and smoked salmon, Ayrshire-cured bacon, homemade sausages from local butcher Mr Mathieson, oatcakes, and homemade scones. Golfing pictures and memorabilia adorn the walls – a reminder that your hosts are happy to book golfing lessons and rounds at 20 different courses.

Anstruther

The Anstruther Fish Bar

Restaurant and takeaway

'The star of the show is haddock, battered or breadcrumbed.'

42-44 Shore Street, Anstruther,
Fife KY10 3AQ
Telephone: +44(0)1333 310518
ansterfishbar@btconnect.com
www.anstrutherfishbar.co.uk

It seems fitting that two fishermen's cottages have been turned into one of the finest fish bars in Scotland. It occupies the ground floor, overlooking the picturesque harbour, and its popularity with locals and tourists is down to its consistently good fish and chips – two years running it has won a Best Fish and Chip Shop in Scotland award. The owners have their own fish-processing business in the fishing village of St Monans, so have access to the freshest and best-quality seafood, including superb crab and lobster landed at nearby Crail.

People travel from miles around for its fare and, in summer months, queues outside stretch right along the street. The interiors are designed for maximum efficiency, with separate takeaway and restaurant sections. Service keeps up with demand, and despite the husle and bustle, you don't feel rushed. The star of the show is haddock, battered or breadcrumbed, but there are plenty of alternative fish. The catch-of-the-day might include tuna, monkfish, halibut, trout, salmon, lemon sole, prawns or dressed crab. You can also enjoy wine or beer with eat-in meals.

Prices: Set lunch £6.30. Restaurant main course from £4.50. House wine £7.50.
Last orders: Food: 22.00.
Closed: Rarely.
Food: Traditional fish and chips.
Other points: No smoking. Children welcome. Public car park opposite. Wheelchair access to the restaurant.
Directions: M90. Nine miles south of St Andrews on the B9131. Next to the Scottish Fisheries Museum. (Map 14)

...for special offers

Anstruther

The Waterfront Restaurant

Restaurant

18-20 Shore Street, Anstruther,
Fife KY10 3EA
Telephone: +44(0)1333 312200
enquiries@anstruther-waterfront.co.uk
www.anstruther-waterfront.co.uk

'Whole sea bass stuffed with garlic and herbs keeps piscivores happy, and carnivores are equally spoilt.'

Rooms: 8. Double/twin room from £25 per person.
Prices: Restaurant main course from £6.50. Snacks from £4.95. House wine £9.95.
Last orders: Food: 22.00.
Closed: Never.
Food: Modern British.
Other points: No smoking. Children welcome.
Directions: Exit 3/A90(M). Take the A92 to Glenrothes, the A911 signed to Leven, then the A917 and B942 to Pittenweem and on to Anstruther. In Anstruther, turn right at the roundabout, go down to the harbour, and the Waterfront is on the left. (Map 14)

The Waterfront's modern glass-and-timber frontage adds a stylish note to the traditional buildings on this attractive street. Just a few steps from Anstruther harbour, and with views over the Firth of Forth, the contemporary theme continues inside, where the bar and restaurant décor is dark chocolate, with oak panelling and plants. Head for a table at the front for harbour views. In keeping with its location, the menu includes Scottish favourites, but also stars international choices.

You can start with cullen skink or sweet-chilli tiger prawns. Mains are an equally eclectic mix: fish and chips, calves' liver or fajitas, but it's the seafood selection that impresses most. A fillet of oven-baked Shetland salmon flavoured with Cajun spice, and a whole sea bass stuffed with garlic and fresh herbs keeps piscivores happy, and carnivores are equally spoilt with Aberdeen Angus beef steaks. The nursery puds are a treat. A short wine list keeps things simple, but caters for most tastes. Cool and contemporary guesthouse rooms and self-catering apartments complete the picture.

Kincardine

Seasons Coffee Shop

Café and takeaway

'Cakes and homemade scones from the tempting display cabinet are irresistible.'

7 Kirk Street, Kincardine-on-Forth,
Fife FK10 4PT
Telephone: +44(0)1259 730720

Inside Leslie Mitch's pretty whitewashed old terrace, you'll find a cosy and inviting ground-floor shop that is traditionally decorated; dark-wood furniture and plenty of local gifts and cards (for sale) adorning an old fireplace and various walls and windowsills. The atmosphere is friendly and homely, and home-cooked, hearty fare to eat in or take away is the mainstay of the menu. At lunchtime, Leslie and her team are kept busy dispensing coffees, of which there are many styles, and light snacks to the local ladies who lunch.

The menu is sensibly limited, and what they serve, they do exceptionally well: soup, perhaps an excellent carrot-and-ginger, followed by a generous prawn sandwich made with chunky brown bread, or a hot panini filled with mixed salad and melted brie or hot crispy bacon, or a bacon roll or filled baguette. Cakes and homemade scones from the tempting display cabinet are irresistible, none more so than the sweet crumbly cream and fruit meringues. Wines come by the small bottle, or there are plenty of refreshing soft drinks and herbal teas.

Last orders: Food: 16.00.
Closed: Sunday and 1-4 January.
Food: Coffee shop, sandwiches and homemade cakes.
Other points: No smoking.
Directions: In the centre of Kincardine.
(Map 14)

...for the latest news

287
MEMBER ENTRY

Kincardine

Unicorn Inn

Village pub

15 Excise Street, Kincardine-on-Forth,
Fife FK10 4LN
Telephone: +44(0)1259 739129
info@theunicorn.co.uk
www.theunicorn.co.uk

'Successfully combines classic rural charm with the contemporary style of a modern dining pub.'

Prices: **Restaurant main course from £8.95.
House wine £12.25.**
Last orders: **Bar: 24.00. Food: lunch 14.00;
dinner 21.00.**
Closed: **Sunday and Monday.**
Food: **Scottish/Irish.**
Real ale: **Schiehallion, Smithwick's Bitter and
Twisted Ales.**
Other points: **No smoking. Children welcome.
Car park. Wheelchair access.**
Directions: **From the south, cross Kincardine
Bridge, and take the first, then the second left.
(Map 14)**

Right next to Kincardine Bridge, in the oldest part of town, Tony and Liz Budde's lovely village inn dates back to 1639 and was the birthplace of Sir Donald Dewar, who invented the vacuum flask. It successfully combines classic rural charm with the contemporary style of a modern dining pub. At ground level is a lounge that features leather sofas around an open fire, and the more casual of two dining areas, The Grill. Its greatest asset lies in the beef and lamb from the Duke of Buccleuch estate, reared by Liz's brother Robert, which scores highly for quality and flavour. Additional selections take in salmon fishcakes with red-pepper rouille, and steak-and-kidney pie.

You'll find the Red Room restaurant upstairs romantically fitted out with deep red curtains and tables clothed in white linen. Nightly menus depend on fresh seafood, meat and game. Start with chicken-liver and cognac parfait with port jelly, before rack of lamb marinated in garlic and olive oil with parsnip purée. A classic pudding, such as cranachan cheesecake, or a plate of Scottish and Irish cheeses should round things off nicely.

www.routiers.co.uk

Harviestoun Brewery,
Alva, 01259 769100
One of the smallest breweries in Britain, Harviestoun is continually up for and winning awards in national competitions, with the fantastically named (and flavoured) Bitter & Twisted winning Champion Beer of Britain at the Great British Beer Festival in 2003. By some to take home from the brewery shop.

Buccleuch Heritage Foods,
Castle Douglas, 01556 503399, www.buccleuchfoods.com
Although not exactly local to the Unicorn, the Buccleuch Estate has close links to Liz and Tony Budde, the owners of the Unicorn. Liz's family have been farmers on the Dumfriesshire Estate for more than 100 years and her brother Robert rears and supplies specially selected cattle, hence why the greatest asset of the Unicorn's Grill Room menu is the quality beef from the estate. The beef is hung for a minimum of 21 days to develop the unique flavour and succulence for which it is famous and all meat is traceable.

Crombies of Edinburgh,
97 Broughton Street, 0131 557 0111
Crombies are third-generation butchers offering a range of nearly 50 varieties of specialist sausages, plus black (and white) pudding, haggis and Lorne sausage.

Ian Mellis Cheesemonger
78 Albion Road, Edinburgh, 0131 661 9955
With shops in Glasgow and Edinburgh, Ian Mellis specialises in high-quality farmhouse cheeses from throughout Britain. The Budde's first-class Scottish and Irish cheesesboard is sourced from Ian Mellis.

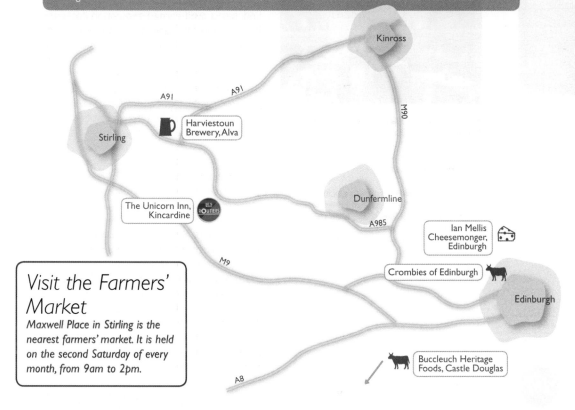

Visit the Farmers' Market

Maxwell Place in Stirling is the nearest farmers' market. It is held on the second Saturday of every month, from 9am to 2pm.

Glasgow

La Parmigiana

447 Great Western Road,
Glasgow G12 8HH
Telephone: +44(0)141 334 0686
s.giovanazzi@btclick.com
www.laparmigiana.co.uk

Italian restaurant

'They do everything well here, from the leather-bound menus to the impeccable service.'

Prices: Set lunch £9.50 and dinner £12.50.
Restaurant main course from £13.50. House wine £12.50.
Last orders: Food: lunch 14.30; dinner 23.00.
Closed: Easter Monday.
Food: Italian.
Directions: Exit 18/M8. Follow signs for West End along Great Western Road, travel over Kelvinbridge and La Parmigiana is on the left. (Map 14)

Established in 1978, this popular and elegant, family-run restaurant near Glasgow's West End has a well-earned reputation for great Italian food. In fact, they do everything well here, from the leather-bound menus to the impeccable service. Given the small size of the kitchen, the menu is sensibly pared down and changes with the seasons. Regulars prefer that Sandro Giovanazzi sticks to favourite dishes and they resist too much change on the menu.

Popular favourites to start include La Parmigiana fish soup with garlic bruschetta, prosciutto di Parma with melon, or spaghetti alla carbonara with olive oil and pancetta. The excellent mains feature fillet of beef with crushed peppercorns and tarragon cream sauce, or risotto with fish and shellfish. Finish with a traditional tiramisu or Cantuccini di Prato biscuits with Tuscan vin santo. Set-price menus at lunch and dinner are very good value. The wine list offers a good selection of Italian favourites, from a prosecco aperitivo to serious Tuscan reds, such as Roccato Vino Da Tavola 'Rocca Delle Macie', with plenty to tempt in between.

Bed and breakfast

Old Ferryman's House

Nethy Bridge Road, Boat of Garten,
Highland PH24 3BY
Telephone: +44(0)1479 831370

'It may be one of the smallest establishments in Les Routiers, but you'll enjoy a big, friendly welcome.'

This traditional stone-built former ferryman's cottage is just across the River Spey from Boat of Garten and is in a truly relaxing setting. Run in tremendous style by Elizabeth Matthews, the cottage has a homely feel throughout. There's a comfortable sitting room filled with flowers, books and magazines and warmed by a wood-burning stove, three small but perfect pine-furnished bedrooms and a large bathroom. The dining room backs on to a lovely garden of cottagey flowers.

No TV is a bonus for those wanting a quiet, get-away-from-it-all break, as are flexible breakfast times, which are a hearty affair of homemade bread and 'grill-up', kippers or kedgeree. Another bonus is the afternoon tea of bran teabreads, shortbread and flapjacks included in the B&B price. Residents also eat well at dinner, starting with, say, cullen skink, followed by wild-venison stroganoff, or wild salmon with herbs, vegetable and salad leaves from the garden in season. Fabulous puds might include raspberry-and-almond roulade. It may be one of the smallest establishments in Les Routiers, but you'll enjoy a big, friendly welcome at this great-value B&B.

Rooms: 4. Double/twin room £50, single £25.
Prices: Set dinner £18.50.
Last orders: Telephone to check.
Closed: Telephone to check.
Food: Modern Scottish.
Other points: No smoking. Children welcome. Dogs welcome overnight. Garden. Car park. Credit cards not accepted.
Directions: Follow the main road through Boat of Garten and across the River Spey; the house is immediately on the right. (Map 14)

...for recipe ideas

Fort William

Four Seasons Country Pub & Restaurant

Country inn

Inchree Centre, Inchree, near Onich,
Fort William, Highland PH33 6SE
Telephone: +44(0)1855 821287
reception@inchreecentre.co.uk
www.inchreecentre.co.uk

'A cosy place for a pint and a decent meal.'

Rooms: 8 chalets. Chalet from £45, hostel family room from £39.
Prices: Set dinner from £11.95 (available to larger parties only). Restaurant main course from £6.95.
Last orders: Food: Dinner 21.30.
Closed: Dining room during the week from November to February.
Food: Modern Scottish.
Real ale: Isle of Skye Brewery Red Cullin, Ben Nevis, Atlas Three Sisters, Cairngorm Trade Winds. Up to two guest beers.
Other points: No smoking. Children welcome. Dogs welcome in the restaurant. Garden. Car park. Internet access. Wheelchair access to the restaurant/pub.
Directions: Eight miles south of Fort William in Onich village. Turn off the A82 at Inchree, a quarter of a mile south of Corran Ferry.
(Map 13)

Outdoor types looking for high-quality budget accommodation in the Glencoe area should look no further than the Inchree Centre, a chalet-and-hostel complex hidden away in a stunning woodland setting with views down Loch Linnhe. What's more, there's a cracking pub-restaurant on site, serving ale from Highland micro-breweries and imaginative evening meals. The simple wood-clad building houses an oak-panelled bar, kitted out with pine pews, traditional dark-wood furniture, a striking pink-and-blue decor, and a rack of maps and walking guidebooks.

As dusk settles and the fire blazes, it's a cosy place for a pint and a decent meal prepared from locally sourced produce. Robust Scottish cooking comes in the form of pork and black-pudding patties with red-onion marmalade to start, with fillet steak and homemade chips to follow, rounded off with the excellent sticky toffee pudding or a plate of Scottish cheeses. Retire to one of the newly refurbished chalets in the grounds and wake up to panoramic views across Loch Linnhe. All are well equipped with TV/DVD, cooker, cutlery and cooking utensils.

Fort William

The Grog & Gruel

Town-centre pub

'Great Scottish micro-brewery ales, hearty pub food and a lively atmosphere.'

66 High Street, Fort William,
Highland PH33 6AE
Telephone: +44(0)1397 705078
greatbeer@grogandgruel.co.uk
www.grogandgruel.co.uk

Active types fed up with conquering peaks should head for The Grog & Gruel, for great Scottish micro-brewery ales, hearty pub food and a lively atmosphere. Its tongue-in-cheek name reflects the relaxed atmosphere and informality of a traditional alehouse. Wooden floors, traditional bench seating and background rock music set the scene in which to enjoy pints of Isle of Skye Black Cuillin and Cairngorm Nessie's Monster Mash, 60 different malt whiskies, and all-day food from the 'alehouse' menu, served in the first-floor restaurant overlooking the High Street.

From starters of Mucho Macho nachos with Hog's Breath chilli beef, and smoked salmon with oatcakes and dill mayonnaise, the menu extends to Tex-Mex chicken fajitas with sour cream and guacamole, house-speciality pizzas, traditional steak-and-ale pie, freshly battered cod with chips, and daily dishes featuring local seafood and Lochaber game. If you're not partial to a decent pint, order a litre pitcher of Tequila Sunrise to accompany your beef-filled burritos. Don't miss the annual beer festivals. Under the same ownership as The Clachaig Inn at Glencoe (see entry).

Prices: Main course from £7.45.
Last orders: Bar: 23.00 (Thursday to Saturday 01.00).
Food: 22.00 Restaurant and 21.00 Bar.
Closed: Rarely.
Food: Mexican/American/Italian.
Real ale: Isle of Skye Brewery Ales, Heather Ales, Atlas Brewery Ales, Caledonian Brewery Ales, Cairngorm Brewery Ales. Up to 10 guest beers.
Other points: No smoking. Children welcome in the restaurant.
Directions: Halfway along Fort William's pedestrianised High Street. (Map 13)

...for events

Glencoe

The Clachaig Inn

Country inn

'Huge log fires provide a roaring welcome.'

Glencoe, Highland PH49 4HX
Telephone: +44(0)1855 811252
inn@clachaig.com
www.clachaig.com

Set in the heart of Glencoe, this 300-year-old inn is a favourite haunt of mountaineers and walkers. The inn has a lively atmosphere and is an activity centre in itself, offering winter mountaineering courses and live folk music. Huge log fires provide a roaring welcome in the cosy, wood-floored lounge bar, and in the rustic, stone-flagged Boots Bar. In the latter, booted walkers can take refuge and enjoy refreshments at a bar dispensing 120 malt whiskies and up to eight cracking real ales from Highland micro-breweries, perhaps Isle of Skye, Cairngorm and Caledonian.

The traditional pub food, served in generous portions, is perfect following a bracing walk, and can be enjoyed in the three bars or restaurant. The choice ranges from filled baguettes, burgers and pasta dishes to local-venison casserole, steak-and-ale pie, and chargrilled steaks with all the trimmings. If you want to sample a local pudding, make room for the homemade apple-and-blackberry crumble. Refurbished bedrooms are split between the main house and chalet-style rooms. in the grounds

Rooms: **23. Double room from £34 per person.**
Prices: **Main course restaurant from £5.85. House wine from £8.25.**
Last orders: **Bar: 23.00 (Friday 24.00, Saturday 23.30). Food: 21.00.**
Closed: **Rarely.**
Food: **Scottish/American/Mexican.**
Real ale: **Atlas Latitude and Three Sisters, Heather Ale from the William's Brothers, Ales from Houston, Cairngorm, An Teallach and Skye Breweries. Up to eight guest beers.**
Other points: **No smoking. Children welcome. Dogs welcome overnight by request. Garden. Car park. Bike shed.**
Directions: **Located in the heart of Glencoe, just off the A82 Glasgow to Fort William Road. (Map 13)**
See pub walk on page 496

Grantown-on-Spey

Tigh-na-Sgiath Country House Hotel

Hotel

Skye of Curr, Dulnain Bridge, by
Grantown-on-Spey, Highland PH26 3PA
Telephone: +44(0)1479 851345
iain@tigh-na-sgiath.co.uk
www.tigh-na-sgiath.co.uk

'The many original features create a stylish and comfortable atmosphere.'

Rooms: 8. Double/twin room from £40.
Prices: Set dinner £31.50 (four courses).
House wine £17.
Last orders: Food: 21.30.
Closed: December and January.
Food: Modern Scottish.
Other points: No smoking. Children welcome.
Dogs welcome overnight. Garden. Car park.
Wheelchair access to the restaurant.
Directions: From Carr Bridge, follow the A938
to Dulnain. Turn right at the post office to Skye
of Curr, and take a second right into Skye of
Curr road. Tigh-na-Sgiath is 400 yards further
on the right. (Map 14)

Just 15 minutes from Aviemore, this elegant house sits in mature gardens with stunning views of the Cairngorm Mountains and Cromdale Hills. Built by a rich shipping family in 1902, it was bought by the Lipton tea family, who owned it until the 1940s before it passed to the Hartley jam family, eventually becoming a hotel in 1969. While its exterior is baronial Victorian, inside, its genteel country-house atmosphere is more evocative of the 1920s.

The many original features, from stone fireplaces and oak panelling to a fine staircase, create a stylish and comfortable atmosphere. The eight bedrooms are tastefully decorated and well appointed. The kitchen offers classic dishes made from home-produced ingredients, such as Highland lamb, beef and game. The daily-changing four-course table d'hôte offers a tower of haggis, neeps and tatties with a Talisker whisky cream, followed by baked fillet of Shetland salmon, and chocolate-and-Cointreau torte. The wine list picks off interesting choices from around the world and there are more than 100 malt whiskies on offer.

Old Smiddy Guest House

Bed and breakfast with tearoom

'Wake up to stunning views and a hearty Scottish breakfast.'

2B Laide, near Achnasheen,
Highland IV22 2NB
Telephone: +44(0)1445 731696
oldsmiddygh@aol.com
www.oldsmiddyguesthouse.co.uk

HIGHLAND

The village of Laide spreads over the slopes of a small peninsula separating Gruinard Bay and Loch Ewe, and the elevated position of this former blacksmith's house makes the most of the views across the bay. The charm of this slate-roofed Highland cottage has not been lost, despite various extensions over the years. New owner Julie Clements has worked wonders, upgrading the en-suite bedrooms, adding a self-catering unit, utilising the dining room as a tearoom, and offering delicious homemade meals using fresh local produce. Expect warm scones and jam on arrival, and four-course evening feasts that may take in fennel, mint and pea soup with homemade walnut bread, local smoked-duck salad, ragout of wild venison, and cranachan – toasted oatmeal, cream and raspberries.

Sleep soundly in one of the stylish bedrooms that are filled with cosseting extras – satellite TV, bathrobes, slippers, thick fluffy towels and fresh flowers. Wake up to stunning views and a hearty Scottish breakfast, perhaps porridge followed by Loch Broom kippers or Julie's 'full Monty' – local sausages, bacon, black pudding and free-range eggs.

Rooms: 3, 1 with private bathroom. Double/twin room from £30 per person, single from £35.
Prices: Set dinner £25 (four courses).
Last orders: Dinner served at 20.00. Afternoon tea served between 14.00 and 17.00 Monday, Wednesday, Friday and Saturday.
Closed: November to February inclusive, excluding Christmas and New Year.
Food: Traditional and Modern Scottish.
Other points: No smoking. Dogs welcome overnight. Garden. Children welcome. Car park. Wheelchair access to the tearoom.
Directions: A9 north from Inverness. Take the A835 towards Ullapool. Turn left at Braemore Junction on to the A832. After 30 miles, go through Laide village and Old Smiddy is the last house on the left. (Map 15)

...for competitions

295
MEMBER ENTRY

Skye Food Link Van,
www.foodlinkvan.co.uk

Skye and Lochalsh has huge potential for fresh local produce – the problem has been how to actually obtain it, especially when the population of 12,000 live in an area that is over 2700 sq km. The solution was found in 2001 when a group of food producers started the Skye Food Link Van. It has been a great success and any producer is eligible to join the group, the simple aim being to make the fantastic local produce of the area available to the public, largely by selling it to restaurants and hotels. The van runs once or twice a week and delivers a mouth-watering range of goodies, from herbs and fruits to fresh oysters and chocolates.

West Highland Dairy,
Achmore, 01599 577203,
www.westhighlanddairy.co.uk

Sheep milk from the dairy's own flock of milking sheep and locally produced cows' milk are manufactured into a wide range of dairy products, including yogurt, ice cream, crème fraîche and award-winning cheeses.

Sleepy Hollow Smokehouse,
Aultbea, 01445 731304,
www.sleepyhollow-smokehouse.co.uk

Sleepy Hollow at Mellon Charles is run by Jenny and Andrew Wiseman and is one of the few truly traditional smokehouses left, using old-fashioned techniques and skills rather than modern electronic kilns. Their smoked salmon is first class and the hot-smoked salmon has won several awards for its unique flavours. As well as smoking and curing fish, the Wisemans supply fresh fish.

Sleepy Hollow
Smokehouse, Aultbea

A832

A896

A863

Portree

A850

The Plockton Hotel,
Plockton

LES
ROUTIERS

West Highland
Dairy, Achmore

A850

Plockton

The Plockton Hotel

Waterfront hotel

Harbour Street, Plockton,
Highland IV52 8TN
Telephone: +44(0)1599 544274
info@plocktonhotel.co.uk
www.plocktonhotel.co.uk

'Real food and wine, real value, real Highland hospitality, and stunning views.'

Real food and wine, real value, real Highland hospitality, and stunning views across Loch Carron to the Torridon Hills make this waterside jewel a difficult place to leave. The hotel commands a beautiful waterfront location in an idyllic National Trust village and Tom and Dorothy Pearson are fully committed to caring for its guests, from fresh flowers in the lobby and hot-water bottles in the beds to cosseting sofas to flop into. Day rooms include a leather-furnished reception lounge, two bars with crackling fires, and the delightful restaurant. Wonderfully comfortable bedrooms have stunning views.

Food reflects the surrounding area. Locally caught shellfish landed at the pier daily, fish from Gairloch and Kinlochbervie, hill-fed lamb and Highland beef and locally made West Highland cheeses feature on comprehensive, daily-changing menus. House specialities embrace traditional fillet steak with whisky, cream and pepper sauce, alongside cream of smoked-fish soup, the celebrated Plockton Smokies, lamb shank with red-wine and rosemary sauce, and perhaps pear, whisky and maple tart among the puddings.

Rooms: 11 rooms in the hotel from £45 per person. 4 rooms in the cottage annex at £30 per person.
Prices: Restaurant main course from £12. Bar snacks from £6.75. House wine £7.95.
Last orders: Bar: 23.00
Closed: Never.
Food: Modern Scottish.
Real ale: Caledonian Deuchar's IPA, Isle of Skye Brewery Hebridean Gold. One guest beer.
Other points: No smoking. Children welcome. Dogs welcome in the bar. Garden. Licence for civil weddings. Wheelchair access to the restaurant/pub and one bedroom.
Directions: Seven miles north along the coast from the Kyle of Lochalsh. (Map 13)

Tongue

Borgie Lodge

Skerray, Tongue, Sutherland,
Highland KW14 7TH
Telephone: +44(0)1641 521332
info@borgielodgehotel.co.uk
www.borgielodgehotel.co.uk

Country-house hotel

'An idyllic Highland retreat for country-pursuits lovers.'

Rooms: 8, 1 with private bathroom. Double/
twin room from £95.
Prices: Set dinner £32. Bar main course from £5.
House wine £12.
Last orders: Bar: afternoon 14.00. Restaurant:
Sunday lunch 14.00; dinner 20.30.
Closed: Rarely.
Food: Modern British.
Other points: No smoking. Children welcome.
Dogs welcome in the bar and overnight.
Garden. Car park. Wheelchair access to the
restaurant.
Directions: From Inverness, take the A9 towards
Tain, the A839 to Lairg and the A836 to Tongue.
Turn left at the second sign for Skerray, and
Borgie Lodge is half a mile along on the right.
(Map 16)

Becky and Daniel Stickland were still settling into this attractive, small and unpretentious hotel when we visited in late 2005. The omens look good for this Edwardian hunting lodge, set beside the River Borgie in a secluded glen on the Countess of Sutherland's estate, as the Sticklands plan to continue its strong tradition as a sporting hotel favoured by the fishing fraternity. In keeping with its location and tradition, it is simply and traditionally furnished with tartan carpets, sporting paintings and stags' antlers, while roaring log fires in cosy lounges add to the charm and atmosphere. Although not opulent, bedrooms are comfortable, well furnished and peaceful, and all but one has a spacious en-suite bathroom.

Dinner is a set four-course affair that shows ambition and careful use of local ingredients, notably estate venison and lobsters from Skerray harbour. A typical meal may feature woodcock-and-pigeon salad with plum chutney, followed by leek-and-potato soup, rack of lamb with redcurrant sauce, and lemon tart with mango coulis. An idyllic Highland retreat for country-pursuits lovers.

Ullapool

The Seaforth

Town-centre pub and takeaway

'Snack on winkles and whitebait or feast on the amazing seafood platters.'

Quay Street, Ullapool, Highland IV26 2UE
Telephone: +44(0)1854 612122
drink@theseaforth.com
www.theseaforth.com

The Seaforth has developed from a basic bar to a thriving pub, seafood restaurant and award-winning chippy (Best Fish & Chips in Radio 4's Food and Farming Awards) since Harry and Brigitte MacRae took over. What's more, it stands on the quayside with stunning views of Loch Broom and the surrounding hills. The extended and modernised 18th-century building takes in a huge ground-floor bar with oak floors and large picture windows, an upstairs bistro for more refined and intimate dining, and The Chippy, a traditional fish-and-chips takeaway. In fact, menus throughout the pub are overwhelmingly biased towards locally caught seafood.

In the bar, snack on winkles and whitebait, or try the oysters, sweet pickled herrings, or feast on the amazing seafood platters. Linger longer in the bistro over seafood soup, fresh lobster or sea bream with tarragon and Pernod. Carnivores can tuck into Highland steaks and lamb rump with red-wine sauce. The Chippy offers the ultimate chip-shop menu – where else can you buy mussels by the kilo, or eat 'takeaway' scallops, lobster and chips, or the best haddock and chips for miles?

Prices: Restaurant main course from £8. Bar snacks from £3.50. House wine from £9.50.
Last orders: Bar: 01.00. Food: 22.00. Times vary according to season.
Closed: 1 January.
Food: Seafood/traditional.
Real ale: Isle of Skye Ales.
Other points: Smoking area. Children welcome. Patio. Car park. Wheelchair access.
Directions: A835 from Inverness. (Map 15)

...for special offers

MEMBER ENTRY
298

Inverness

River House Restaurant

Restaurant

1 Greig Street, Inverness IV3 5PT
Telephone: +44(0)1463 222033
allanlittle@tesco.net

'The River House enjoys an enviable location in this vibrant city.'

Prices: Set lunch £14.65. Set dinner £28.75. House wine £16.25.
Last orders: Food: lunch 14.30 (Tuesday to Friday); dinner 22.00 (Tuesday to Sunday).
Closed: Monday. Saturday and Sunday lunch.
Food: Contemporary Scottish.
Other points: No smoking. Children welcome. Wheelchair access.
Directions: A9. From the Kessick Bridge roundabout, follow the dual carriageway to Inverness and Beauly. At the third roundabout, take the first exit on to Welsh Street. Follow the road along the river and River House is near the footbridge. (Map 14)

The River House enjoys an enviable location in this vibrant city, its big windowed frontage overlooking the River Ness, the Greig Street footbridge and the bustling city. Beyond the narrow side door and a heavy velvet curtain you'll find a Victorian-style dining room, decorated in dark greens and rich reds, and dominated by chef-proprietor Alan Little's sparkling open-plan kitchen and serving counter. Expect a jovial welcome, plenty of cordial banter between Alan and the kitchen and his regular diners, and service that is attentive, efficient and relaxed.

Alan's menu offers a curious mix of traditional Scottish dishes, which utilise the best local produce available, and a well-balanced Asian influence, with various stir-fry techniques and good Asian ingredients evident on the eclectic menu. His classic Scottish dishes highlight local estate reared game, beef, lamb and organically farmed vegetables direct from farms surrounding Inverness, Scottish cheeses from Summer Isles Foods, and fresh fish and shellfish from Mallaig on the west coast. Menus are sensibly short and well-executed dishes offer good value for money.

Trafford Bank Guesthouse

Bed and breakfast

96 Fairfield Road, Inverness IV3 5LL
Telephone: +44(0)1463 241414
info@traffordbankguesthouse.co.uk
www.traffordbankguesthouse.co.uk

'A magnificent guest lounge boasts a fabulous marble fireplace and antique furniture.'

Within walking distance of booming Inverness centre, Trafford Bank Guesthouse was the official residence of the Bishop of Moray and Ross-shire. This fine Victorian house, finished in reddish-pink sandstone, is surrounded by mature gardens, and combines contemporary styling with traditional designs. A modern take on tartans and furnishings makes this a lighter, brighter version of a traditional Scottish country house. Bedrooms are individually decorated and full of cossetting extras – CD/DVD player, plasma TV, mini fridge, internet connection, and smart en-suite facilities.

Downstairs, a magnificent guest lounge boasts a fabulous marble fireplace and antique furniture. Another lounge area down the hall has a long dining table and chairs designed by owner Lorraine Freel. The same chairs can be found in the modern conservatory dining room, which seats up to 16 people. This is the place to enjoy a substantial breakfast of local produce: Stornaway black and fruit puddings from a local butcher, Auchultibuie kippers, bacon from a farmers' market and a selection of home-made preserves, including whisky marmalade and Cawdor honey.

Rooms: 5. Double/twin room from £40, single room from £50. Prices quoted are per person per night.
Closed: Never.
Other points: No smoking. Children welcome. Garden. Car park.
Directions: A9. From Longman roundabout, follow the A82 Fort William signs. Cross the River Ness and turn left on to Kenneth Street. Fairfield Road is on the right. (Map 14)

...for the latest news

Inverness

Westbourne Guest House

Bed and breakfast

50 Huntly Street, Inverness IV3 5HS
Telephone: +44(0)1463 220700
richard@westbourne.org.uk
www.westbourne.org.uk

'Rooms have a colour TV, hairdryer, beverage tray with sweeties, fluffy towels and safes.'

Rooms: 10. Double/twin room from £30 per person.
Last orders: Breakfast: 7.30-8.30 (Monday to Friday); 8.00-9.00 (Saturday and Sunday), or by arrangement.
Closed: Rarely.
Other points: No smoking. Children welcome. Dogs welcome overnight. Garden. Car park. Wheelchair access.
Directions: Take the A9 to Kessock Bridge roundabout and follow the signs to Inverness. Go straight over three roundabouts and, at the fourth, take the first exit on to Wells Street, which becomes Huntly Street. (Map 14)

This spick-and-span modern house boasts some fabulous river views and maintains a genuine character feel. The Paxton family has lived on this site for generations, and in 1998, Richard Paxton decided to rebuild the house to create an up-to-date, purpose-built guesthouse. The bedrooms are individually styled with a tartan scheme and offer an exceptional level of accommodation. All the rooms have a colour TV, hairdryer, beverage tray with sweeties, fluffy towels and safes. Superior beds make for a very comfortable stay.

Downstairs is a cosy residents' lounge with internet access, books and games. The spacious breakfast room is light and bright and furnished with cheerful bistro-style furniture, with scenes of Inverness decorating the walls. The hearty Highlander breakfast is prepared from fresh local ingredients and will set you up for the day, whatever your outdoor pursuits. Richard has an encyclopaedic knowledge of the local area and can suggest tours that take in beautiful scenery and distilleries, and advise on wildlife excursions and walks.

Hotel Eilean Iarmain

Waterside hotel

'A magnificent location with breathtaking views.'

Eilean Iarmain, Isle Ornsay, Sleat,
Isle of Skye IV43 8QR
Telephone: +44(0)1471 833332
hotel@eileaniarmain.co.uk
www.eileaniarmain.co.uk

Situated in a tiny seafront hamlet, this white-painted hotel has a magnificent location with breathtaking views across the sea loch. Rural chic sums up traditional interiors that combine simplicity and style. The 16 bedrooms are all smartly individual and there are four suites in the converted stables with bedrooms upstairs and sitting rooms below. The bustling An Pranban bar is a relaxing place to enjoy one of 30 local malt whiskies, including their own blend, Te Bheag.

The bar food is first rate. At lunchtimes, tuck into sandwiches and homemade soups, hearty casseroles, steaks and local seafood. The dining room has a refined air and head chef Steffan Bux serves fine food. Local seafood includes oysters from the hotel's own beds and shellfish from its private stone pier. Game, especially venison, is from the estate. A typical dinner might include grilled seafood sausage on cucumber pickle with a Glendale organic-herb salad, followed by grilled calves' liver with crisp bacon and thyme mousseline. Finish with a decadent rich warm chocolate-and-Armagnac tart or some superb local Scottish cheese.

Rooms: 12. Double/twin room from £60 per person, single occupancy £90. 4 suites in restored stables £200.
Prices: Set lunch £16.50 and dinner £31. House wine £16.
Last orders: Bar: 23.00. Food: lunch 14.30; dinner 21.00.
Closed: Never.
Food: Modern Scottish.
Real ale: McEwans.
Other points: Smoking area. Children welcome. Garden. Car park.
Directions: 40 miles from Portree and seven miles from Broadford on the A851. (Map 13)

...for recipe ideas

Dunbar

Creel Restaurant

Restaurant

The Harbour, 25 Lamer Street, Dunbar,
East Lothian EH42 1HG
Telephone: +44(0)1368 863279
creel@fsmail.net
www.creelrestaurant.co.uk

'The revamped Creel Restaurant is putting this harbourside location on the culinary map.'

Prices: Set lunch £9.95 (two courses).
Restaurant main course from £8.25.
Last orders: Food: lunch 14.00 (Sunday 14.30); dinner 20.30 (Friday and Saturday 21.00).
Closed: Closed Sunday evening, Monday and Tuesday.
Food: Modern Scottish.
Other points: Smoking area. Children welcome. Wheelchair access.
Directions: Take the A1 to Dunbar. Follow the signs for the town centre, go to the end of the high street and on to the harbour. (Map 14)

Cobbled streets and quaint fishermen's cottages make the pretty harbour town of Dunbar, one of the oldest settlements on the East Lothian coast, an attractive proposition. Now the revamped Creel Restaurant is also putting this harbourside location on the culinary map. Set in an end-of-terrace former cottage, the Creel has been given a traditional-with-a-contemporary-twist makeover – a taste of things to come on its popular menu. Gavin Howat's delicious lunchtime line-up is increasingly enticing business customers out of the city.

The menu is a modern but unpretentious collection of dishes using fresh local produce. Interesting touches include sweet potato in the traditional lamb stew or chilli jam served with a goat's cheese and rocket bruschetta. Fish and local beef are fine choices, perhaps roast cod sautéed in garlic butter with chorizo and chargrilled Scotch beef with peppercorn-and-brandy sauce, and it's pleasing to see that most of the main courses don't nudge higher than £10; starters mostly stay within the £5 bracket, too. A fairly priced wine list has a good mix of Old and New World choices.

www.routiers.co.uk

Blair Atholl

Atholl Arms Hotel

Hotel

'If you're looking for genuine highland grandeur, then look no further.'

Old North Road, Blair Atholl,
Perth & Kinross PH18 5SG
Telephone: +44(0)1796 481205
enquiries@athollarmshotel.co.uk
www.athollarmshotel.co.uk

If you're looking for genuine Highland grandeur, then look no further than this imposing Victorian hotel, which stands proudly at the northern end of the village, close to Blair Castle. A smart establishment in a commanding position, this fine, gabled, granite-stone building was until recently owned by the Atholl Estate and remains big on heritage. Popular with sporting groups, regular shooting and stalking on the Atholl Estate can be arranged by the hotel.

The interiors reflect the house's Victorian and Scottish heritage and are sumptuously decorated in deep burgundies and greens, with walls covered in baronial-style accessories, and tartan making a tasteful appearance throughout. The bedrooms are smartly attired, as are the Bothy Bar and Baronial Dining Room, where you can sample the best of local produce from Blair Atholl estate game, such as venison pan fried with Dunsyre Blue Cheese, Tombuie Smokehouse meats and cheeses, fish from Kerrachers, and shellfish from Skye, and perhaps langoustines in garlic-and-parsley butter. The hospitality and atmosphere are amazing.

Rooms: 31. Double/twin room from £50, single from £35, family from £65.
Prices: Set lunch from £12 and dinner from £20. Restaurant main course from £10.95. Bar main course from £6.75. House wine £10.50.
Last orders: Bar: 23.00 (Friday and Saturday 23.45). Food: 21.30.
Closed: Rarely.
Food: Modern Scottish.
Real ale: Moulin Ales.
Other points: Smoking area. Children welcome. Dogs welcome. Garden. Car park. Wheelchair access.
Directions: A9 Inverness. Six miles north of Pitlochry on the A9, turn right at the T-junction and follow signs for Blair Castle. The Atholl Arms is 200 yards past the main gate on the left. (Map 14)

...for events

304

Comrie

The Royal Hotel

Hotel

Melville Square, Comrie,
Perth & Kinross PH6 2DN
Telephone: +44(0)1764 679200
reception@royalhotel.co.uk
www.royalhotel.co.uk

'A book-lined library with sofas is a cosy place for relaxation or a wee dram.'

Rooms: 11. Double/twin room £65 per person, single £80. Four-poster suite from £85 per person.
Prices: Restaurant main course from £9.95. Bar main course from £6.95. House wine £11.95.
Last orders: Bar: 23.00 (Friday and Saturday 23.45). Food: lunch 14.00; dinner 21.00.
Closed: Rarely.
Food: Modern/traditional English.
Real ale: Deuchar's IPA.
Other points: No smoking. Children welcome. Dogs welcome in the bar and overnight. Garden. Car park. Wheelchair access to the restaurant.
Directions: From the A9 at Greenloaning, take the A822 heading for Crieff, then the B827 to Comrie. (Map 14)

Once a coaching inn that played host to Queen Victoria, this beautifully appointed hotel offers a country house ambience within an attractive town-centre setting. Period antiques, paintings and stylish soft furnishings are complemented by the Milsom family and their staff's cheerful, helpful hospitality. The cosy lounge bar, along with the wood-and-stone public bar, are the focus of the local community, offering an informal atmosphere and a warm welcome. A book-lined library with sofas and low tables is a cosy place for relaxation or a wee dram.

In the conservatory-style brasserie, cullen skink, rack of lamb with roasted root vegetables and rosemary sauce or braised oxtail stew may be washed down with a glass of Deuchar's IPA or one of 170 Highland malts. Dinner in the intimate restaurant can be a fixed-price three-course affair or taken from a seasonal carte that makes full use of the markets' seasonal produce, from fresh fish, meats and game to Tobermory cheddar and local farm fruits and vegetables. Beautifully appointed bedrooms feature furnishings by local craftsmen, and rich fabrics.

Dunkeld

The Pend

Bed and breakfast

5 Brae Street, Dunkeld,
Perth & Kinross PH8 OBA
Telephone: +44(0)1350 727586
molly@thepend.sol.co.uk
www.thepend.com

*'Its small scale allows for genuine
friendliness and a homely feel.'*

With its classic good looks and leisure options, this hotel, set in the attractive Perthshire village of Dunkeld on the banks of the River Tay, offers quite an itinerary of activities – hunting, fishing and shooting on local estates, and picturesque walks. The hotel has an appealing lack of pretentiousness and its small scale allows for genuine friendliness and a homely feel. All the bedrooms are beautifully decorated, with antique furniture here as well as in the lounge-dining room, and cosseting extras such as a mini fridge, bathrobes and quality toiletries.

The traditional cooking is based around quality ingredients from local suppliers – the smoked salmon comes from the Dunkeld smokery just across the road, then there's local Bestwick game, beef, lamb, pork and soft fruits from nearby farms, homegrown vegetables and exquisite local cheeses. From the daily-changing table d'hôte comes mains of pan-fried Orkney salmon, Balemund Farm organic lamb chops or rib-eye steak. There is no bar, but a fully stocked drinks cabinet runs on an honesty basis, and there's a 100-bin list of wines.

Rooms: 3. Rooms £35 per person. £60 per person dinner bed and breakfast.
Prices: Set dinner (four courses) from £25.
Closed: Rarely.
Food: Traditional with French/Italian influences.
Other points: Smoking area. Children welcome. Dogs welcome overnight. Car park.
Directions: 12 miles north of Perth on the A9. Cross the river into Dunkeld and take the second right into Brae Street. (Map 14)

...for competitions

Perth

The Famous Bein Inn

Glen Farg, Perth,
Perth & Kinross PH2 9PY
Telephone: +44 (0)1577 830216
stay@beininn.com
www.beininn.com

Country inn

'Rock-music fans travel miles to visit the basement museum filled with rock memorabilia.'

Rooms: 12. Double room from £70, single from £45, family from £65.
Prices: Set lunch £14 and dinner £18. Restaurant main course from £10.95. Bar main course from £5.95. House wine £10.50.
Last orders: Bar: afternoon 14.00; evening 23.00 (open all day at weekend). Food: lunch 14.00; dinner 21.00 (Sunday food served all day).
Closed: Rarely.
Real ale: Inveralmond Independence.
Other points: Smoking area. Children welcome. Dogs welcome overnight. Car park. Wheelchair access.
Directions: Exit 9/M90. Take the exit for Glenfarg and drive through the village. The Famous Bein Inn is 1 1/2 miles into the wooded glen. (Map 14)

Originally built as a resting place for travellers on the traditional route north from Edinburgh to the Highlands, this remote drovers' inn is an institution and local landmark. Standing alone in a deep-wooded glen, just five minutes' drive from the M90, David Mundell's hotel has become famous for live-music sessions, attracting some top recording artists. Rock-music fans travel miles to visit David's Rock Bar, a basement museum filled with rock memorabilia – the walls are plastered with signed photographs, backstage passes and rock star posters.

Décor is a tad more traditional in the MacGregor Bar, with its tartan carpet and comfortable sofas, and in the more formal Balvaird Restaurant. Food is honest and home cooked, the simple menus appealing to a loyal local clientele and passing travellers. Expect lunchtime sandwiches and light meals, such as a generous salad of three smoked meats or the inn's classic stilton beefburger with hand-cut thick chips, to be followed with one of the indulgent homemade puddings. In keeping, en-suite bedrooms are clean, tidy and unpretentious.

The Old Mill Inn

Town-centre pub

'Don't miss the Highland buffet night on Thursdays and the regular wine-tasting dinners.'

Mill Lane, Pitlochry,
Perth & Kinross PH16 5BH
Telephone: +44(0)1796 474020
enquiries@highlandperthshire.com
www.old-mill-inn.co.uk

In the heart of Pitlochry and accessed from the High Street along a paved path, the Old Mill, as its name suggests, is a refurbished 17th-century corn mill, replete with working water wheel and gushing burn. Like the town, the pub draws the crowds and the Smaile family work hard to meet their needs, as well as endeavouring to create a more individual inn. Space is not a problem – there's a coffee shop, an upstairs bistro, a bustling bar area offering Scottish ales and 150 malt whiskies, a function room, and a big terrace and garden for summer barbecues.

Menus are broad and cosmopolitan, with basic pub meals listed alongside more imaginative homemade dishes that utilise fresh, local produce. Typically, these include fresh haddock, black-pudding and rösti stack, Dunkeld lamb chops, Perthshire venison sausages, and local butcher meats, including beef from named farms in the area. Don't miss the Highland buffet night on Thursdays and the regular wine-tasting dinners. En-suite bedrooms are comfortable and well equipped.

Rooms: 6. Double/twin room from £50, single from £30, family from £70.
Prices: Restaurant main course from £5.95. Bar snacks from £2.95. House wine £11.95.
Last orders: Bar: 23.00. Food: 22.00.
Closed: Rarely.
Food: Modern British.
Real ale: Tetley's Bitter, Jennings Bitter, Hook Norton Best Bitter. Five guest beers.
Other points: No smoking. Children welcome. Dogs welcome overnight. Garden. Car park. Wheelchair access.
Directions: A9, Pitlochry. Situated in the centre of Pitlochry behind the post office. Parking available behind the inn. (Map 14)

...for special offers

MEMBER
308
ENTRY

Tyndrum

Green Welly Stop Restaurant

Café and shop

Tyndrum, Crianlarich,
Perth & Kinross FK20 8RY
Telephone: +44(0)1838 400271
thegreenwellystop@
tyndrum12.freeserve.co.uk
www.thegreenwellystop.co.uk

'An amazing selection of whiskies, locally smoked salmon, haggis and Scottish preserves.'

Prices: Main course from £5. Snack from £2.95.
House wine £2.70 for a small bottle.
Last orders: Food: 17.30.
Closed: Rarely.
Food: Traditional Scottish.
Other points: Smoking area. Children welcome.
Patio. Car park.
Directions: On the A82, in the centre of the village. (Map 14)

Run as a family business and now into its third generation, this all day café-restaurant and outdoor-equipment shop is a welcome pit-stop if you're en route to Oban or Fort William. The family prides itself on making everything on site and the menu of home-cooked Scottish dishes is dictated by what's available locally and seasonally. The daily-changing menu offers fresh soups, perhaps Scotch broth, curried apple and parsnip, Tattie Drottle or cullen skink.

The baking is excellent, with scones ranging from plain, to fruit, treacle, and cheese, with date-and-walnut slice, banana loaf, Border tart and Orkney broonie widening the tempting choice of cakes even further. Main courses include hearty portions of traditional favourites such as lasagne, pasta Bolognese or haggis 'n' neeps. Desserts may be boozy bread-and-butter pudding or Atholl Brose trifle. There's an amazing selection of whiskies, locally smoked salmon, haggis and Scottish preserves to buy in the shop, as well as snacks such as homemade butter fudge or Mackie's ice cream to take away.

Mansfield House Hotel

Country-house hotel

'The comforts extend to the bedrooms, which come with TVs and a range of cossetting extras.'

Weensland Road, Hawick,
Scottish Borders TD9 8LB
Telephone: +44(0)1450 360400
ian@mansfield-house.com
www.mansfield-house.com

This handsome Victorian mansion stands tall and proud on a hillside overlooking Hawick. The interiors match the grandeur of the exterior, but the traditional and lavish furnishings are combined with 21st-century amenities. The house has been in the MacKinnon family since 1985 and they have restored its character, successfully turning it into a comfortable hotel. The classicly styled sitting room features ornate cornicing, an open fire and deep sofas and chairs. The comforts extend to the bedrooms, which are spacious and well decorated, and come with TVs and a range of cossetting extras.

In the kitchen, Sheila MacKinnon uses seasonal local produce, notably first-class meats from surrounding farms, to ensure her up-to-date menu offers only the freshest flavours. Monthly-changing dinner menus could take in Teviot smoked salmon with capers, navarin of venison with roast root vegetables and a rich wine sauce, and rhubarb tart or coffee-date pudding to finish. A separate traditional bar is used for informal meals. The wine list is a good mix of France and the New World at keen prices.

Rooms: 12. Double room from £80, single from £45, family room from £105.
Prices: Set lunch £19.50 and dinner £25. House wine £10.50.
Last orders: Lounge bar: 21.00. Food: lunch 14.00; dinner 21.00 (Sunday 20.00).
Closed: Rarely.
Food: Traditional Scottish.
Other points: No smoking. Children welcome. Dogs welcome overnight. Garden. Car park. Licence for civil weddings/partnerships. Wheelchair access to the restaurant.
Directions: Take the A7 to Hawick, then the A698 to Denholm/Jedburgh; the hotel is one mile along on the right. (Map 12)

...for the latest news

Falkirk

La Picardie

French restaurant

12 Union Road, Camelon, Falkirk,
Stirlingshire FK1 4PG
Telephone: +44(0)1324 631666
info@lapicardie.co.uk
www.lapicardie.co.uk

'For a flavour of France, look no further than this chic, rustic restaurant.'

Prices: Set dinner from £20. Restaurant main course from £11. House wine £8.99.
Last orders: Food: 21.00. Reservations required.
Closed: First week in January and first two weeks of July.
Food: French.
Other points: No smoking. Wheelchair access.
Directions: M9 and M876. One mile from the Falkirk Wheel. (Map 14)

For a flavour of France, look no further than this chic, rustic restaurant. Its brasserie-style menu uses local ingredients to conjure up classic French dishes, and they've proved popular with locals and visitors alike. The hearty food is offered at exceptionally keen prices that are not very much dearer than if you cooked them at home. You can enjoy an excellent-value two-course lunch, choosing from homemade pâté or scallops St Jacques to start, followed by Provençal beef stew or pork with camembert sauce.

The evening menu widens the choice with more French favourites. Start with soup or garlic mushrooms, followed by entrecôte with pepper sauce or chicken with tarragon sauce. Simplicity is the key. Bread, chilled water and coffee are all included in the price. Good, easy-drinking wines come from France and, at £8.99, the house wine is a steal. The restaurant is cosy and the space is cleverly used; the tiny galley kitchen opens on to the dining rooms, so you can see chef Duncan Cochrane in action. The atmosphere and good food make for a pleasant dining experience that won't break the bank.

Balivanich

Stepping Stone Restaurant

Seafood restaurant

'Offers that much-needed warmth and welcome in these blustery parts.'

Benbecula, Balivanich,
Western Isles H57 5DA
Telephone: +44(0)1870 603377
steppingstonehs7@tiscali.co.uk

In the group of islands that make up the Western Isles, Benbecula is regarded as a stepping stone between North and South Uist, hence the restaurant's name. If you arrive by air, you won't miss the Stepping Stone as it's one of the first places you'll see as you leave the airport. It was purpose built, but it's been stylishly designed and offers that much-needed warmth and welcome in these blustery parts. Inside, the wood-and-glass structure feels like a spacious log cabin.

It's split into two eating levels: the Food Base is an informal café where you can enjoy all-day snacks, sandwiches, homebaked cakes, and fish and chips to eat in or take away, while Sinteag, the no-smoking restaurant on the higher level, turns out scintillating food based around locally caught fish. Menus are presented in a simple style, whether it's fillet of sole with a shrimp sauce, or scallops with bacon and cheese. Other specialities include Uist venison cooked in red wine. The Maclead family also own the renowned town bakery that makes the famous oatcakes sold all over Scotland and served here in the restaurant with delectable Scottish cheese.

Prices: Sunday lunch £11.95. Set dinner £21.75 (five courses). House wine £8.50.
Last orders: Food: 21.00.
Closed: Rarely.
Food: Traditional Scottish and seafood.
Other points: No smoking. Children welcome. Garden. Car park.
Directions: On the island of Benbecula, on the airport road, five minutes from the ferry and the airport at Balivanich. (Map 15)

...for recipe ideas

Wales

Cardiff

The Thai House Restaurant

Thai restaurant

3-5 Guildford Crescent,
Churchill Crescent, Cardiff CF10 2HJ
Telephone: +44(0)2920 387 404
info@thaihouse.biz
www.thaihouse.biz

'The innovative combination of Thai flavourings and Welsh ingredients quickly gained a loyal following.'

Prices: Set lunch £10 and dinner from £26. Restaurant main course from £11. House wine £11.50.
Last orders: Food: lunch 14.30; dinner 23.00.
Closed: Sunday and four days over Christmas.
Food: Thai.
Other points: Smoking area. Children welcome. Wheelchair access.
Directions: In the centre of Cardiff, just off Churchill Way. The Thai House Restaurant is next to the Ibis Hotel and opposite the stage door of Cardiff International Arena. (Map 4)

The innovative combination of Thai flavourings and Welsh ingredients quickly gained Noi Ramasut and his wife Arlene a loyal following when they opened for business in 1985. Stylish and contemporary, the stunning reclaimed floor of this cutting-edge establishment is from the capital's Philharmonic Hall. Difficulties sourcing Thai ingredients were solved when Noi set up an importing business – now many of the fresh herbs, spices and vegetables are flown in fresh from Bangkok every week.

Skilled staff cook these in the traditional way, so whether it's a gai yarng som dam (a marinated whole poussin, grilled and served with traditional salad), a peppery ner pat prik (topside of beef flash-fried with basil and garlic in soy sauce), or starters of beek gai (Thai chicken wings stuffed with seasoned mince), you know you are getting the real thing. Innovation is evident, as Cardigan Bay sea bass and mackerel, Welsh beef and lamb are used in the regional Thai dishes. The Chang beer and well-chosen wines are great matches for the spicy offerings.

313

Ty Mawr Country Hotel

Hotel

'Open fires, tiled floors and beamed ceilings are all beautifully restored.'

Brechfa, Carmarthen,
Carmarthenshire SA32 7RA
Telephone: +44(0)1267 202332
info@wales-country-hotel.co.uk
www.wales-country-hotel.co.uk

Steve Thomas and Annabel Viney have breathed new life into this wonderful 15th-century house, set in a peaceful location in the Cothi Valley. It's been a smallholding, grammar school and farmhouse, but has come into its own as a small, stylish hotel. All the bedrooms have been beautifully decorated, and are well appointed and comfortable. Downstairs, the character of the house has been maintained, with open fires, tiled floors and beamed ceilings all beautifully restored.

The food, sourced and cooked by Steve, is amazing. The set, daily-changing menus feature starters of duck pâté with cranberry confit, and seared scallops with lime-and-herb crust, then mains of River Teifi sewin with cucumber, organic Fferm Tyllwyd Welsh black fillet steak with mushroom and red-wine sauce, and roast partridge with chestnut gravy. Welsh cheeses or lemon-ricotta cheesecake are fine finishes. The new bar dispenses decent wines and Steve's micro-brewery beers. Ty Mawr is well placed for exploring the south and west Wales countryside.

Rooms: **5. Double/twin room from £95, single from £65.00.**
Prices: **Set lunch £16.50 and dinner £29. House wine £11.75.**
Last orders: **Food: Lunch 14.00; dinner 2100.**
Closed: **Never.**
Food: **Modern British.**
Other points: **Smoking area. Children over 12 welcome (no children in the bar). Dogs welcome. Garden. Car park.**
Directions: **M4. From the A40/A48, take the B4310 north. Ty Mawr is in the centre of Brechfa on the left. (Map 7)**

Llanarthne

The Fig Tree

Restaurant-with-rooms

Dryslwyn Fawr, Llanarthne,
Carmarthenshire SA32 8JQ
Telephone: +44(0)1558 668187
enquiries@thefigtreerestaurant.co.uk
www.thefigtreerestaurant.co.uk

'The restaurant has built up an excellent reputation for fine food.'

Rooms: **5. Double/twin room from £50.**
Prices: **Restaurant main course from £10. House wine £10.95.**
Last orders: **Food: lunch 14.00; dinner: 21.00.**
Closed: **Sunday evening and all day Monday.**
Food: **Modern British/European.**
Other points: **Smoking area. Children welcome. Garden. Car park. Licence for civil weddings. Wheelchair access.**
Directions: **Exit 49/M4. Between Carmarthen and Llandeilo. Just off the A40 by Dryslwyn Castle, signposted off the B4300. (Map 7)**

Nestling in the stunningly beautiful Towy Valley, with views of Dryslwyn Castle and Paxton's Tower, the restaurant is situated on an old model farm, dating back to the 13th century, although most of the remaining structures are from the 17th century. The restaurant in the farm's courtyard joins the existing four self-catering holiday cottages. It is housed in a creeper-clad building and dining on three levels is brasserie-style. The décor makes the most of the original features, such as worn flagstone floors, stone walls and lots of natural wood.

Under the skilful leadership of chef Tom French, the restaurant has built up an excellent reputation for fine food. His commitment to using local ingredients has paid off. At lunch, tuck into the menu of soups, salads and lighter dishes, plus fish and superb steaks. Specials are on offer at lunch and for the sophisticated dinner menus. Start with warm bacon and pan-fried asparagus tartlet, perhaps, before moving on to a Welsh Black fillet steak topped with Italian blue cheese. Monthly jazz nights and Sunday brunches are proving popular.

Jabajak Restaurant and Country Retreat

Countryside retreat

'A meeting of the exotic, hi-tech and rural.'

Banc y Ilain, Llanboidy, Whitland,
Carmarthenshire SA34 0ED
Telephone: +44(0)1994 448786
info@jabajak.co.uk
www.jabajak.co.uk

This countryside retreat is a meeting of the exotic, hi-tech and rural. Well-travelled hosts Amanda and Julian Stuart-Robson have fully renovated this farmhouse, successfully combining a mix of North African furniture and objects with the latest technology – DVD players and wide-screen satellite TVs, great sound systems, internet connections and other home comforts. En-suite accommodation is spacious, comfortable and generously kitted out with extras. They can also cater for conferences and weddings, and the honeymoon suite is a romantic treat with its real fire and private decked area.

The restaurant is also something special. It takes up the old carriage house, stable and milking parlour, and combines oak furniture with stone and slate surfaces. Cooking makes the most of high-quality local and fully traceable ingredients. Take our advice and don't leave without trying the Welsh Celtic Pride steaks. Jabajak grows a lot of its own herbs and fruit, plus there's a judicious use of Mediterranean produce. The well-selected wine list is fairly priced. Breakfasts are the full-English kind or lighter, continental options.

Rooms: **5. Double/twin room from £75. Family room from £100.**
Prices: **Set lunch £12.50. Set dinner £15.50. Restaurant main course from £12.50. House wine £9.95.**
Last orders: **Food: 21.30.**
Closed: **Rarely.**
Food: **Modern British/European.**
Other points: **Smoking area. Children welcome. Garden. Car park. Wheelchair access.**
Directions: **Exit 49/M4. Continue on the A48 to Carmarthen and then on to the A40 to St Clears and Whitland. Turn left for Llanboidy, and Jabajak is 2 1/2 miles along on the right. (Map 7)**

...for competitions

316

Aberaeron

Hive on the Quay

Cadwgan Place, Aberaeron,
Ceredigion SA46 0BU
Telephone: +44(0)1545 570445
hiveon.thequay@btinternet.com
www.hiveonthequay.co.uk

Harbourside café-restaurant

'Everything is delicious, from the crab soup to the local-lobster salad.'

Prices: **Main course from £7.50. Snack from £5. House wine £12.**
Last orders: **Café/restaurant: 15.00 from spring bank holiday to mid-September; Dinner 21.00 in August.**
Closed: **From the fourth week of September to spring bank holiday.**
Food: **British (especially Welsh) and regional European.**
Other points: **No smoking. Children welcome. Garden/courtyard. Licence for civil weddings. Wheelchair access.**
Directions: **At the end of the M4. Continue to Carmarthen and Llandysul and take the A487 coast road to Aberaeron. Take the first left after the river bridge to the harbour and The Hive. Street parking available. (Map 7)**

The Holgate family's peerless seasonal quayside café celebrated 30 years of business in 2006. Set on the seafront at Aberaeron's sheltered inner harbour, seafood has been key to its longevity and success. Supplies are local and come via their harbourside fish shop, which is stocked with the freshest Cardigan Bay crabs and lobster. The other big draw is its honey ice cream, made from locally farmed honey.

The Hive offers a compact lunch and dinner menu, but it's the sort of line-up where everything is delicious, from the crab soup to the local-lobster salad. The daily specials menu features local meats, salads, vegetables, cheeses, yogurts and milk. Choices range from simple hot crab on toast or herrings in oatmeal with orange-and-onion salad, to poached chicken with summer vegetables and aïoli, and sea bass with pesto topping. The drinks list is full of pleasant surprises, such as the organic mead and lager, and a selection of organic wines. Sarah Holgate and her team make their bread and cakes almost entirely from organic produce. Summer seating is available in the sheltered courtyard.

www.routiers.co.uk

Aberystwyth

Le Vignoble

Restaurant

'It's simple, stylish and a pleasant backdrop for the brasserie-style food.'

31 Eastgate Street, Aberystwyth,
Ceredigion SY23 2AR
Telephone: +44(0)1970 630800
medinarees@mac.com
www.theorangery.uk.com

Owned by the same team behind The Orangery café/bistro (in Aberystwyth's old Talbot Hotel), Le Vignoble is housed in a Victorian shop which benefits from a high glass front and recessed entrance. This means the interior is filled with west-coast light, which complements the mushroom walls, clothed tables and expensive cutlery and glasses. It's simple, stylish and a pleasant backdrop for the brasserie-style food. All of the Welsh Black beef on the menu comes from the owners' own farm, as do the soft fruits and wild garlic in season, and there are plans to open a bakery.

The menu is refreshingly short and to the point: leek, parmesan and mascarpone tartlet is served with vine tomatoes and white truffle oil, and a main course of half a local lobster arrives with chips, mixed leaves and saffron aïoli, while pan-fried wild sea bass is accompanied with roasted red-pepper coulis. Dessert could be lemon posset with Pimms-and-lemonade granita or fresh strawberries and orange on vanilla French toast. The extensive wine list is packed with Gallic delights.

Prices: Set lunch £16. Restaurant main course from £12.50. House wine £10.95.
Last orders: Food: lunch 14.00; dinner 22.00.
Closed: All day Sunday and Monday, lunch Tuesday, Christmas and New Year.
Food: French.
Other points: No smoking. Children welcome. Wheelchair access.
Directions: The restaurant is situated in Aberystwyth town centre on Eastgate Street, which runs parallel to and one block behind the Promenade. (Map 7)

...for special offers

MEMBER ENTRY 318

Betws-y-Coed

Penmachno Hall

Penmachno, Betws-y-Coed,
Conwy LL24 OPU
Telephone: +44(0)1690 760410
stay@penmachnohall.co.uk
www.penmachnohall.co.uk

★

Bed and breakfast

'The location is ideal for those wanting an effortlessly relaxing break.'

Rooms: **3. Double/twin room from £70.**
Prices: **Set dinner (five courses) from £25.
Afternoon teas from £5. House wine from
£9.90.**
Last orders: **Dinner served 19.30 for 20.00 (by
prior arrangement only).**
Closed: **Last two weeks in October 2006
– telephone for confirmation.**
Food: **Fresh local produce.**
Other points: **No smoking. Children welcome.
Garden. Car park.**
Directions: **Take the B4406 to Penmachno. At
'The Eagles', take the turning to the right of the
pub. Penmachno Hall is just after the Rectory
bridge. (Map 7)**

Those wanting quiet contemplation will appreciate the rural setting of this former rectory in Snowdonia National Park. With magnificent views, the Glasgwm River burbling by out front and the pretty village of Penmachno just down the road, the location is ideal for those wanting an effortlessly relaxing break. Owners Simon Awdry, a wine merchant, and his wife Lauraine have updated this Victorian house to create a rustic but stylish three-bedroom B&B.

In the refreshingly bright morning and dining rooms, you can enjoy the spoils of the area: hearty home-cooked breakfasts and dinners are freshly prepared using local meats and vegetables, and as generous on quantity as they are on quality. As well as lamb, chicken and beef, you'll find a good choice of fish and vegetarian mains, followed by comforting crumbles, plus the most fabulous local cheese selection. Afternoon teas and nibbles are also available. The three bedrooms have an exotic feel through their colour schemes and fabrics, and are well appointed. Forgotten-my-toothbrush types can buy low-cost toiletries at reception.

Betws-y-Coed

The Royal Oak Hotel

Hotel

'Bedrooms have a restful décor, with quality fabrics and furnishings and spotless en-suite bathrooms.'

Holyhead Road, Betws-y-Coed,
Conwy LL24 0AY
Telephone: +44(0)1690 710219
royaloakmail@btopenworld.com
www.royaloakhotel.net

In the heart of this old town, against a stunning backdrop of mountains and moorland, sits this solid stone former Victorian coaching inn, which is now a handsome hotel. It overlooks the River Llugwy and successfully caters for a wide-ranging clientele, from locals and business guests to the tourists and walkers that flock to Snowdonia in summer. Dining options include the smart, conservatory-style Grill Bar for all-day bistro/café-style meals and the Llugwy Restaurant in the main building while, to the rear, is the Stables Lodge and Bar, with its outside terrace, that serves fine ales and traditional bar food.

Dinner in the restaurant could take in pan-fried rabbit loin with vanilla risotto, followed by monkfish with herb mash and lemon cream, and Welsh farm cheeses with homemade bara brith. Ingredients are carefully sourced from local suppliers, notably beef and lamb from surrounding farms and game from shoots at Conwy and on Anglesey. Bedrooms have a restful décor, with quality fabrics and furnishings and spotless en-suite bathrooms. There are simpler rooms in the Lodge for hikers and mountaineers.

Rooms: **27. Double/twin room from £40 per person, single room from £65. Family room from £50 per adult.**
Prices: **Set lunch £11.95. Restaurant main course from £12.95. Bar main course from £5.50. House wine £12.75.**
Last orders: **Bar: 21.30 (Friday and Saturday 21.45). Restaurant: 21.00. Restaurant open Wednesday to Saturday evening only.**
Closed: **Rarely.**
Food: **Modern British.**
Real ale: **Greene King Old Speckled Hen.**
Other points: **Smoking area. Children welcome. Car park. Licence for civil weddings. Wheelchair access to the restaurant and overnight.**
Directions: **Exit 19/A55. Take the A470 to Llanrwst. Four miles south of Llanrwst, turn right to join the A5. The hotel is a mile along on the left. (Map 7)**

...for the latest news

Capel Curig

St Curigs Church

Bed and breakfast

Capel Curig, Betws-y-Coed,
Conwy LL24 OEL
Telephone: +44(0)1690 720469
alice@alicedouglas.com
www.stcurigschurch.com

'You have an outdoor whirlpool hot-tub to ease those aching muscles.'

Rooms: **4. Double/twin room from £65, single from £37.50.**
Prices: **Set dinner £25.**
Closed: **Rarely.**
Food: **Traditional French.**
Other points: **Smoking area. Children welcome. Dogs welcome. Garden. Car park.**
Directions: **M56. Take the A55 towards Llandudno. At the junction with Llandudno, take the A470 to Betws-y-Coed and then the A5 to Capel Curig. St Curigs is at the western end of the village, opposite the junction with A4086. (Map 7)**

St Curigs is a unique B&B in the heart of Snowdonia, for it is a deconsecrated 19th-century church, sympathetically renovated by Alice Douglas and offering accommodation in four impressive and very cosy en-suite bedrooms. All are furnished and decorated to a high standard. Two have hand-carved four-poster beds, some retain architectural features such as a pulpit embedded in the wall, while all sport quality fabrics and linen and under-floor heating. The dining room and lounge feature a towering ceiling, stained-glass windows and a lavishly decorated mosaic.

Delicious evening meals are provided on request and rely on local supplies, and may feature charcuterie, followed by monkfish with a lime and créme fraîche sauce. Robust breakfasts use quality sausages and eggs from their own chickens, and should set even the most active types up for a day's hiking or mountain biking – Pen-y-Pass and access to the Snowdon Horseshoe is just 10 minutes' drive away. On your return, you have drying facilities, and an outdoor whirlpool hot-tub to ease those aching muscles.

321

Country inn

The Groes Inn

Tyn-y-Groes, Conwy LL32 8TN
Telephone: +44(0)1492 650545
enquiries@groesinn.com
www.groesinn.com

'Belt-loosening puds include an excellent bread-and-butter pudding made with bara brith (Welsh fruit bread).'

Claiming to be the first licensed house in Wales, 'Taverne-y-Groes' (by the cross) boasts a history unbroken since 1573 and is now family-run by Dawn Humphreys and her son Justin. The building, which enjoys splendid views of the Conwy estuary, contains much 16th- and 17th-century interior timberwork in a succession of low-ceilinged rooms that have been extended to include a formal dining room and a conservatory.

Daily chalkboards and menus proclaim promising bar meals, ranging from Anglesey gammon and eggs and lasagne to braised shoulder of Welsh lamb on minted-pea purée. Belt-loosening puds include an excellent bread-and-butter pudding made with bara brith (Welsh fruit bread). Book ahead for the popular three-course set Sunday lunch and the nightly table d'hôte menu. Lamb, venison, game and fish are all sourced from local suppliers and the bread is homemade. The 14 individually decorated and well-appointed en-suite bedrooms are located in the modern building next door. Expect good fabrics, comfortable sofas, bathrooms with bidets, and views across fields to Snowdonia.

Rooms: 14. Double/twin room from £95, single from £79. Family room from £95.
Prices: Sunday lunch £16.95. Set dinner £28. (4 courses). House wine half carafe £8.65.
Last orders: Bar: afternoon 15.00; evening 23.00 (open all day weekends in summer). Food: lunch 14.15; dinner 21.00.
Closed: Rarely.
Food: Welsh.
Real ale: Burton Ale, Tetley's Bitter.
Other points: Smoking area. Dogs welcome overnight. Garden. Car park. Wheelchair access.
Directions: A55. Take the Conwy exit and go over the river on to the B5106. Turn directly left at the castle, and the hotel is two miles along on the right-hand side. (Map 7)

...for recipe ideas

Llandudno

Dunoon Hotel

Seaside hotel

Gloddaeth Street, Llandudno,
Conwy LL30 2DW
Telephone: +44(0)1492 860787
reservations@dunoonhotel.co.uk
www.dunoonhotel.co.uk

'Chandeliers, draped windows and linen-clothed tables make for elegant dining.'

Rooms: **48. Double room from £86, single from £57.**
Prices: **Set Sunday lunch £15.50 (four courses plus coffee) and set dinner £19.50 (five courses plus coffee). House wine £12.50.**
Last orders: **Food: lunch 14.00; dinner 20.00.**
Closed: **From mid December to mid March.**
Food: **Traditional British.**
Other points: **Smoking area. Children welcome. Garden/patio. Car park. Wheelchair access.**
Directions: **Turn left off Llandudno Promenade near the pier. Continue straight on at the next two roundabouts; the hotel is 200 yards along on the right. (Map 7)**

Set a block or two back from the seafront, this splendid gable-ended mansion is one of many fine examples of Victorian architecture that define this traditional resort town. The charm of this old-fashioned seaside hotel has been maintained by young and enthusiastic owners, Rhys and Charlotte Williams, who have embraced a philosophy of 'if it ain't broke, don't fix it', retaining long-serving staff and an appreciation of what Llandudno did best in its Victorian heyday. Smart oak-panelled public rooms include the Welsh Dresser Bar, which sports a magnificent cooking range. There's a relaxing reading lounge and a panelled lounge with an open fire and cosy corners.

In the restaurant, chandeliers, draped windows and linen-clothed tables make for elegant dining. Chef Mark Martin produces two five-course dinners. This may include a salad of beef tomatoes with feta and basil or chicken-liver pâté, mains of Welsh chop with rosemary-and-redcurrant sauce or sea bream with braised fennel and saffron cream sauce, followed by bread-and-butter pudding or delicious cheeses.

St George

The Kinmel Arms

Restaurant-with-rooms

'Country furniture and polished wood floors give a real buzz to the place.'

St George, Abergele, Conwy LL22 9BP
Telephone: +44(0)1745 832207
info@thekinmelarms.co.uk
www.thekinmelarms.co.uk

Tucked away in the beautiful Elwy Valley, this refurbished 17th-century coaching inn continues to flourish under enthusiastic and dedicated owners Tim Watson and Lynn Cunnah-Watson. In a setting of country furniture and polished wood floors that lend a real charm to the place, everything operates on clean, uncluttered lines around a slate-topped bar offering quality real ales and exceptional wines. Brasserie-style lunches and inventive evening meals may be taken in the cosy lounge, a quieter segregated dining area or the sunny conservatory.

A range of sandwiches and snacks, or 'boat-sinking battered cod' with tartare sauce make for a more than adequate lunch, with perhaps braised ham hock with white wine and herb sauce, or the award-winning dish of Welsh lamb's liver in a rich Guinness-and-mushroom jus, as a mainstay of a full-blown evening feast. Look out for market-fresh fish and local meats on the chalkboards. Four stunning, individually designed suites sport handmade beds, DVD and broadband, luxurious bathrooms, a balcony or patio and views over the wooded Kinmel Estate.

Rooms: **4 suites.**
Prices: **Set Sunday lunch £13.95. Restaurant main course from £9. Bar main course from £9. House wine £11.50.**
Last orders: **Bar: afternoon 15.00 (Sunday 17.30); evening 23.00. Food: lunch 14.00; dinner 21.30 (Sunday 16.00).**
Closed: **Monday.**
Food: **Traditional British/Welsh/French.**
Real ale: **Facer's Dark Mild, Conwy Castle Bitter, Tetley's Bitter. Three guest beers.**
Other points: **No smoking. Children welcome. Dogs welcome in the bar on request. Garden. Car park. Wheelchair access.**
Directions: **Exit 16/M56. Take the A5517 and then the A550 to the A55; St George is two miles south-east of Abergele. (Map 7)**

...for events

Prestatyn

Nant Hall Restaurant & Bar

Nant Hall Road, Prestatyn,
Denbighshire LL19 9LD
Telephone: +44(0)1745 886766
mail@nanthall.com
www.nanthall.com

Restaurant and bar

'The choice here is staggering, but the staff pull off everything with aplomb.'

Prices: **Restaurant main course from £8.95. House wine £11.95.**
Last orders: **Bar: 23.00. Food: Dinner 21.30 (22.00 at weekends).**
Closed: **25-26 December.**
Food: **Modern British.**
Real ale: **Conwy Castle Bitter.**
Other points: **Smoking area. Children welcome. Garden. Car park. Wheelchair access.**
Directions: **A55. Exit on to the A548 to Prestatyn. Nant Hall is on the Old Coast Road. (Map 7)**

No expense has been spared by owners Peter Lavin and Graham Tinsley in transforming Nant Hall. The airy, open-plan interiors, which are split into different rooms, can cater for more than 200 covers and there are rooms for formal dining and others with sofa seating by fires for relaxed pre-dinner drinks. Throughout, vivid wallpapers contrast attractively with polished wooden floors. The bar is imposing and well lit, and has tables with chairs and banquettes. Pick from a well-chosen and fairly priced selection of wine, or enjoy one of the two real ales from Conwy's micro-brewery.

Local dishes and ingredients also feature strongly on the menu and, alongside international bar staples such as Greek salad, you will find local specialities, such as dressed Conwy crab and Edwards of Conwy's award-winning pork-and-leek sausages. A separate section is reserved for the fine local seafood and there are children's meals. Homemade puddings and excellent local cheeses round things off nicely. The choice here is staggering, but the waiting and kitchen staff pull of feverything with aplomb.

www.routiers.co.uk

St Asaph

Drapers Café-Bar

All-day café

'This bright and cheerful café-bar is the perfect spot for refuelling.'

Tweedmill Factory Outlets,
Llannerch Park, St Asaph,
Denbighshire LL17 0UY
Telephone: +44(0)1745 731005
enquiries@tweedmill.co.uk
www.tweedmill.co.uk

There's a Mediterranean feel to the 100-seater Drapers Café-Bar, which is a part of the Tweedmill Factory Outlet. Located in the old tweed mill, this complex is a star attraction for the Welsh Tourist Board and offers plenty of shopping opportunities. The bright and cheerful café-bar is the perfect spot for refuelling, with plants, pine furniture and a large, south-facing patio with beautiful views across a designated Area of Outstanding Natural Beauty.

The menu changes daily and dishes are prepared using fresh local ingredients. Daily specials could include leek-and-potato soup or grilled chicken breast filled with Welsh cheese wrapped in smoked bacon and served with a leek sauce, followed by meringue nest with fresh strawberries and cream. Snacks and light meals run to scrambled eggs with smoked salmon; cheese, chive and bacon bagels; chestnut and mixed-bean savoury loaf; and filled jacket potatoes, with Welsh ice cream among the choice of puddings. It's a popular place for tired and weary shoppers, but big enough to accommodate quite a crowd without the service suffering.

Prices: **Main course from £5.65. House wine £7.95.**
Last orders: **Food: 16.30 (Thursday 19.30, Sunday 16.00).**
Closed: **25 December.**
Food: **Modern British.**
Other points: **Smoking area. Children welcome. Patios. Car park. Wheelchair access.**
Directions: **Two miles south of St Asaph on the A525 to Denbigh. Follow the brown tourist-information signs from the A55. (Map 7)**

...for competitions

326

Aberdyfi

Penhelig Arms

Seaside inn

Aberdyfi, Gwynedd LL35 OLT
Telephone: +44(0)1654 767215
info@penheligarms.com
www.penheligarms.com

'Constantly updated and improved with style, it ranks among the finest of Welsh inns.'

Rooms: 14. Double/twin room from £118 including dinner.
Prices: Set lunch from £13.50 (two courses) and dinner £28. Restaurant main course from £8.95. Bar snack from £4.95. House wine £11.
Last orders: Bar: afternoon 15.30; evening 23.00. Food: lunch 14.30; dinner 21.30.
Closed: Rarely.
Food: Welsh and seafood.
Real ale: Adnams Broadside, Hancock's HB, Greene King Abbot Ale, Felinfoel Double Dragon Ale. Two guest beers.
Other points: Smoking area. Children welcome. Dogs welcome. Car park. Wheelchair access.
Directions: Take the A493 to Aberdyfi from the A487 in Machynlleth. (Map 7)

Robert and Sally Hughes's wonderful 18th-century waterside inn is the place to go if you're looking for 'location, location, location' along this stretch of magnificent Welsh coastline. It stands back from the tiny harbour and enjoys superb views across the Dyfi estuary. Constantly updated and improved with style, it ranks among the finest of Welsh inns. In the Fisherman's Bar, locals and visitors alike congregate to enjoy traditional ales, first-class wines and imaginative bar food.

This is a true 'local' also, in that fresh fish, meats, fruit, vegetables and bakery goods all arrive at the door from local suppliers, featuring within minutes, it seems, on the daily menus that provide such excellent value for money. Expect a host of choices: roast cod with king prawns, chilli and mint, whole black bream roasted with rosemary and olive oil, chargrilled Welsh Black fillet steak with béarnaise sauce, and panna cotta with blackberry compote being typical temptations. In addition to 14 spacious and beautifully appointed bedrooms, there's a stylish loft-style apartment with its own private terrace for watching the sunsets over the bay.

327

GWYNEDD

Bae Abermaw

Hotel

'Well-presented bedrooms, most of which have fabulous sea views.'

Panorama Road, Barmouth,
Gwynedd LL42 1DQ
Telephone: +44(0)1341 280550
enquiries@baeabermaw.com
www.baeabermaw.com

Perched on Panorama Hill, with views across Cardigan Bay, Bae Abermaw combines the old and the new to great effect. Its imposing Victorian exterior hides a comfortable contemporary interior of polished-wood floors and log-burning marble-and-slate fireplaces. White is the dominant colour in the well-presented bedrooms, most of which have fabulous sea views, while others look towards Snowdonia National Park.

Food is another compelling reason to visit Bae Abermaw. Chef David Banks is passionate about using local produce in a range of modern and traditional dishes, such as magnificent sewin from the Mawddach Estuary, mountain lamb braised with white wine and garlic, and Welsh Black beef served with a port-and-juniper wine sauce. Many of the vegetables and herbs are grown in the hotel's own or local gardens. Puddings are sumptuous and may include dark bitter-chocolate tart with raspberry sauce. There is also a good choice of Welsh cheeses. Proprietor Richard Drinkwater is a man with an eye for quality and price when it comes to his well-chosen wine list.

Rooms: 14. Double/twin room from £110, single from £80.
Prices: Set dinner £23.50. Restaurant main course from £16. House wine from £11.50.
Last orders: Dinner: 21.00.
Closed: Rarely.
Food: Modern British.
Other points: No smoking. Children welcome. Garden. Car park. Licence for civil weddings. Wheelchair access.
Directions: From the M54 at Shrewsbury, take the A458 to Welshpool, then the A470 to Dolgellau. Bypass Dolgellau and, at the Llanelltyd roundabout, take the A496 to Barmouth.
(Map 7)

...for special offers

Barmouth

The Bistro

Church Street, Barmouth,
Gwynedd LL42 1EW
Telephone: +44(0)1341 281009
info@bistro-barmouth.co.uk
www.bistro-barmouth.co.uk

Bistro

'Its lively daytime vibe turns into a cosy, romantic atmosphere in the evenings.'

Prices: **Restaurant main course from £10.95. Vegetarian main course from £9.95. Starter from £3.95. House wine £11.95. Special dietary requirements with advance notice.**
Last orders: **Food: 21.30.**
Closed: **lunchtime and Wednesday all day.**
Food: **Modern British with Mediterranean influences.**
Other points: **No smoking. Children welcome.**
Directions: **In the town centre. Some street parking, free at night. (Map 7)**

The cheery French-bistro style is perfect for this 18-seater restaurant that is big on atmosphere and friendliness. Its lively daytime vibe turns into a cosy, romantic atmosphere in the evenings. Owners Gareth Palmer and Rosemary Heath are keen on sourcing good ingredients, and this is evident in their flavoursome dishes. Conwy and North Sea fish is delivered from Llandudno, the spring lamb and aged Welsh Black beef come from local farms, while the organic herbs and salad come from local growers.

The food ranges from starters of black pudding, bacon-and-egg tartlet and asparagus wrapped in smoked salmon with lemon-and-dill dressing to satisfying main dishes such as pork-and-garlic sausages on parsley mash with red-onion gravy, seafood pie, and roast confit of duck on hoisin noodles. Puddings – perhaps warm chocolate tart or raspberry crème brûlée – are exemplary and the plate of impressive Welsh cheeses is always popular. The Bistro attracts a loyal clientele, so booking is a must, especially at weekends.

329

Barmouth

Llwyndu Farmhouse

Bed and breakfast

'Boasts stunning, uninterrupted views of beach and sea.'

Llanaber, Barmouth, Gwynedd LL42 1RR
Telephone: +44(0)1341 280144
intouch@llwyndu-farmhouse.co.uk
www.llwyndu-farmhouse.co.uk

This 16th-century farmstead boasts stunning, uninterrupted views of beach and sea. Walk through the slate-built porch and heavy wooden door and you'll find yourself in the modest great hall, which now doubles up as a dining room. Stone walls, Welsh settles, beamed ceilings and fireplaces are just some of the original features in this characterful place. Peter and Paula Thompson have been here for 21 years.

Peter does the cooking and it's simple, unpretentious and generous, and makes good use of local seafood, homegrown vegetables and Welsh cheeses. You could start with chicken livers and grapes in butter and sherry, followed by salmon, smoked haddock and prawns in a lightly curried cream sauce, or duck with plum-and-ginger sauce. Finish with brandy-snap baskets with a mango syllabub and tropical fruits. If the wine list doesn't tempt you, try the Red Kite beer from the local Bragdy brewery. The six bedrooms are well presented, with comfortable beds and well-equipped bathrooms, and some enjoy sea views. Hearty breakfasts should set you up for long beach walks.

Rooms: **6. Double/twin room from £80. Family room from £110.**
Prices: **Set dinner £25.95. House wine £9.25.**
Last orders: **Food: dinner 18.00.**
Closed: **Rarely.**
Food: **Modern and traditional British.**
Other points: **No smoking. Children welcome. Dogs welcome overnight. Garden. Car park.**
Directions: **Two miles north of Barmouth on the A496. Where the street lights and the speed restriction finish, the farmhouse is the next property on the right-hand side. (Map 7)**

...for the latest news

330
MEMBER ENTRY

Abergavenny

Hunters Moon Inn

Country inn

Llangattock Lingoed, Abergavenny,
Monmouthshire NP7 8RR
Telephone: +44(0)1873 821499
huntersmooninn@btinternet.com
www.hunters-moon-inn.co.uk

'Limestone walls and soft lighting make a congenial setting for dining.'

Rooms: **4. Double/twin room from £50, single from £25.**
Prices: **Restaurant main course from £8. House wine £10.**
Last orders: **Bar: afternoon 14.00; evening 23.00. Food: lunch 14.30; dinner 21.00.**
Closed: **Sunday evening, all day Monday, 25 December evening.**
Food: **Traditional/modern British.**
Real ale: **Brains Rev James.**
Other points: **Smoking area. Children welcome. Dogs welcome in the bar. Garden. Car park. Skittle alley. Wheelchair access to the restaurant/pub (not WC).**
Directions: **Take the A40 to Abergavenny, then the B4347 to Llanvetherine and follow the signs to Llangattock Lingoed. (Map 5)**

Set on the Offa's Dyke path, this traditional rural local has been tastefully renovated to make the most of its historic setting and the 13th-century building itself. A solid oak door leads through to a traditional bar with a tiled floor and a warming log fire. The comfortable, oak-beamed dining area with limestone walls and soft lighting makes a congenial setting for dining.

The menu revolves around what's available locally, notably Hereford steak – a house favourite that is hung for 28 days for a fuller flavour. Most ingredients are quality Welsh homegrown and reared and the menu majors on robust dishes best suited to pub dining. Faggots and peas or homemade cottage pie and chips are satisfyingly good, as are gammon steak with fresh duck egg and chips, or rack of lamb. Whisky bread-and-butter pudding and crumbles continue the comfort theme. The well-kept ales are Welsh, too, and include Brains Rev James, while Gwatkin's cider and perry make for a rustic treat. Draught De Konnick beer from Belgium and Lindeboom lager from Holland add an international flavour.

Abergavenny

Llansantffraed Court Hotel

Country-house hotel

'The main glitz and gloss is saved for the food.'

Llanvihangel Gobion, Clytha, Abergavenny,
Monmouthshire NP7 9BA
Telephone: +44(0)1873 840678
reception@llch.co.uk
www.llch.co.uk

Family owned and set in 20 acres of manicured grounds, this impressive country-house hotel is making a name for itself with its fine dining. The listed building has well-proportioned rooms with a sense of grandeur. Comfortable en-suite bedrooms are refurbished on a rolling basis, but the main glitz and gloss is saved for the food, which utilises the top-quality produce on the doorstep, and delivers exquisite flavours from the amuses-bouches and canapés through to the petits fours.

After a fino sherry in the delightful bar, head through to the dining room; the chintzy look suits the spacious setting and sophisticated menu. Confit leg of Wye Valley duckling with pickled red cabbage is followed by noisettes of Monmouth lamb with thyme jus, or Gower monkfish saltimbocca. Puddings are formidably good – try the orange panna cotta with figs poached in red wine – plus there's a fine choice of mostly Welsh cheeses. The wine list focuses on accessibility with much in the fair-price bracket, but with blow-out options, too. The table d'hôte menus offer excellent value.

Rooms: 21. Double/twin room from £112, single £86, family from £130.
Prices: Set lunch £16.50 and dinner £29.50. Restaurant main course from £16. Bar snacks from £7. House wine £15.
Last orders: Food: lunch 14.00; dinner 20.45.
Closed: Never.
Food: Modern Welsh.
Real ale: Felinfoel Double Dragon Ale. One guest beer.
Other points: No smoking. Children welcome. Dogs welcome overnight. Garden. Car park. Licence for civil weddings/partnerships. Wheelchair access. Trout and salmon fishing.
Directions: Exit 24/M4. From the junction of the A40 and A465 at Abergavenny, follow the signs from the roundabout to Usk on the B4598. The hotel is four miles along on the right. (Map 5)

...for recipe ideas

Abergavenny

Llanwenarth Hotel & Riverside Restaurant

Hotel

Brecon Road, Abergavenny,
Monmouthshire NP8 1EP
Telephone: +44(0)1873 810550
info@llanwenarthhotel.com
www.llanwenarthhotel.com

'Scallops with Thai curry, coconut and lemongrass broth get things off to a flying start.'

Rooms: 17. Double/twin room from £85, single from £65, family from £110.
Prices: Set lunch £12.95 and dinner £14.25. Restaurant main course from £9.45. House wine £11.95.
Last orders: Food: lunch 14.00 (Sunday 15.00); dinner: 21.30 (Sunday 21.00).
Closed: Rarely.
Food: Modern British.
Other points: Smoking area in the bar. Children welcome. Terrace. Car park. Wheelchair access.
Directions: Take the A40 out of Abergavenny and head towards Brecon. The hotel is two miles along on the left. (Map 5)

Perched high above the River Usk, midway between Abergavenny and Crickhowell, the new-look hotel and restaurant (formerly known as The Pantrhiwgoch) continues to go from strength to strength, following extensive refurbishment in 2004. Floor-to-ceiling windows in the cheery-looking bistro-style restaurant and the sunny summer terrace offer wonderful views across the Usk Valley.

The food is much improved and chef Jon West's dishes are strong on local ingredients and on simple but effective presentation. Confit duck leg on pak choi with ginger, soy and plum essence, or scallops with Thai curry, coconut and lemongrass broth get things off to a flying start. The menu varies with the seasons, but avoids clichés, as seen in the Welsh lamb platter – cutlets, braised stuffed breast in red wine, sautéed kidney and sweetbreads in creamy mustard sauce. There's also local venison with blueberry compote, and indulgent puddings such as a chocolate mousse-filled choux bun. The wine list offers a good house option and attractive half bottles. Most of the tasteful and well-appointed bedrooms overlook the river.

www.routiers.co.uk

Llansoy

The Star Inn

Country pub

'What a great location this is.'

Llanfihangel-tor-y-Mynydd, Llansoy,
near Usk, Monmouthshire NP15 1DT
Telephone: +44(0)1291 650256
thestar.inn@virgin.net

What a great location this is. Drop down from the head of the Valley Road, which runs parallel to the Lower Wye Valley Road, and you are in the rural heart of Monmouthshire, with its rolling hills and valley views. This old roadside inn has been providing passers-by with food and drink for three and a half centuries: John Wesley stayed here during his travels around Monmouth. Stone-built with a traditional slate roof, the interior retains original features. A deeply carved mock-Jacobean counter is flanked by a large stone fireplace and, to the left, a small carpeted lounge leads to the traditional public bar.

The rest of the space is used for diners, who can choose from menus that use plenty of local produce, including potatoes and eggs from the farm opposite, and beef and lamb from a neighbouring farm. Expect generous portions from the extensive menu, which touches all bases. Braised ox cheek with Guinness and mushroom is a hearty main course, as is an Indonesian fish curry with mussels and king prawns. The Star is under the same ownership as The Crown at Whitebrook (see entry).

Prices: Restaurant main course from £8.95. Bar main course from £6.95. House wine £10.95.
Last orders: Bar: 23.00. Food: lunch 15.00 (Friday and Saturday 15.30, Sunday 16.30); dinner 21.30.
Closed: Never.
Food: Traditional and Modern British.
Real ale: Brains Rev James, Greene King Old Speckled Hen, Bass.
Other points: Smoking area. Garden. Children welcome. Car park. Wheelchair access.
Directions: Exit 24/M4. Take the A449 signposted to the Midlands. At the first exit, take the A4472 to Usk and then the immediate right on to the B4235 for Chepstow. Take the second left to Llansoy and, at the crossroads, turn right. (Map 5)

...for events

Monmouth

Misbah Tandoori

Bangladeshi restaurant

9 Priory Street, Monmouth,
Monmouthshire NP25 3BR
Telephone: +44(0)1600 714940/772346
info@misbahtandoori.co.uk
www.misbahtandoori.co.uk

'The menu features old tandoori favourites, and an extensive range of constantly changing specials.'

Prices: **Set lunch from £5.95. Restaurant main course from £5.50. House wine £10.95.**
Last orders: **Food: lunch 14.00; dinner 22.30 (Friday and Saturday 23.00).**
Closed: **Rarely.**
Food: **Bangladeshi and Indian.**
Other points: **No smoking. Children welcome. Private room. Wheelchair access.**
Directions: **Exit 24/M4. A449 to Monmouth. The restaurant is near Monmouth Castle and Market Square. (Map 5)**

Situated in a Grade II-listed building in the oldest part of the historic market town of Monmouth, the Misbah Tandoori has been run Mr Miah for the past 15 years. He has worked hard to improve the already high quality of the food and change with the times by incorporating local ingredients into the menu and bringing the best chefs from northern Bangladesh to train the kitchen team. Recently updated, the dining room has plain, neutral colours and modern lighting.

Although the menu features old tandoori favourites, there's an extensive range of constantly changing specials. Hidden among the Anglo-South Asian dishes such as chicken tikka mossalla and butter chicken, are Bengali items such as Bengal king prawn, Bengal fish mossalla and a number of vegetarian items, such as the garlicky potato dish rosuni aloo mossalla and the South Indian-style modhu-mothi (mixed vegetables cooked with spinach, coconut, cheese and tomato). Mr Miah likes to keep up with the times and has introduced a choice of balti dishes, including one featuring chicken and chickpeas.

Pilgrims

Restaurant

'Dishes that emerge from the kitchen are well presented and full of gutsy flavours.'

24 Church Street, Monmouth,
Monmouthshire NP25 3BU
Telephone: +44(0)1600 772744

With just 26 covers, this fetching restaurant may be intimate, but it certainly packs a punch with its simple, well-executed cooking. The dishes that emerge from the kitchen are well presented and full of gutsy flavours. There is an emphasis on local producers, with meat, vegetables and herbs, cider, perry and beer coming from Wales or Herefordshire. Dairy products come from Bower Farm at Grosmont – including the Jersey cream used in the heart-stopping crème brûlée.

Although there is a mid-week fixed-price menu with three choices per course, the à la carte holds plenty of distractions in starters such as mussels cooked in Gwatkin's cider, potted smoked trout or seared scallops with orange and rocket. Main courses take in beef en croute – a fillet of Herefordshire beef with stilton cheese encased in puff pastry and served with a claret-and-thyme infusion – and lemon sole pan-fried in lemon butter with capers and anchovies. At the time of going to print Pilgrims was under new ownership and the name had been changed to Twenty Four.

Prices: **Set dinner available Wednesday and Thursday evening, £14.95. Restaurant main course from £10.95. House wine £10.95.**
Last orders: **Food: lunch 14.15 (Friday and Saturday only); dinner 21.15 (Wednesday to Saturday only).**
Closed: **Sunday, Monday, Tuesday all day, Wednesday and Thursday lunch and month of January.**
Food: **Modern British.**
Real ale: **Wye Valley Butty Bach, Wye Valley Dorothy Goodbody.**
Other points: **No smoking. Children welcome. Wheelchair access.**
Directions: **Exit 24/M4. Take the A449 towards Monmouth and then the A40 into Monmouth. Turn into the one-way system, then left into St James Street and right into St Mary's Street. (Map 5)**

Monmouth

The Stonemill

Rockfield, Monmouth,
Monmouthshire NP25 5SW
Telephone: +44(0)1600 716273
www.thestonemill.co.uk

Restaurant

'A stylish setting for some stunning food.'

Rooms: **6 self-catering cottages. Double/twin room from £40, single from £35.**
Prices: **Set lunch £12.95. Set dinner £16.95. Restaurant main course from £12.50. House wine £11.95.**
Last orders: **Food: lunch 14.00; dinner 21.30.**
Closed: **Sunday evening, all day Monday and two weeks in January.**
Food: **Modern British.**
Other points: **No smoking. Children welcome. Garden. Car park. Licence for civil weddings/ partnerships. Wheelchair access.**
Directions: **M50 north and M4 south. From the centre of Monmouth, head out on the B4233 to Rockfield, Hendre and Abergavenny. The Stonemill is on the right after 2 1/2 miles. (Map 5)**

Housed in a converted 16th-century farm cider barn, with the original millstone as a centrepiece, this restaurant is a stylish setting for some stunning food. Service is friendly and the enthusiastic kitchen team do justice to the excellent ingredients available locally. Thanks to its deepest Monmouthshire location, quality local produce features to great effect in the good-value set menu and a fairly priced carte.

Starters of homemade gnocchi, rich hare sauce and parmesan or stuffed Hendre pig's trotter with wild mushrooms and truffle oil set the standards bar high, and the mains continue to showcase local glories to their best. Monmouthshire lamb, perhaps with pak choi and mint pesto, is one of the foundations of the menu and is joined by Hendre venison, served with a rich game-and-chocolate sauce, and local Longhorn beef accompanied by braised oxtail and parsley cream. Puddings are traditional, for example, sticky toffee pudding with toffee sauce. A fine selection of Welsh cheeses is a good alternative. There are six beautifully appointed self-catering cottages in the grounds.

Local farm meats
Quality, traditionally farmed meats are sourced from farms within a 10-mile of the restaurant. Longhorn beef comes from Frank Sutton at Parc Grace Dieu Farm at The Hendre; free-range Large White pigs from Tump Farm near Monmouth supply the pork; free-range chickens are from Madgotts Farm in Redbrook; and lamb is sourced from New House Farm at Dingestow.

Local shoots
Seasonal game from local shoots includes wild venison from woodlands across Monmouthshire, rabbits shot at Gwelehog and Usk, and mallard from various shoots across the county.

Honey, mushrooms and vegetables
The delicious honey is supplied by Ted and Olive Barrell, who keep hives within two miles of the Stonemill. Bees feed on meadow flowers and tree blossom between the restaurant and the River Trothy. Forager Raoul Van Denbroucke (The Wild One), gathers wild mushrooms in and around the Forest of Dean. Seasonal vegetables are supplied by Crwys Garden Produce at The Hendre, near Monmouth, 01432 275443.

Vin Sullivan Foods,
Abergavenny and Blaenavon, 01495 792792, www.vin-sullivan.co.uk
From humble beginnings at their shop in Abergavenny's High Street, which opened in 1960 and continues to thrive, Vin Sullivan Foods now produce, package and distribute over 5,000 products from an industrial-estate unit in Blaenavon. High-class gourmet products are supplied, including the Stonemill's excellent Welsh cheese-board selection.

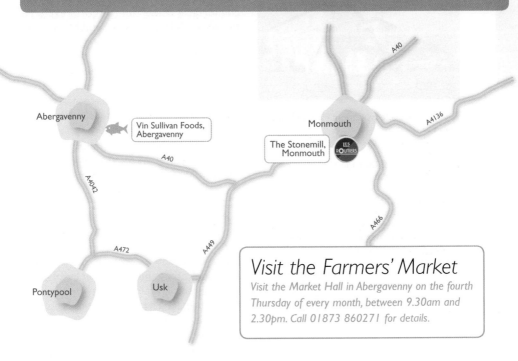

Abergavenny

Vin Sullivan Foods,
Abergavenny

A40

A4042

A472

Pontypool

A449

Usk

Monmouth

A40

A4136

The Stonemill,
Monmouth

LES ROUTIERS

A466

Visit the Farmers' Market
Visit the Market Hall in Abergavenny on the fourth Thursday of every month, between 9.30am and 2.30pm. Call 01873 860271 for details.

Raglan

The Beaufort Arms
Coaching Inn and Restaurant

Village inn

High Street, Raglan,
Monmouthshire NP15 2DY
Telephone: +44(0)1291 690412
thebeauforthotel@hotmail.com
www.beaufortraglan.co.uk

'The overall quality and presentation is well above average.'

Rooms: 15. Double/twin room from £65, single from £55.
Prices: Main course from £4.95. House wine £9.75.
Last orders: Bar: 23.00. Food: lunch 15.00; dinner: 21.00 (Friday and Saturday 21.30).
Closed: Rarely.
Food: Modern British.
Real ale: Brains Rev James, Fuller's London Pride. Guest beers change weekly.
Other points: Smoking area. Children welcome. Garden. Car park. Wheelchair access to the restaurant/pub.
Directions: One minute from the junction of the A40 from Abergavenny and the A449 to Monmouth. South to Newport and the M4 and north to the M50, M5 and M6. (Map 5)

The Lewis family's immaculately refurbished 16th-century inn offers a relaxing and very comfortable base for visitors exploring the Wye Valley, the Vale of Usk and the Brecon Beacons. Individually furnished en-suite bedrooms have been stylishly upgraded; south-facing rooms offer soothing rural views. Period features include an impressive carved oak bar and a huge fireplace taken from Raglan Castle, which blend well with design-led furniture and fabrics to add a modern feel to the bars, brasserie and private dining area. Add decent wines, local real ales and a sun-trap terrace and you have a vibrant inn.

Chefs are committed to using first-class local ingredients, notably meat from surrounding farms and Welsh cheeses. Menus comprise good bar food, such as steak and béarnaise panini, crab terrine and hake in beer batter, alongside robust and more inventive modern dishes listed on chalkboards. In the brasserie, imaginative cooking produces highlights such as oxtails braised in red wine and rosemary, roast turbot with asparagus velouté, and rich chocolate tart. The overall quality and presentation is well above average.

Skenfrith

The Bell at Skenfrith

Country inn

'Wonderful seasonal menus and some seriously good cooking.'

Skenfrith, Abergavenny,
Monmouthshire NP7 8UH
Telephone: +44(0)1600 750235
enquiries@skenfrith.co.uk
www.skenfrith.co.uk

Since re-opening in 2001, following careful restoration and refurbishment by Janet and William Hutchings, this handsome 17th-century inn has become a favoured retreat in the beautiful Welsh borders. It occupies a picturesque spot by the River Monnow and oozes all the charming allure of an old Welsh inn, with slate floors, old settles and fireside easy chairs in the stylish open-plan bar and dining area. However, it's the food, wine and bedrooms that really steal the show.

A commitment to sourcing produce within a five-mile radius of the inn, and from their new organic kitchen garden, results in wonderful seasonal menus and some seriously good cooking. Bar lunches bring Old Spot pork sandwiches or venison steak with cranberry jus, followed by apple tart. The dining-room menu showcases local ingredients in ham-hock terrine with fig compote, followed by braised belly pork, roast venison with port reduction, and baked bass with smoked almond and vanilla butter. William's wine list is superb. The eight en-suite bedrooms are luxuriously appointed and enjoy river or mountain views.

Rooms: **8. Double/twin/suite from £100, single from £75.**

Prices: **Sunday lunch £21.50. Restaurant main course from £14. Bar snacks from £7.50. House wine from £12.**

Last orders: **Bar: 23.00. Food: lunch 14.30; dinner 21.30 (Sunday 21.00).**

Closed: **Two weeks at the end of January/early February and Mondays from November-March.**

Food: **Modern British.**

Real ale: **Breconshire Golden Valley, Freeminer Best Bitter, Timothy Taylor Landlord.**

Other points: **No smoking. Children welcome. Dogs welcome. Garden. Car park. Wheelchair access to the restaurant.**

Directions: **From the A40 at Monmouth, take the A466 towards Hereford. After five miles, turn left on to the B4521 towards Abergavenny. The Bell is two miles further, on the banks of the River Monnow. (Map 5)**

See pub walk on page 498

...for special offers

339
MEMBER ENTRY

Usk

Greyhound Inn Hotel

Llantrissant, Usk,
Monmouthshire NP15 1LE
Telephone: +44(0)1291 672505
enquiry@greyhound-inn.com
www.greyhound-inn.com

Country inn

'Alfresco drinking is a real treat among the colourful flower borders and hanging baskets.'

Rooms: 10. Double room from £74, single from £52.
Prices: Bar main course from £7. House wine from £12.
Last orders: Food: lunch 14.15 (Monday to Sunday); dinner 22.30.
Closed: No food Sunday evening (bar open 19.00-22.30).
Food: Traditional Welsh.
Real ale: Bass, Flowers Original, Greene King Abbot Ale, Brains Bitter. One guest beer.
Other points: Smoking area. Children welcome. Dogs welcome in the bar. Garden. Car park. Wheelchair access.
Directions: Exit 24/M4. From Usk town square, take the second left and follow signs to Llantrissant for 2 1/2 miles. (Map 5)

Originally a traditional 17th-century Welsh longhouse and later a staging post for coaches, the Greyhound occupies a stunning hillside position, surrounded by woodland and pasture in the beautiful Usk Valley. Much extended, with a split-level bar and a succession of drinking and eating rooms, the pub is noted for open fires and a comfortable atmosphere. Visitors will find a printed bar menu detailing traditional pub favourites alongside interesting home-cooked specials listed on chalkboards.

The kitchen uses fresh produce from first-class suppliers, including locally grown fruit and vegetables, and venison from the Welsh Venison Centre. Look out for the venison-and-ale pie, Welsh lamb cutlets with redcurrant and red-wine sauce, and local pheasant in season. Puds are a gooey and retro selection of profiteroles, banana split and gateaux. Conversion of the former stables has produced spacious en-suite bedrooms, all decorated in a cottage style that suit the rural location. Summer alfresco drinking is a real treat among the colourful flower borders and hanging baskets of the garden.

www.routiers.co.uk

Restaurant-with-rooms

'The modern British and French dishes are elegantly presented and big on flavour.'

The Crown at Whitebrook

Whitebrook, Monmouth,
Monmouthshire NP25 4TX
Telephone: +44(0)1600 860254
info@crownatwhitebrook.co.uk
www.crownatwhitebrook.co.uk

Set in three acres of gardens and pasture in a small village five miles from Monmouth, The Crown was one of Britain's first 'restaurants with rooms'. Situated in a historic valley where, in 1607, mills were built along the brook to produce brass wire, the building was modernised in 1973, but has seen further improvements since. The tiny dining room is a model of restraint, with muted colours and modern drawings on the walls.

The modern British and French dishes are elegantly presented and big on flavour: pan-fried calves' kidneys arrive on tomato couscous with pumpkin and chorizo. They may be followed by slow-braised belly of veal on Puy lentils with turnip, onion and parmesan. Desserts such as confit of rhubarb with Granny Smith apple sorbet, tarragon and black Muscat may tempt, but a cheese trolley of up to 15 British cheeses – many of them Welsh – may distract you further. Suppliers include the Welsh Venison Centre, the local butcher and grocer, and fruits and ale from Kingston Farm up the road. The food here is complemented by an extensive and interesting wine list. There are eight plain, but stylish rooms.

Rooms: **8. Double/twin room from £100, single from £65.**
Prices: **Set lunch £22.50. Set dinner £37.50. House wine £16.**
Last orders: **Bar: afternoon 15.00; evening 23.00. Food: lunch 14.00; dinner 21.00 (Friday and Saturday 21.15, no food Sunday evening).**
Closed: **Monday. 26 December to 8 January.**
Food: **Modern British and French.**
Real ale: **Greene King Old Speckled Hen, Marston's Pedigree, Wye Valley Dorothy Goodbody's Golden Ale.**
Other points: **Smoking area. Children over 12 welcome. Garden. Car park. Wheelchair access restaurant only.**
Directions: **Exit 2/M48. A466 towards Monmouth. From Monmouth, take the B4293 towards Trelleck and turn right at the signpost to Whitebrook and follow the road for two miles. (Map 5)**

Trefin

Oriel-y-Felin Gallery and Tea Room

Teashop

15 Ffordd-y-Felin, Trefin, near St Davids,
Pembrokeshire SA62 5AX
Telephone: +44(0)1348 837500
gallery@oriel-y-felin.com
www.oriel-y-felin.com

'This tearoom is a blueprint for perfection.'

Prices: Salads, soups, baguettes, puddings and teas from £4.
Last orders: Food: 16.45.
Closed: Monday. End of October to Easter.
Food: Light lunches, specialist teas and coffees.
Other points: No smoking. Children welcome. Dogs welcome on the patio. Wheelchair access.
Directions: A487 St. Davids to Fishguard Road. 1/4 mile west of the Square and Compass Inn, take the road to Trefin, then turn sharp left after the village hall. The gallery is 50 yards on the left. (Map 7)

There are many reasons to visit Oriel-y-Felin – its proximity to the Pembrokeshire Coastal Path, the two galleries displaying pieces by local artists, and, top of the list, the fine food at incredibly fair prices and an excellent selection of teas. The menu offered in this spick-and-span and welcoming tearoom is a collection of light dishes and a range of superbly prepared beverages. The ingredients, though, are what turn the ordinary into the extraordinary.

The beef sandwich alone is a culinary triumph, made using organic bread from an artisan baker in Carmarthen and excellent beef – and then there's the locally sourced bacon and ham. The homemade beefburger is also worth travelling for, as is the Abercastle crab. In fact, sandwich, burger or salad, nothing disappoints. On the sweet side, we highly recommend the delicious Welsh cakes, chocolate brûlée and apple-and-gooseberry treacle crunch. Even die-hard drinkers are catered for, with a perfectly acceptable and reasonably priced house red and white. In fact, this tearoom is a blueprint for perfection.

Wolfscastle Country Hotel

Country-house hotel

'You are assured a friendly Welsh welcome and staff ensure everything runs like clockwork.'

Wolfscastle, Haverfordwest,
Pembrokeshire SA62 5LZ
Telephone: +44(0)1437 741225
enquiries@wolfscastle.com
www.wolfscastle.com

Well hidden from the A40, this converted Welsh stone vicarage is a perfect base for touring the rugged Pembrokeshire coastline and is a handy stopover en route to or from the Emerald Isle. Family run for more than 25 years, you are assured a friendly Welsh welcome and staff ensure everything runs like clockwork. Bedrooms include three executive suites that are among the most spacious and agreeable in the area and they come with thoughtful extras – state-of-the-art TVs, videos and finger-touch bedside lighting make for a relaxing stay.

The menus follow an 'eat what you like, where you like' policy. Dishes incorporate fresh fish and seafood from nearby Milford Haven, local organic vegetables and herbs and Preseli lamb and beef. The choice is extensive, from a starter of Llangloffan cheese-and-chive pâté with onion-and-ginger marmalade to traditional game pie or roast loin of lamb with laverbread and port-and-orange jus. These are offered in the clubby bar and elegant restaurant. As well as delicious desserts, there's always a superb choice of Welsh cheeses, and a decent list of wines.

Rooms: **20. Double room from £85 to £115, single from £60 to £80.**
Prices: **Main course from £8.50. House wine £10.**
Last orders: **Food: lunch 14.00; dinner 21.00.**
Closed: **Never.**
Food: **Global.**
Other points: **Smoking area. Garden. Children welcome. Dogs welcome. Car park. Licence for civil weddings/partnerships. Wheelchair access to the restaurant/pub.**
Directions: **Signed off the A40 midway between Haverfordwest and Fishguard in the village of Wolfscastle. (Map 7)**

...for recipe ideas

Brecon

The Felin Fach Griffin

Country inn

Felin Fach, Brecon, Powys LD3 0UB
Telephone: +44(0)1874 620111
enquiries@eatdrinksleep.ltd.uk
www.eatdrinksleep.ltd.uk

'Innovative food brings together quality ingredients and mouth-watering combinations.'

Rooms: **7. Double room from £97.50, single from £67.50. Four-poster room £125.**
Prices: **Main course lunch from £7.95. Main course dinner from £12.95. Starters from £4.50. House wine £11.95.**
Last orders: **Bar: afternoon 15.00; evening 23.00. Food: lunch 14.30; dinner 21.30 (Sunday 21.00).**
Closed: **Monday lunch (except bank holidays).**
Food: **Modern British.**
Real ale: **CWRW Haf, OSB (Old Style Bitter), Tomos Watkin's Ales.**
Other points: **Smoking area. Children welcome. Dogs welcome. Garden. Car park. Wheelchair access to the restaurant/pub.**
Directions: **Four miles north-east of Brecon on the A470. The inn is the large terracotta building on the left. (Map 7)**

Brothers Charles and Edmund Inkin have created something very special out of this former farmhouse. A smart, ochre-coloured inn with rooms, the Felin Fach Griffin is one of the new breed of contemporary Welsh inns and it attracts a healthy mix of walkers, foodies and well-heeled City types looking for a weekend retreat. Its innovative food brings together quality ingredients and mouth-watering combinations, while upstairs you can stay in chic, individually designed bedrooms. Flagstone floors, open fireplaces and stripped pine beams create an inn with character and personality.

The ethos in the kitchen is to use fresh local ingredients and keep it simple to maintain freshness and flavours. There's even a kitchen garden a mere 29 paces from the kitchen. Chalkboard menus may list Black Mountains Smokery smoked salmon tartare and Welsh minute steak with braised leeks and chips, in a béarnaise sauce for lunch. Suppers may consist of dressed Portland crab with Granny Smith, celery and Melba toast, or loin of Welsh lamb with sweet-potato mash, with rhubarb and Grand Marnier fool to finish.

Welsh Venison Centre,
Middlewood Farm, Bwlch, Brecon Powys, 01874 730929, www.welshvenisoncentre.com
Sells quality-assured farmed venison either diced, in shoulder steaks, chops, mince, sausages and burgers, plus other cuts. Contrary to popular opinion, this is a low-fat, low-cholesterol meat, rich in iron. The shop is open Monday to Saturday.

Black Mountains Smokery,
Crickhowell, Unit 1, Leslie House Elvitec Estate, 01873 811566, www.smoked-foods.co.uk
Traditional smoking methods and hand filleting and slicing from quality ingredients make for a fine product collection. Wonderful smoked salmon and duck.

Bower Farm Dairy,
Grosmont, 01981 240219
Victor and Val Collinson have developed a local market for their dairy produce, with milk from a herd of pedigree Jersey cows from which they make cream, clotted cream, yogurt and crème fraîche. They also produce rare-breed Gloucester Old Spot pork.

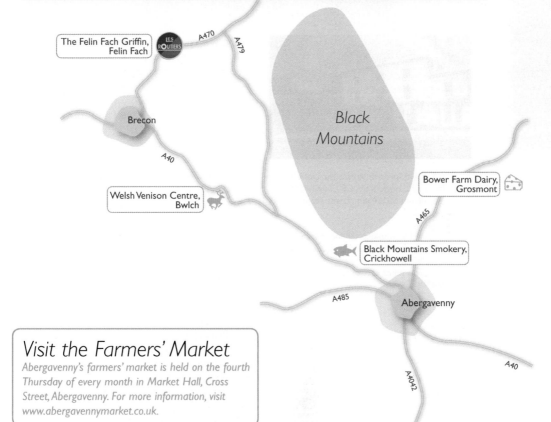

Visit the Farmers' Market

Abergavenny's farmers' market is held on the fourth Thursday of every month in Market Hall, Cross Street, Abergavenny. For more information, visit www.abergavennymarket.co.uk.

Crickhowell

Glangrwyney Court

Bed and breakfast

Glangrwyney, Crickhowell, Powys NP8 IES
Telephone: +44(0)1873 811288
info@glancourt.co.uk
www.glancourt.co.uk

'The wow factor starts at the gate of this lovely property.'

Rooms: **5, 1 with private bathroom. Double room from £70, single from £50, family £95.**
Prices: **Set dinner £25. Main course from £12.50. House wine £10.**
Closed: **Rarely.**
Other points: **No smoking. Children welcome. Garden. Car park. Boules and croquet. Licence for civil weddings.**
Directions: **Two miles east of Crickhowell off the A40. (Map 5)**

Glangrwyney Court has all the elements of a fine B&B and more. It's set in an elegant Georgian mansion sympathetically refurbished by Christina Jackson. The wow factor starts at the gate of this lovely property, approached along an attractive tree-lined drive that runs through gorgeous gardens. Christina is the perfect host, proud of her home in which visitors are treated as personal guests. The lounges, with just the right amount of chintz, are supremely comfortable. These are complemented by five opulently decorated en-suite bedrooms that are romantic in style and have lovely views over the grounds. Thoughtful added extras include bathrobes, quality toiletries, a clock radio, a hairdryer and a DVD player.

Breakfast is quite an occasion, thanks to the sourcing of fabulous ingredients from the Black Mountains Smokery, local honey, vegetables and fruit. Christina's set dinners are available by prior arrangement, or you can dine very well in nearby Crickhowell. Overall, this guesthouse offers excellent value for money for this level of comfort and outlook.

www.routiers.co.uk

Crickhowell

Ty Croeso Hotel

Hotel

The Dardy, Crickhowell, Powys NP8 1PU
Telephone: +44(0)1873 810573
info@ty-croeso.co.uk
www.ty-croeso.co.uk

'Enjoy drinks in the lounge bar, or on the pretty sun terrace in summer.'

Translated from the Welsh as House of Welcome, Linda Jarrett's small and intimate hotel deserves its name. Set high into a hillside overlooking Crickhowell and the Usk Valley, this former workhouse infirmary of Victorian origin sports eight neat and comfortable bedrooms that are undergoing promising refurbishment – most command stunning mountain views.

Linda has injected the required passion and energy since taking over in 2005 to improve and re-establish the business. Bedrooms are being updated and a new kitchen has been installed for long-serving chef Lisa Grenfell to produce her excellent-value Taste of Wales dinner menu, which highlights produce sourced within a 10-mile radius of the hotel. Enjoy drinks in the lounge bar, or on the pretty sun terrace in summer, and then tuck into twice-baked cheese-and-laverbread soufflé, followed by rib-eye steak with a mustard-and-pepper crust or lamb shank cooked in red wine, and finish with rhubarb-and-lemon tart. A peaceful stroll beside the Brecon Canal just below the hotel should stimulate a healthy appetite for dinner.

Rooms: **8. Double/twin room from £68, single from £42. Family room from £100.**
Prices: **Set dinner £18. Restaurant main course from £9.50. House wine £10.95.**
Last orders: **Dinner: 21.00.**
Closed: **Rarely.**
Food: **Modern British.**
Real ale: **Breconshire Brewery.**
Other points: **No-smoking area. Children welcome. Car park. Wheelchair access.**
Directions: **Exit 24/M4. Take the A449 then the A40 to Crickhowell. Turn left at the Shell petrol station, go across the bridge, right at the lights and then first left. (Map 7)**

...for events

346

Machynlleth

The Wynnstay Hotel & Restaurant

Town-centre inn

Heol Maengwyn, Machynlleth,
Powys SY20 8AE
Telephone: +44(0)1654 702941
info@wynnstay-hotel.com
www.wynnstay-hotel.com

'Puddings are seriously good: a pineapple triptych or curd tart with mara des bois strawberries.'

Rooms: **23. Double/twin room from £80, single from £55, family from £80.**
Prices: **Set lunch £12.95 (Sundays only) and dinner £25. Main course from £9.95. House wine £13.95.**
Last orders: **Bar: afternoon 14.00; evening 23.00. Food: lunch 14.00; dinner 21.00. Pizzeria 21.30.**
Closed: **1 January.**
Food: **Welsh with Italian influences. Real pizzas.**
Real ale: **Greene King Old Speckled Hen, Brains Rev James, Greene King IPA.**
Other points: **Smoking area. Children welcome. Dogs welcome. Car park. Wheelchair access to the restaurant/pub. Pizzeria with wood-fired oven.**
Directions: **Last exit/M54. Follow signs to Newtown, continue on the A470 to Machynlleth. Wynnstay is on the left as you approach the Clock Tower. (Map 7)**

Once a coaching inn for the Shrewsbury Stage, this rambling, Tardis-like Georgian building has long been a place for the weary traveller to rest and feast. Since the arrival of owners Charles and Sheila Dark and chef Gareth Johns in 2000, it has been moving effortlessly up the culinary ladder of mid-Wales and draws a discerning local clientele.

Lunches and dinners in the non-smoking and smoking bars and restaurant include plenty of local ingredients: rillettes of Dyfi sewin, Rhydlewis smoked salmon with garlic, chive and yogurt dressing and Bay scallops with wilted Ynyslas chard demonstrate keen local sourcing, as do breast of Bacheiddon mallard with red wine and chocolate, and Conwy mussels with leeks and white wine. A separate pizza menu widens the choice. Puddings are seriously good: a pineapple triptych or curd tart with mara des bois strawberries. And there's a good selection of Welsh cheeses. The overhauled wine list has much to please fans of all things Italian, from light, bright Prosecco to a rich and satisfying Brunello di Montalcino. The en-suite rooms are simply appointed and keenly priced.

www.routiers.co.uk

Food Producers

The recipes you cook are only as good as the ingredients you use, and we can help you source the best. Our directory of food producers and farm shops around the country brings you a market garden of fresh produce, the best local cheeses, meats and products. So, whether you want to pick your own fruits, buy a picnic hamper of goodies or garden plants, we have pinpointed the top suppliers.

The Rare Breeds Survival Trust was set up as a charity in 1973 to protect Britain's native livestock breeds for future generations. A non-Government funded body the RBST lists over 70 rare breed cows, pigs, sheep, poultry, goats and horses on its 'watch list'. It also set up the Traditional Breeds Meat Marketing Company, which accredits independent butchers to stock and market rare and traditional breeds and reassure the public about traceability, as a means of conservation. Encouraging people to eat meat from rare breeds creates a demand that means that more farmers keep more of them.

Thurstaston, Cheshire

Church Farm Organics

Church Lane, Thurstaston, Wirral,
Cheshire CH61 0HW
Telephone: +44(0)151 6487838
sales@churchfarm.org.uk
www.churchfarm.org.uk

Hours: Tuesday-Friday 10.00-17.00. Saturday
9.00-17.00. Sunday 11.00-17.00.
Other points: Plants and shrubs for sale. PYO.
Parking. Coffee shop. Farm animals. Disabled
access.
Directions: Exit 4/M53, to Clatterbridge. Take
the A540 Chester to Heswall road. Continue
until you reach Thurstaston, then follow the
brown tourist-information signs. (Map 9, 348)

This 60-acre organic farm is set in a
conservation area, but the main reason
to visit is the 2,000 grocery products
available from the farm shop. All the fruit
and vegetables are organic, as are meats,
cheese and grocery lines. You will find all
the top brands here, too, from Richard
Woodall's bacons, sausages and hams to
Cartmel sticky toffee pudding. The shop
also runs a box scheme and has a caravan
and camping site.

Truro, Cornwall

Callestick Farm Cornish Dairy Ice Cream

Callestick, Truro, Cornwall TR4 9LL
Telephone: +44(0)1872 573126
info@callestickfarm.co.uk
www.callestickfarm.co.uk

Hours: Monday-Friday 9.00-17.00. In summer
Saturday and Sunday afternoon.
Other points: Farm shop.
Directions: North of Truro between the A30
and the A3075. (Map 3, 349)

This award-winning, family-run Cornish ice
cream maker uses the freshest milk and
cream from the farm and the finest fruits.
Stop off at the café and ice-cream parlour
to sample its flagship luxury clotted cream
range, as well as premium ice creams such
as Jamaican rum-and-raisin or crunchy
honeycomb. A delicatessen stocks the
entire range, as well as other tasty Cornish
foodstuffs. Watch the ice cream being
made from a viewing area.

www.routiers.co.uk

Grange-over-Sands, Cumbria

The Hazelmere Café and Bakery

1 Yewbarrow Terrace, Grange-over-Sands,
Cumbria LA11 6ED
Telephone: +44(0)15395 32972
hazelmeregrange@yahoo.co.uk
www.hazelmerecafe.co.uk

Hours: Monday-Saturday 9.00-16.30 in winter,
9.00-17.00 in summer.
Directions: Exit 36/M6, then take the A590,
then the B5277, signposted to Grange-over-
Sands. Pass Grange station and at the mini
roundabout take the first exit. The café is
25 yards along on the right. (Map 9, 350)

Grasmere, Cumbria

Sarah Nelson's Original Celebrated Grasmere Gingerbread

The Gingerbread Shop, Church Cottage,
Grasmere, Cumbria LA22 9SW
Telephone: +44(0)15394 35428
sarahnelson@grasmeregingerbread.co.uk
www.grasmeregingerbread.co.uk

Hours: Monday-Saturday 9.15-17.30. Sunday
12.30-17.30. (Shorter hours in winter).
Other points: Shop. Mail order.
Directions: Exit 36/M6. A590 to A591 through
Windermere/Ambleside. (Map 12, 351)

From Lakeland plum bread to authentic French sticks, up to 40 different breads are baked in Dorothy and Ian Stubley's bakery every morning. In the café next door, a mouthwatering display of traditionally made cakes includes an award-winning Cumbrian rum nicky. They can all be washed down with one of the 30 or so single-estate teas sourced by Dorothy. From the menu of savoury dishes, try potted Morecambe Bay shrimps or grilled Cumbrian goat's cheese.

The picturesque village of Grasmere may be famous as the home of William Wordsworth, but it's equally renowned for Sarah Nelson's Original Celebrated Gingerbread. This tiny shop has been in the same family for the past 80 years. Many have tried to copy the world-famous secret gingerbread recipe, but no one has ever come close to the intensely flavoured confection that comes wrapped in parchment paper. Homemade fudges and Kendal Mint Cake are also available.

...for competitions

Kendal, Cumbria

Low Sizergh Barn

Low Sizergh Farm, Sizergh, Kendal,
Cumbria LA8 8AE
Telephone: +44(0)15395 60426
apark@lowsizerghbarn.co.uk
www.lowsizerghbarn.co.uk

Hours: Daily 9.00-17.30.
Other points: Farm shop. Car park. Farm trail.
Craft gallery. Tearoom.
Directions: Situated on the A591, three miles
south of Kendal and three miles from exit
36 on the M6. Follow the A590 and brown
tourist-information signs for Sizergh Castle
then Low Sizergh Barn. (Map 12, 352)

Penrith, Cumbria

The Watermill

Little Salkeld, Penrith, Cumbria CA10 1NN
Telephone: +44(0)1768 881523
organicflour@aol.com
www.organicmill.com

Hours: Daily 10.30-17.00.
Other points: Shop. Mail order. Mill tours.
Directions: Six miles from exit 40/M6. Take the
A686 for five miles to Langwathby, turn left
at the village green and the mill is two miles
further on. (Map 12, 353)

This late 17th-century barn shop is packed with speciality foods, crafts and gifts. Awarded UK Farm Retailer of the Year 2005, its shelves are laden with Cumbrian produce, including cheeses and ice cream made from the farm's organic milk, and vegetables fresh from the fields. The tearoom uses homegrown ingredients to good effect. To see the cows being milked, arrive at around 3.45pm. There are local ceramics, paintings, baskets and rugs aplenty in the craft shop.

Registered with the Biodynamic Agriculture Association, Nick and Ana Jones' restored mill produces a wide range of biodynamic and organic flours, including wholewheat and rye. The shop stocks an array of organic produce: porridge oats, oatmeal, dried fruit and nuts, teas and coffees, and herbs and spices. The food served in the tearoom is completely organic and vegetarian. Try the miller's lunch of Loch Arthur cheese and homemade chutney, or homemade soup with various breads.

Pamphill, Dorset

Pamphill Dairy Farm Shop, Restaurant and Butchery

Pamphill, Wimborne, Dorset BH21 4ED
Telephone: +44(0)1202 880618
info@pamphilldairy.com
www.pamphilldairy.com

Hours: Daily 8.30-17.30.
Other points: Garden centre. Ample parking.
Children's play area. Scenic walks. Picnic area.
Easy access and facilities for disabled.
Directions: From Wimborne, take the B3082.
Turn left at Pamphill post office and look out
for signs. (Map 4, 354)

In 1983, the Richardsons converted old
farm buildings into a farm shop to sell
produce grown on the farm as well as that
from local growers and artisans. Expect
to find orchard and soft fruits, vegetables,
eggs, homemade cakes and jams, dairy
produce and locally baked bread and
honey. A butchery sells fresh meats, notably
beef from the Ruby Red North Devons of
Kingston Lacy Park. A tearoom is situated
in the former milking parlour.

427

...for special offers

Cirencester, Gloucestershire

The Butts Farm Shop

Near South Cerney, Cirencester,
Gloucestershire GL7 5QE
Telephone: +44(0)1285 862224
gary@buttsfarmshop.com
www.thebuttsfarmshop.com

Hours: Tuesday-Friday 10.00-18.00. Saturday
8.30-12.00.
Other points: Farm shop. Mail order. Car
park. Farm open to public February-October.
Delivery to London restaurants twice a week.
Directions: Alongside the A419 Gloucester
to Swindon M4-M5 link road; just outside
Cirencester near South Cerney. (Map 5, 355)

At Butts Farm, butcher Gary Wallace and livestock breeder Judy Hancox farm rare breeds of cattle, sheep, pigs and poultry in the traditional way to produce meat of exceptional quality and flavour. Fully traceable traditional and rare-breed meats, home-cured and oak-smoked bacon, sausages and cooked meats are available through the farm shop, as well as locally grown vegetables and fruits, and their Cotswold Gourmet Mail Order service. The farm is open to the public.

Cirencester, Gloucestershire

Chesterton Farm Shop

Chesterton Farm, Cirencester,
Gloucestershire GL7 6JP
Telephone: +44(0)1285 653003
www.chestertonfarm.co.uk

Hours: 8.30-17.00. Saturday 8.00-16.00.
Closed Sunday.
Other points: Farm shop. Rare-breed butcher.
Directions: Situated on the southern outskirts
of Cirencester town, off Chesterton Lane.
Follow the A433 out of Cirencester (to
Tetbury). Chesterton Lane is situated on the
left between the last two roundabouts.
(Map 5, 356)

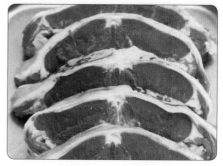

This farm shop majors in traditional British and rare-breed meats and has a policy of selling only fully traceable meats. Among its prime-meat choices are Gloucester Old Spot pork, Tamworth pork, Dorset Down lamb, and its famous dry-cured bacon and ribs of beef. Alongside the butchers is a well-stocked fruit and vegetable farm shop offering an excellent choice of locally grown fresh produce. It also sells delicious home-baked cakes, ice cream, free-range eggs, nibbles and olives.

Cirencester, Gloucestershire

The Organic Farm Shop & Café

Abbey Home Farm, Burford Road,
Cirencester, Gloucestershire GL7 5HF
Telephone: +44(0)1285 640441
cargofco@aol.com
www.theorganicfarmshop.co.uk

Hours: Tuesday and Wednesday 9.00-17.00.
Thursday and Friday 9.00-18.30. Saturday
9.00-16.00.
Directions: Two miles north-east of
Cirencester off the B4425 on the road
to Bibury. (Map 5, 357)

Huntley, Gloucestershire

The Country Butcher

Ross Road, Huntley,
Gloucestershire GL19 3DZ
Telephone: +44(0)1452 831023
sales@countrybutcher.co.uk
www.countrybutcher.co.uk

Hours: Tuesday-Saturday 9.00-17.30.
Other points: Shop.
Directions: A40. West of Gloucester.
(Map 5, 358)

The aim of The Organic Farm Shop and Café is to provide visitors with a complete and different shopping experience. The 15-acre market garden produces 200 varieties of vegetables and fruits each year, as well as herbs and cut flowers. All organic beef, pork and lamb reared on the farm, giving complete traceability, and eggs come from three flocks of free-range Black Rocks. The garden inspires the simple, seasonal menus at the organic café.

Dave Tomlins is a traditional country butcher providing high-quality meat, home-cured bacon and delicious hand-made sausages. At The Country Butcher, prime Hereford and Scotch beef is hung for 21 days and comes with complete traceability, pork is from Gloucester Old Spot pigs and lamb is traditionally produced. Dave uses traditional methods in his other products, too. He has been an award-winning sausage maker for 35 years and his home-cured bacon has also picked up medals.

...for the latest news

Basingstoke, Hampshire

Laverstoke Park Produce

Laverstoke Park, Overton,
Hampshire RG25 3DR
Telephone: +44(0)1256 772800
info@laverstokepark.co.uk
www.laverstokepark.co.uk

Hours: Tuesday-Saturday 8.00-17.30. Sunday
10.00-16.00.
Other points: Farm shop. Farmers' market.
Online/mail order. Delivery. Car park.
Directions: Exit 8/M3. Take the A303, the first
exit towards Overton, for two miles, and the
farm shop is on the right. Or, two miles south
from the traffic lights at Overton. (Map 5, 359)

Titchfield, Hampshire

Garsons

Fontley Road, Titchfield,
Hampshire PO15 6QX
Telephone: +44(0)1329 844336
titchfield@garsons.co.uk
www.garsons.co.uk

Hours: Monday-Saturday 9.00-18.00 (winter
17.00). Sunday 10.30-16.30.
Other points: Farm shop. Garden centre.
Restaurant. Pet centre.
Directions: Exit 9/M27. From the A27, turn
into Mill Lane which leads to Fontley Road.
(Map 5, 360)

Set within 2,500 organic acres of rolling Hampshire farmland, Laverstoke Park farm shop stocks choice cuts of award-winning organic meats, including wild boar, water buffalo, Aberdeen Angus beef, Hebridean lamb and Middle White pork. Add to that a large choice of organic fruit and vegetables, hand-picked strawberries, buffalo-milk ice cream made on the farm and local cheeses, and the result is a one-stop shopping experience of great-tasting food grown, produced and nurtured without compromise.

Garsons Farms Shop prides itself on the wide selection of Hampshire produce it sells, including jams and preserves, local cheeses, cakes, luxury ice creams, Scottish smoked salmon, chocolates and beers. Breads and pastries arrive daily from a local bakery. The garden centre allows green-fingered visitors to stock up on plants, furniture, barbecues and clothing, and The Terrace Restaurant is the place to relax and take refreshment. Look out, too, for the Copnor Tropicals Pet Centre.

Ledbury,
Herefordshire

Llandinabo Farm Shop

21 The Homend, Ledbury,
Herefordshire HR8 1BN
Telephone: +44(0)1531 632744
info@tbmm.plus.com
www.rarebreedsbutcher.com

Hours: Monday and Saturday 8.00-16.00.
Tuesday-Friday 8.00-17.00.
Directions: A449. In the centre of Ledbury,
on the same side of the street as the market
house. (Map 5, 361)

An accredited butcher of the Rare Breeds
Survival Trust, John Miles specialises in the
highest-quality meat. All beef, lamb, pork
and bacon are from pure-bred traditional
breeds, most of them from local farms.
Breeds vary, but beef could be from
Dexter or Belted Galloway herds, lamb
from Wiltshire Horn or Balwen, and pork
from Tamworth or Berkshire pigs. It all
makes for delicious meat that is guaranteed
to have an old-fashioned depth of flavour.

...for recipe ideas

431

Market Harborough, Leicestershire

Farndon Fields Farm Shop

Farndon Fields Farm, Farndon Road, Market
Harborough, Leicestershire LE16 9NP
Telephone: +44(0)1858 464838
office@farndonfields.co.uk

Hours: **Monday-Saturday 8.00-18.00. Sunday
and bank holidays10.00-16.00. Closed
Christmas, New Year and Easter Sunday.**
Other points: **Butchers. Plant centre.**
Directions: **Exit 20/M1. A427 to Market
Harborough. Right at the first roundabout,
right at the next roundabout. The farm is a 1/4
mile along on the right. (Map 8, 362)**

From a farmhouse garage selling potatoes
and vegetables, this thriving business has
expanded rapidly. Now housed in a large,
purpose-built shop, the range of produce
includes a wider choice of vegetables and a
full selection of salads and fruits all grown on
the 250-acre site. These are supplemented
by cakes and bread, rare-breed meats from
local farms, cheeses, jams, chutneys, honey,
sauces and other deli products. The garden
centre sells cut flowers, plants, composts
and pots.

New Ferry, Merseyside

Edge & Son

61 New Chester Road, New Ferry,
Wirral, Merseyside CH62 1AB
Telephone: +44(0)151 645 3044
callum@traditionalmeat.com
www.traditionalmeat.com

Hours: Monday-Friday 8.00-17.00. Saturday
8.00-16.00.
Other points: Shop. Mail order. Delivery.
Directions: A41. Four miles from Birkenhead.
(Map 9, 363)

Tradition plays a major part in the success of the Edge family butchery business, which has operated from the same premises since John Edge founded it in 1844. Today, Callum Edge runs the business in much the same way, slaughtering their own quality, pure British breed livestock sourced from low intensive or organic grassland farms from across Cheshire, Wales and the Wirral. Meat is traditional hung to improve its flavour and texture.

Swafield, Norfolk

Tavern Tasty Meats Ltd

The Farm Shop, The Street, Swafield,
Norfolk NR28 0PG
Telephone: +44(0)1692 405444
roger@tavern.fsbusiness.co.uk
www.taverntasty.co.uk

Hours: Tuesday, Thursday and Friday
8.00-16.00. Saturday 8.00-13.00.
Other points: Shop. Mail order. Delivery.
(Map 10, 364)

Norfolk's only accredited rare-breeds butcher, Roger Human's Tavern Tasty Meats supplies traditional-breed beef, lamb, pork, bacon and ham. All meat comes from the butcher's own farm or small Norfolk producers and each animal is totally traceable. The shop, which is housed in a former village pub, also sells 12 different varieties of sausage, plus delicious pork pies. All products are available at Roger's new shop in Holt (44 Bull Street), as well as selected farmers' markets.

...for events

433

Corbridge, Northumberland

Brocksbushes Fruit Farm

Brocksbushes Farm, Corbridge,
Northumberland NE43 7UB
Telephone: +44(0)1434 633100
acd@brocksbushes.co.uk
www.brocksbushes.co.uk

Hours: **Daily 9.30-19.00 (winter 18.00).**
Other points: **Farm shop. PYO. Parking.
Picnic area. Tea room.**
Directions: **16 miles west of Newcastle-
upon-Tyne, on the A69. The entrance is off
the Styford roundabout, five miles east of
Hexham. (Map 12, 365)**

Stocksfield, Northumberland

North Acomb Farm Shop

North Acomb Farm, Bywell, near Corbridge,
Stocksfield, Northumberland NE43 7UF
Telephone: +44(0)1661 843181
info@northacombfarmshop.co.uk
www.northacombfarmshop.co.uk

Hours: **Tuesday-Saturday 9.30-17.00.
Sunday 9.30-13.00.**
Directions: **15 miles west of Newcastle,
5 miles east of Corbridge. From A69, take
the B6309 in the direction Bywell/Stocksfield.
The farm shop is signposted. (Map 12, 366)**

The range of homemade foods at
Brocksbushes is irresistible. Farm-fresh
poultry and game in season is another
draw, as are the pick-your-own berry fruits.
Stock up on its grocery lines, fresh fruit
and vegetables, much of it organic, and
wines from around the world, or order gift
hampers to be delivered by post. You can
sample the farm's homemade specialities in
its tearoom before stocking up with plants
at the new plantary.

For more than 26 years, Robin and Caroline
Baty have sold produce from their family-
run working farm. They offer the best-
quality Aberdeen Angus beef, traditionally
fed lamb and pork, free-range chickens,
geese, duck and game in season, dry-cured
bacon and gammon, fresh dairy products
and vegetables. Also, carefully selected
items from the delicatessen, gift items and
greeting cards. Caroline produces the most
delicious home-cooked dishes and Robin's
own-recipe burgers, black puddings and
sausages are legendary.

Abingdon, Oxfordshire

Millets Farm Centre

Kingston Road, Frilford, Abingdon,
Oxfordshire OX13 5PD
Telephone: +44(0)1865 391266
carter@milletsfarmcentre.com
www.milletsfarmcentre.com

Hours: Daily 9.00-18.00 in summer 9.00-17.00
in winter. PYO available June-September. Maze
open June-early September.
Other points: Farm shop. PYO. Car park. Play
area. Farm zoo. Restaurants. Garden centre.
Picnic area. Woodland walk. Maze.
Directions: Four miles west of Abingdon
on the A415 (follow the brown tourist-
information signs). (Map 5, 367)

From May to October, Millets Farm
has more than 50 acres of 30 different
fruits and vegetables for pick-your-own
harvesting. The extensive farm shop stocks
the same produce, alongside breads and
cakes from the bakery, cheeses from the
delicatessen, locally sourced meat from the
butchers and wet fish from the fishmongers.
There's also a wine department. As well as
two restaurants and a farm shop, there is a
garden centre, a children's zoo, a trout lake
and a maze.

Bicester, Oxfordshire

J M Walman Butcher

1 Station Road, Launton, Bicester,
Oxfordshire OX26 5DS
Telephone: +44(0)1869 252619

Hours: Tuesday and Thursday 8.00-17.00.
Friday 8.00-17.30. Saturday 8.00-14.00.
Sunday 9.30-12.00.
Other points: Shop.
Directions: Exit 9/M40. Go anti-clockwise
on the Bicester Ring Road. Take the third
roundabout signposted Launton. (Map 5, 368)

Licensed game dealer and butcher John
Walman may have won national gold
standard awards for his homemade sausages
and burgers, but his Bicester shop draws
customers from across a wide area for his
traditional breed meats, namely beef, lamb
and pork, and free-range poultry. The shop
is much more than a traditional butcher's,
with a new deli counter offering English
and Continental cheeses, olives, pâtés and
homemade pies and home-cooked meats.

Hailey, Oxfordshire

Shaken Oak Products

Shaken Oak Farm, Old North Leigh Lane,
Hailey, Witney, Oxfordshire OX29 9UX
Telephone: +44(0)1993 868043
shakenoak@lycos.co.uk
www.shakenoak.co.uk

Hours: Weekends and by appointment.
Other points: Farm shop. Farmers' market.
Mail order. Delivery. Car park.
Directions: From Witney, take the B4022.
Before Hailey, turn right into Poffley End. Turn
right at the next crossroads (about one mile
on) and take the left fork up the lane to the
farm. (Map 5, 369)

This Cotswold farm is simply a must for
mustard-lovers. The owners started making
mustard as a hobby for family and friends,
but it has become a full-time business.
Only the best ingredients are used in
the range, which is gluten-free and free
from preservatives, colouring or artificial
ingredients. The selection includes: Original;
Mustard with Garlic; Honey Mustard;
Mustard with Herbs; Old Hooky Beer
Mustard; Mustard with Ginger; Hot Mustard;
Tarragon Mustard; and Chilli Mustard.

Market Drayton, Shropshire

Buttercross Farm Foods

Shiffords Grange Farm, Red Bull,
Market Drayton, Shropshire TF9 2QS
Telephone: +44(0)1630 656670
info@buttercross.com
www.buttercross.com

Hours: **Daily 8.30-17.00.**
Other points: **Farm shop. Mail order. Delivery.
Car park. Wholesalers.**
Directions: **Approximately 1 1/2 miles east of
Market Drayton on the A53. (Map 9, 370)**

Animal welfare has always been important
to Buttercross, which specialises in fresh,
free-range and rare-breed pork, dry-
cured bacon, quality hams and gammons,
sausages and black pudding. All the
produce is prepared on the farm from
the outdoor, free-range herd of pigs. The
aim of Buttercross is to 'revive the links
between farmer and consumer for fresher
local food'. The new farm shop offers a full
range of butchery produce complemented
by other local food.

...for special offers

North Cadbury, Somerset

J A & E Montgomery Cheeses

Manor Farm, Woolston Road, North Cadbury,
Yeovil, Somerset BA22 7DW
Telephone: +44(0)1963 440243
jamie@montycheese.fsnet.co.uk

Hours: Closed Wednesday, Saturday and
Sunday afternoons.
Other points: Shop. Mail order.
Directions: One mile off the A303 between
Wincanton and Sparkford. Coming into North
Cadbury, turn right into Woolston Road and
the shop is on the left. (Map 4, 371)

The Montgomery family has been farming
in Somerset since 1911 and Jamie is the
third generation to produce hand-made
traditional unpasteurised cheeses and
butter. All are made from the milk of the
family's own herd of cows – Friesian milk
for the cheddar (the Supreme Champion
in the British Cheese Awards 2004) and
rich milk from Jersey cows for the equally
revered Ogle Shield – a softer, pungent,
rind-washed cheese with a creamy flavour.

438

Lichfield, Staffordshire

The Old Stables Farm Shop & Bakery

Packington Moor Farm, Packington, Lichfield, Staffordshire WS14 9QB
Telephone: +44(0)1543 481223
john@packingtonmoor-events.co.uk
www.packingtonmoor-events.co.uk

Hours: Tuesday-Friday 8.00-18.00. Saturday 8.00-17.30. Closed Sunday and Monday.
Other points: Farm shop. Farmers' market. Delivery. Car park. Play area. Picnic area.
Directions: Between the A51 and the A5, near Whittington Army Barracks. (Map 8, 372)

John and Rosemary Barnes's farm provides a rich harvest of pick-your-own fruits throughout the summer. Their fruity line-up includes blackcurrants, redcurrants, strawberries, raspberries and gooseberries. You can also buy these in the farm shop, along with a winning selection of cheeses, cream, free-range eggs, meat and poultry, locally baked breads, cakes, pies, homemade ice creams and other grocery lines. Light refreshments are served – alfresco in fine weather – and there's a large picnic area.

...for the latest news

Bury St Edmunds, Suffolk

The Denham Estate

Denham, Bury St Edmunds, Suffolk IP29 5EQ
Telephone: +44(0)1284 810231
venison@denhamestate.co.uk
www.denhamestate.co.uk

Other points: **Delivery for trade orders to East Anglia, London and Thames Valley.** (Map 6, 373)

Occupying 1,200 acres, The Denham Estate is home to 3,000 fallow deer, reared in an extensive natural, free-range and stress-free environment and grazed in meadows rich in clover, rye and timothy grasses. It's little wonder that chefs and gourmets consider Denham fallow venison the finest of all venison meats. Available to trade customers only for 12 months of the year, Denham supplies some of the finest hotels and restaurants in London and south-east England.

Newmarket, Suffolk

Powters Ltd

Wellington Street, Newmarket, Suffolk CB8 0HT
Telephone: +44(0)1638 662418
sales@powters.co.uk
www.powters.co.uk

Hours: Monday-Saturday 7.00-17.00.
Other points: Shop. Mail order. Car park.
Directions: Wellington Street is on one corner of Market Square, next to the shopping centre. Parking available on Market Square (except Tuesday and Saturday). (Map 6, 374)

Sausages have been produced in the racing town of Newmarket as long as racehorses. Powters has led the field since the 1880s, when Grant Powter's great grandfather set up the butchers shop. Powters still make their famous sausage to the original recipe, combining fresh local pork with a secret blend of herbs and spices. Other delights include Aberdeen Angus beef, lamb from Romney Marsh, Gloucester Old Spot pork, poultry, game, home-cooked hams, sweet-cured bacon, cheeses, olives and oven-ready meals.

Esher, Surrey

Garsons

Winterdown Road, Esher, Surrey KT10 8LS
Telephone: +44(0)1372 464389
info@garsons.co.uk
www.garsons.co.uk

Hours: 9.00-18.00 (winter 17.00). Sunday
11.00-17.00.
Other points: Farm shop. Garden centre. PYO.
Directions: Turn on to West End Lane from
the A307 Esher to Cobham road or from the
A244 Esher to Hersham road. Winterdon
Road is a turning off West End Lane by The
Prince of Wales pub. (Map 6, 375)

Godalming, Surrey

Secretts Farm Shop

Chapel Lane, Milford, Surrey GU8 5HU
Telephone: +44(0)1483 520500
info@secretts.co.uk
www.secretts.co.uk

Hours: Monday-Saturday 9.00-17.30. Sunday
and bank holidays 11.00-17.00.
Other points: Farm shop. Gift shop. Flower
shop. Garden centre. PYO. Car park. Play area.
Picnic area. Tearoom. Restaurant.
Directions: Just off the A3 approximately six
miles south of Guildford. (Map 6, 376)

Garson Farm boasts more than 40 different crops of pick-your-own fruit, vegetables and flowers between May and September. Garsons Farm Shop, housed in renovated old farm buildings, prides itself on its selection of fresh and locally produced foods. Meats and dairy products are available, along with fresh fruit, vegetables, cakes and ice creams. And if you're a keen gardener, visit the garden centre, which sells plants, garden tools, barbecues, furniture, clothing and giftware. There's also a restaurant on site.

This farm shop is crammed with fruit, vegetables, herbs and salads picked in the market garden each day. The pick-your-own fruit and vegetable section is available from June to September, and an extensive delicatessen offers 300 cheeses, cooked meats, salads and delicious individual dishes prepared in the kitchens. Garden furniture and barbecues can be bought at the garden centre. Next to the farm shop is Eliza's, a recreation of a 1930s tearoom, serving sandwiches, light lunches and afternoon teas.

...for recipe ideas

Newcastle-upon-Tyne, Tyne & Wear

George Payne Butchers

27 Princes Road, Brunton Park, Gosforth,
Newcastle-upon-Tyne, Tyne & Wear NE3 5TT
Telephone: +44(0)191 236 2992
george@georgepaynebutchers.co.uk
www.georgepaynebutchers.co.uk

Hours: Monday-Thursday 7.30-17.00. Friday
7.30-17.30. Saturday 7.30-14.00.
Other points: Shop.
Directions: Situated in North Gosforth,
two minutes' drive from the A1 and the
racecourse. (Map 12, 377)

A traditional butcher for 40 years, George Payne prides himself on traceability and sourcing meat direct from the farm. This 'gate-to-plate' partnership with local producers means that he stocks the very best meat available to him. Galloway and Longhorn beef comes from East Farm at Great Whittington, White-faced Woodland lambs come from Irthington, Carlisle and Saddleback pork comes from Tom Burn at Hunting Hall. Organic free-range chickens are also available, as well as delicious, award-winning sausages.

Coventry, Warwickshire

Berkswell Traditional Farmstead Meats

Larges Farm, Back Lane, Meriden,
Warwickshire CV7 7LD
Telephone: +44(0)1676 522409
www.farmsteadmeats.co.uk

Hours: Tuesday-Saturday 8.00-5.30.
Other points: Farm shop.
Directions: Off the A45 between Coventry
and Stonebridge, a short drive from the NEC.
(Map 8, 378)

Philip Tuckey is Warwickshire's only accredited traditional-breeds butcher and he continues 400 years of family involvement in farming and butchery. His farm shop stocks a range of traceable beef, pork and lamb from local farmers, including Longhorn beef and pork from Tamworth and Gloucester Old Spot pigs. All sausages and burgers are homemade, as is the dry-cured bacon, and there is a selection of cheeses, including Fowlers of Earlswood and Berkswell ewe's-milk cheese.

WARWICKSHIRE

...for events

Birmingham, West Midlands

Roger Brown Ltd

16 Lonsdale Road, Harborne, Birmingham,
West Midlands B17 9RA
Telephone: +44(0)121 427 2057/1252

Hours: Tuesday-Friday 8.00-17.30.
Saturday 7.00-16.00.
Other points: Shops.
(Map 9, 379)

A past winner of 'Birmingham's Best Family Butcher' and a proud member of Traditional Breeds Meat Marketing, Roger Brown specialises in quality meat with full traceability. Such provenance shows in the delicious Longhorn beef, Welsh salt-marsh lamb and free-range Suffolk pigs. All sausages are homemade, as is the dry-cured bacon and traditional oak-smoked bacon. This traditional family butcher also has a shop at its head office in Northfield Road in Harborne, Birmingham.

Pulborough, West Sussex

Nutbourne Vineyards

Gay Street, Pulborough,
West Sussex RH20 2HH
Telephone: +44(0)1798 815196
sales@nutbournevineyards.com
www.nutbournevineyards.com

Hours: Monday-Friday 14.00-17.00.
Weekends and bank holidays 11.00-17.00.
May to October.
Other points: Shop.
Directions: Off the A283, near Pulborough.
(Map 6, 380)

Set in the lovely grounds of Nutbourne Manor, with its lakes, wild fowl and family of llamas, the 18 acres of vines that make up the Nutbourne Vineyards produce seven different types of grapes. The gentle slopes are protected by the South Downs and enjoy the same fertile soil as the Champagne region of France. These distinctive, award-winning dry white wines – and one sparkling wine – are available to buy at the Windmill Shop.

Turners Hill, West Sussex

Tulleys Farm

Turners Hill Road, Turners Hill, Crawley,
West Sussex RH10 4PD
Telephone: +44(0)1342 718472
info@tulleysfarm.com
www.tulleysfarm.com

Hours: Shop daily 9.00-18.00 in summer, 17.00 in winter. Tearoom daily 9.30-17.00 in summer, 16.30 in winter. PYO June-October daily 9.00-18.00.
Other points: Farm shop. PYO. Tearoom.
Directions: Exit10/M23. A264 to East Grinstead. B2928 to Turners Hill. B2110 at the centre, right at the church towards Worth.
(Map 6, 381)

Pick-your-own soft fruits and vegetables are available at this well-stocked farm shop in a converted dairy. It also sells a range of fresh and local produce and gifts. A farmhouse kitchen-style tearoom is open all year round for tea, coffee, cakes, salads and hot meals, with the added bonus of a patio and relaxing garden in which to enjoy refreshments. At peak seasonal times, enjoy refreshments in the Hayrack Espresso Snack Bar, built into an old rustic cart lodge.

...for competitions

Marlborough, Wiltshire

Sumbler Bros

11 London Road, Marlborough,
Wiltshire SN8 1PH
Telephone: +44(0)1672 512185
john@sumblerbros.co.uk
www.sumblerbros.co.uk

Hours: Monday, Tuesday, Thursday, Friday
7.00-17.30. Wednesday 7.00-13.30. Saturday
7.00-15.00.
Other points: Shop. Delivery. Car park.
Directions: On the main A4 London road
between the roundabouts and opposite
ATS Tyre Service. (Map 5, 382)

Winner of the 2005 Countryside Alliance
Best Rural Retailer for Wessex, this
traditional, long-established butchers only
sells non-intensified farmed beef, lamb
and pork, and free-range chicken. It also
makes a good range of well-flavoured and
textured sausages, and sells the excellent
Sandridge Farm Wiltshire bacon.

Castle Douglas, Dumfries and Galloway

Craigadam Country Larder

Castle Douglas,
Dumfries and Galloway DG7 3HU
Telephone: +44(0)1556 650233
inquiry@craigadam.com
www.craigadam.com

Hours: Daily 10.00–16.00.
Other points: Farm shop. Mail order.
Directions: M74. A75 to Dumfries. Follow signs to Castle Douglas. After nine miles, go through the village of Crocketford and turn right on to the A712. Craigadam is two miles along on the right. (Map 11, 383)

Richard and Celia Pickup offer an extensive range of game and organic lamb products at the shop on this working farm. As well as farm-assured cuts of lamb, seasonal game is abundant, from oven-ready wild pigeon, snipe, woodcock or mallard to prime cuts of wild roe-deer venison. Celia has won awards for her cooking, which can be enjoyed in the family's elegant, 18th-century country house, with its seven en-suite bedrooms and self-catering cottage.

...for special offers

Walks

Clutton Hill, Bath

To Greyfield Wood from The Hunters Rest

From the word go, the views on this spectacular walk are breathtaking. Weave your way down to the village of Clutton, then follow a lengthy stretch of the popular Limestone Link path through a long valley to reach peaceful Greyfield Wood, with its fascinating industrial heritage and array of plants and flowers.

1

From the pub, cross over to the footpath opposite and follow it alongside a fence beside a white cottage. Cross two more stiles as you descend to reach double gates and the road. Don't go through them. Instead, swing left by the waymarker and follow the path down the field, keeping a line of trees on the right. Continue to a kissing gate on the right.

2

Cross the track here to another gate and drop down the field to the next gate by a barn. Continue down the slope, crossing a paddock to reach woodland. Cross a footbridge and follow the path through the trees. Soon swing left at some steps and emerge from the trees. Cross over a woodland path to a stile and keep ahead between houses to the road.

3

Turn right, pass the entrance to The Ramblers and turn left immediately beyond a line of cottages. Go down the field, across a stream to a gate and up the slope, keeping to the left. Pass through a gate and continue uphill to Pennyquick Cottage. Cross two stiles and turn left to the stile in the field corner and a lane. Follow it ahead through the village of Clutton. Cross the road junction into Church Lane and make for St Augustine's.

4

Go round the left bend, cross a stream and just beyond it, the road swings right. Veer off to the left here to follow the Limestone Link. Take the obvious track towards farm outbuildings, pass to the left of them and continue on the well-used trail, crossing a number of stiles and negotiating a variety of gates. Eventually, you will come to a kissing gate and a few paces beyond is a gate with a footbridge spanning the stream.

5

Cross the bridge and the field beyond it towards woodland and pass through a gate, following the broad path through Greyfield Wood. Cross a wide track and continue to an information board on the edge of the wood. Follow the track ahead and when you reach the road turn left and walk through Greyfield.

6

When you reach a footpath sign, veer off to the right up the lane. At a junction, keep left and follow Cuckoo Lane. When you reach Clutton Hill, turn left at the junction and drop down to a path on the right, immediately beyond houses. Go diagonally up the field slope, or round the right edge if it is ploughed, to a gap in the hedge, turn left along the lane and return to the pub. For pub see entry 2

fact file

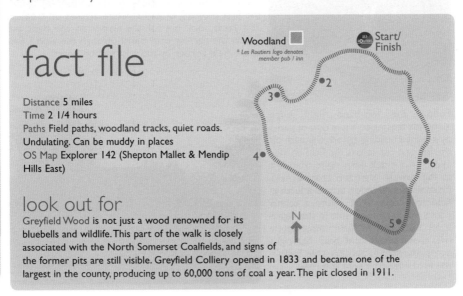

Woodland ▪
* Les Routiers logo denotes
member pub / inn

Start/Finish

Distance **5 miles**
Time **2 1/4 hours**
Paths **Field paths, woodland tracks, quiet roads. Undulating. Can be muddy in places**
OS Map **Explorer 142 (Shepton Mallet & Mendip Hills East)**

look out for

Greyfield Wood is not just a wood renowned for its bluebells and wildlife. This part of the walk is closely associated with the North Somerset Coalfields, and signs of the former pits are still visible. Greyfield Colliery opened in 1833 and became one of the largest in the county, producing up to 60,000 tons of coal a year. The pit closed in 1911.

...for the latest news

Marlow, Buckinghamshire
Into the Chilterns from The Royal Oak

A glorious walk that explores the peaceful woodland and unspoilt valleys that characterise the gently undulating countryside of the east Chiltern Hills.

Turn left along the road from the pub, then left again into Bovingdon Green. Turn right at the fork at the end of the green. The lane soon becoming a track. At a house called Pommery, keep left along a fenced path. Ignore the stile on the left, continue alongside woodland and soon enter Davenport Wood. Follow the main path marked by white arrows on trees, drop down to a junction of paths and keep ahead. Shortly, at a crossing of paths, take the arrowed path (Chiltern Way CW) right, following white arrows to a road.

Cross the road and proceed ahead, following the CW arrows, and descend steeply to a stile. Follow a fenced path to a stile, turn left along the field edge, crossing two more stiles to a road. Turn right, then left along a track into Homefield Wood (Nature Reserve). Ignore the first crossing of paths (white arrows on tree). In 200 yards, look out for the arrow on the right and follow the narrow path uphill through the wood. Exit at the field corner by the information board.

Follow the left-hand field edge alongside fencing to a junction of paths by a ruined building. Ignore the path on the left and cut across the field corner ahead to a track. Turn right, then left at the 'private' sign and cross a field. Maintain the direction across a further field to a stile. Skirt round a tennis court and head for a stile in the right-hand field corner. Turn immediately left, cross a stile and bear half-right across the field to another stile. Follow the field edge to a stile and road.

4

Turn right, pass Chisbridge Farm and descend to a junction in a valley bottom. Turn right for 200 yards, being aware of traffic, and then left along a metalled track by Walnut Cottage, signed Bluey's Farm. Keep right at a junction and soon take the arrowed bridleway right through a gate. Descend in front of a fine house and climb the stile on your right at a crossing of paths/bridleways. Walk alongside fencing, go through two gates and Shillingridge Wood.

5

Reach a wide bridleway at the end of the wood and keep left up the steep hill. Bear right at the top along a metalled track by a cottage. On reaching a house, take the arrowed bridleway left and head downhill on a narrow path through trees. Gently climb past more properties, with the track soon becoming tarmac. Bear off right, following the CW arrows, at a sharp left bend and descend to a road. Cross straight over, the narrow path climbing steeply. At the top, keep left past a house and soon fork right (note the CW arrows) and you will see the pub ahead.
For pub see entry 16

fact file

look out for

Some of the route follows the Chiltern Way, a circular, 168-mile (275km) walk that criss-crosses the Chiltern Hills from Hemel Hempstead.
Red kites are thriving in the Chiltern Hills and you will see them riding the thermals high above the fields and woodland. Part of Homefield Wood is a nature reserve and during April and May, you will see a field (just beyond the entrance on the right) carpeted with primroses.

Distance 6 1/2 miles
Time 2 1/2 hours
Paths Field and woodland paths, bridleways, short stretches of road
OS Map Explorer 172 (Chiltern Hills East)

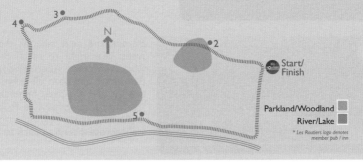

N

Start/Finish

Parkland/Woodland
River/Lake

* Les Routiers logo denotes member pub / inn

...for recipe ideas

Romaldkirk, Co Durham

Through Teesdale from The Rose and Crown

An invigorating ramble through the heart of Teesdale, exploring rough hillside pastures dotted with isolated farmsteads, and the sheltered wooded valley beside the swiftly flowing River Tees.

1

Turn left on leaving the inn and follow the dead-end lane ahead to the left of the green. Take the arrowed path left opposite Klein Cottage and follow the walled path down to a footbridge and stile. Continue ahead across pasture behind the cemetery and bear right alongside the wall, heading uphill to a stile. Head across the field to a stile and follow the wall on your right, high above the River Tees with views of Eggleston Hall, to reach a gate beyond a stone building.

2 Turn right along the road, cross the bridge and climb the stile right to follow the Teesdale Way along a metalled drive. Just before a gate, cross the stile on the left and ascend steps through trees, the path eventually reaching a stile and field. Continue ahead beside the wall to a stile and follow the path uphill towards farm buildings. Beyond a stile, keep right along the wall and pass to the rear of the farmhouse.

3

Follow the arrow (on a telegraph pole) to a gate and bear slightly right, following the path through rough pasture to cross a beck, then a wall stile. Head gently downhill to a stile and bear slightly left following the waymarker across the field to a visible stone stile. Bear left then right with the arrow, cross a stile and proceed ahead beside the wall above Shipley Wood.

4

Beyond the next stile, at the edge of the trees, bear right to reach the Perry Myre Rock viewpoint. Alternatively, keep to the path ahead and bear left down a track. Cross a beck and the stile immediately on your right. Cross a further stile, follow the defined path downhill towards Cotherstone and walk across a caravan park to a gate.

fact file

Distance **6 miles**
Time **3 hours**
Paths **Old moorland roads, field paths, lanes**
OS Map **Explorer OL31 (North Pennines)**

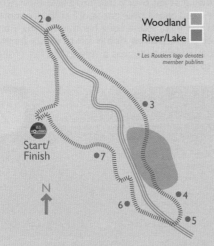

Woodland
River/Lake

Les Routiers logo denotes member pub/inn

Start/
Finish

N

look out for

Romaldkirk One of the prettiest villages to be found in upper Teesdale.
Eggleston Hall Dominates the riverside scene and its gardens can be visited.
Woden Croft One of the infamous 'Yorkshire Schools' featured in Charles Dickens' novel *Nicholas Nickleby*.

5

Head downhill along the track, bearing right at the bottom to cross the footbridge over the River Tees. Follow the Teesdale Way right along the bank, then uphill to a stile. Keep parallel with the river, cross a stile and bear left down stone steps to cross a beck via stepping stones. Climb the next stile and follow the path uphill to a gate to the right of a stone building. Go through the gate ahead and pass in front of Woden Croft.

6

Cross the drive, pass in front of cottages and keep right of a corrugated barn to a stile. Beyond the next stile ahead, bear immediately right downhill into woodland beside the River Tees. Follow the undulating woodland path – narrow and slippery in places – close to the river. Eventually, leave the river, cross a stile and keep to the right-hand field edge to pass a derelict cottage.

7

Go through a gate and follow the grassy track left uphill. Bear off right to a tiny gate and head across the field to a further gate. Maintain this direction and soon bear slightly right through trees to a gate. Join a narrow path and follow this back into Romaldkirk.
For pub see entry 27

...for events

St Breward, Cornwall

A moorland and valley ramble from The Old Inn

A varied exploration of the western fringes of Bodmin Moor, through pasture fields and delightful wooded valleys, with expansive views over the moor's highest land and towards the north Cornwall coast.

Walk uphill from the pub. Turn right just before the church; then first left over a stile into a field. Bear right to a stile, keep ahead over two more stiles. Continue ahead to the next stile among hawthorns, into a big field. Keep ahead, bearing slightly left to pass a granite gatepost in a bank, and cross a stile to the left of the gate on to a lane.

Turn right and follow the lane through Treswallock Farm. Descend to cross the stream and turn left over a stile into marshy ground. Cross the stile ahead and bear right, following the wall of Mellon farmhouse. Pass through a gate and bear diagonally left across the field. Cross a stile, a narrow meadow, and another stile on to a lane.

Keep ahead over a stile, looking right for Rough Tor and Alex Tor. Continue up the field, aiming for a gate just left of conifers. The track leads to Corgelly Farm; turn right. After 50 yards, turn left over a stile. Keep ahead, downhill (with a big metal barn on your left), parallel to the hedge-bank. Cross the stream on a wooden bridge. Keep ahead for 20 yards, then turn left along the field bottom, aiming for a stile on to a track.

Turn left uphill through Newton and reach a lane. Turn left again. Where the lane bears away left, bear right up a rough track. Pass between farm buildings; keep ahead through a gate on a grassy track across open ground. Pass over the hilltop and keep left of the gorse-filled track as it descends towards a wall.

www.routiers.co.uk

5

Turn left. Where the wall bears away right, keep ahead over a stile. Bear left uphill to a post/steps over a wall. Keep ahead and cross the next wall corner on steps, with St Breward Church tower directly ahead. Go straight across the next big field, descending through a gate left of an open barn. Follow the track downhill, passing through the right of three gates. Keep ahead, descending to meet a tarmac way through a gate.

Turn right. Descend over a cattle grid, ascend to a road. Turn left uphill. 100 yards beyond a sharp right bend, bear right on to a track. At the house entrance, turn left on to a narrow footpath. Eventually meet a path junction and turn right downhill to Fellover. Bear left and keep straight on above the Camel Valley. Reach a lane by the tropical-bird farm; bear right to pass through the Chapel and continue uphill.

6

7 Turn left uphill past the holy well. Pass through a gate with a house on your left. After 100 yards, turn left through a gate and bear right over a stile. Continue uphill, over a stile, through playing fields. Cross a stile on to a track and follow the path ahead to the pub.
For pub see entry 37

fact file

Distance 5 1/2 miles
Time 2 1/2 hours
Paths Field paths, tracks, farm lanes, grassland, woodland paths
OS Map Explorer 109 (Bodmin Moor) Note: waymarking is inconsistent, so use an OS map.

look out for

St Breward Church Dates from Norman times and is dedicated to the 6th-century saint, said to have been martyred in the neighbourhood.
Holy Well of St James Thought to have been visited by pilgrims en route to Santiago de Compostela in Spain.

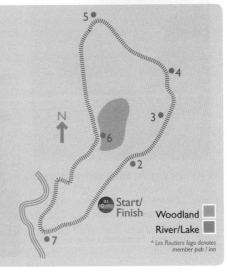

Start/Finish
Woodland
River/Lake
* Les Routiers logo denotes member pub / inn

...for competitions

Treen, Cornwall
Along the coastal path to Zennor

A beautiful coastal walk from The Gurnard's Head, taking in some of the magnificent Cornish coastal path, combining a few steep climbs over rugged terrain, and a gentle return journey across wide pastures. Spend time at Zennor exploring the church and tiny Wayside Museum.

Leave the inn and turn left along the dead-end lane through the hamlet. Take the arrowed path left, signed Gurnards Head, just beyond Treen Farm, crossing two stone stiles to a field. Follow the left-hand field edge, drop down stone steps and continue along the field edge with fine coastal views to a stone stile. Proceed through bracken and bear right at a fork of paths. Zig-zag downhill to join the coast path.

Turn left for Gurnards Head, otherwise follow the coast path right and soon pass the ruins of an old chapel and a mine. Pass to the rear of a house, cross the access track and keep to the coast path. Ascend, then descend towards Porthglaze Cove and climb to the next headland and a house.

Keep to the coast path and pass round Pendour Cove. Climb steps close to a house to join a track. Turn left to reach Zennor Head. Turn right and walk towards Zennor village.

Pass through a farm and bear right to the church. Keep right passing The Tinner's Arms and the Wayside Museum. Ascend steeply to the B-road, keep right and shortly take the arrowed footpath right opposite Trewey Farm.

5

Walk along the track beside the farmyard, cross a stone stile by a gate and keep to the right-hand field edge. Follow the yellow-arrowed route across several fields and stone stiles, eventually reaching a stoney track. Proceed past houses to the B-road.

6

Turn right and take care through the hamlet of Boswednack. Keep to the road and take the arrowed path right across a stone stile. Follow the path across fields towards the inn, eventually crossing a stile in front of the inn.
For pub see entry 38

fact file

Distance **4 miles**
Time **2 hours**
Paths **challenging coast path, field paths and tracks**
OS Map **Explorer 7 (Land's End)**

Start/Finish

* Les Routiers logo denotes member pub / inn

look out for

Tin mines Below Treen you can see a disused shaft and a ruined engine house of a tin mine built in the early 19th century to exploit the rich veins or 'lodes' of tin within the hard granite rock along this rugged coastline. The last working tin mine, Geevor at Pendeen, closed in 1992, ending 3,000 years of continuous mining activity. It is now a museum and you can enjoy a tour of the surface and underground mine with experienced guides.

Zennor shelters in a hollow between rugged, boulder-strewn moorland and the rocky coast. Zennor church was built in the 12th century, probably on the site of an ancient chapel. It is famous for the mermaid chair in the side chapel, and the romantic legend that goes with it. The Wayside Museum is a quaint private museum that explores life in Zennor from 3000BC to the 1930s. It contains a traditional Cornish kitchen and an exhibition of domestic and mining implements. DH Lawrence drank at The Tinner's Arms when he lived nearby during the First World War, writing *Women in Love*.

...for special offers

Eskdale, Cumbria
From The Boot Inn to Burnmoor Tarn

Here's a walk with a steep climb. Your reward is to stand beside a remote tarn in the shadows of England's highest peaks, with views to die for and a return leg through a sublime valley and lake-speckled moors.

From the inn, walk up to the old packhorse bridge beside the watermill. Go through the gate beyond this and turn right. In about 100 yards, go through the bridlegate on your right. The track rises gradually through a series of gates beside oak woods high above the lively Whillan Beck, finally passing through a last wall to continue across gently sloping moorland.

At the first fork, keep ahead-right along the lesser path, walking in line towards the towering Scafell. Keep right at the next fork, passing well above the footbridge at Lambford. Occasional cairns mark the route. Eventually, the remote Burnmoor Tarn is revealed. To your right, Scafell scrapes the sky; ahead are the stunning peaks clustering at Wasdale Head. (An additional 2 miles return walk to the low horizon beyond Burnmoor Tarn reveals this wonderful panorama).

fact file

Distance **6 1/2 miles**
Time **3 1/2 hours**
Paths **Rough paths, moorland tracks, one short road section**
OS Map **Explorer OL6 (The English Lakes, South-Western Area)**

Railway
Woodland
River/Lake

Les Routiers logo denotes member pub / inn

N

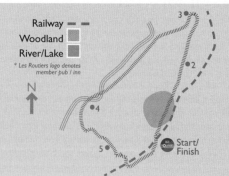

3 Above the near shoreline, turn left to walk to Burnmoor Lodge. Pass just left of this and take a narrow path to the right. This soon crests a gentle rise to reveal hidden Miterdale. Pick a way down to the bank of the infant River Mite and trace a path along either side of the water. You'll ultimately need to be on the left bank to take a ladder stile near to fir woods. Walk ahead to find a stile beside a tree. Don't take this; rather turn uphill to follow the wall around to a gate at the edge of woods. Stay on this old stony lane as the woods peel away.

4

Continue along this to a gate; keep ahead to a second gate. Don't go through this; instead, turn left up alongside the wall, commencing a lengthy and potentially boggy climb up to a forestry road at a woodland gate. Remain outside the woods to the point where the trees and wall turn away right. Here, bear left along an indistinct path which circles to the left of a knoll. Fork right in 200 yards through a dip in the low ridge and walk ahead to a lone rowan tree. A more obvious path now passes left of reedy Siney Tarn and crests a rise to reveal lovely Blea Tarn.

Pass right of the tarn and pick up a path that passes to the right of the snout of the knoll beyond the tarn. This bends left to start a series of lazy zigzags down into Eskdale. At the bottom, go through a gate and cross the railway to Beckfoot Station. Turn left along the road, pass Dalegarth Station to find the turn for Boot beside Brook House Inn.
For pub see entry 46

5

look out for
Built in the 16th century, Boot Watermill is said to be the oldest working mill in England.
Burnmoor Tarn One of the largest and most remote of the tarns of Lakeland.
Miterdale Has views up its valley to Scafell and glimpses of statuesque Great Gable.

...for the latest news

Chagford, Devon
The Teign Gorge and Castle Drogo

This peaceful walk from Sandy Park Inn through the Teign Valley explores the wooded river bank, rich in flora and fauna, and a panoramic high-level track that offers stunning views towards Dartmoor's high tors and into the Teign Gorge

Turn right out of the pub along the lane through the hamlet. Cross the waymarked stile on your left and follow the grassy path alongside fencing as it curves left beside a stream to reach the River Teign and Dogmarsh Bridge. Cross the road, go through the gate and enter National Trust land (Castle Drogo). Keep to the grassy path beside the river for 1/2 mile to reach a gate and bridge.

Take the arrowed path right for Castle Drogo. Gently ascend, merge with a drive by a thatched cottage and keep ahead along the metalled lane. In 400 yards, take the path sharp right through a gate signed Castle Drogo.

Keep to the main path (Hunter's Path) as it bends left and gradually climbs across high moorland above the wooded Teign Valley. Pause at conveniently placed benches to absorb the beautiful views and, if wishing to visit Castle Drogo (National Trust), take the signed path left to reach castle grounds.

4

Remain on the path to Piddledown Common and a junction of paths. Continue along the high-level track, signed to Fingle Bridge. At a fork of paths, follow the path right and steeply descend through woodland into the valley.

5

On reaching a metalled lane, turn right to reach Fingle Bridge and pub/café. Just before the bridge, go through the gate on your right and follow the delightful wooded path beside the River Teign for 1 1/2 miles, looking out for dippers and wagtails. Reach the bridge and waymarker you passed earlier and keep to the riverside path, retracing your steps back to the pub.

For pub see entry 65

fact file

Distance **5 1/2 miles**
Time **2 1/2 hours (longer if visiting Castle Drogo)**
Paths **woodland, riverside & moorland paths, tracks.**
OS Map **Outdoor Leisure 28: Dartmoor**

Start/Finish

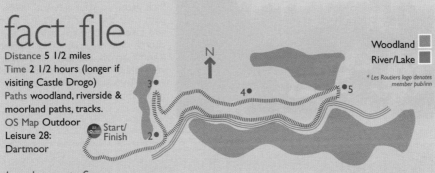

Woodland
River/Lake

* Les Routiers logo denotes member pub/inn

look out for

Fingle Bridge – An unspoilt beauty spot deep in the beautiful wooded Teign Gorge, where this 16th-century granite bridge, previously used by pack-horses, straddles the fast-flowing Teign River. Spring is a wonderful time to explore the riverside paths and woodland, with carpets of daffodils and bluebells, and a wealth of birdlife to look at.

Castle Drogo – This imposing granite castle stands on a rocky crag 900ft above the River Teign. It is a combination of medieval might and 21st-century luxury as it was the last stately home to be built in England. It was built for Julius Drewe, founder of Home and Colonial Stores, in 1930 by Sir Edward Lutyens and its highly individual style is best appreciated from the inside. There are wonderful views from the terrace and gardens.

...for recipe ideas

Kelmscott, Gloucestershire
From The Plough at Kelmscott to Lechlade

This easy ramble beside the River Thames takes in St Mary's Church at Buscot, historic Lechlade and Kelmscott Manor, once the home of William Morris, founder of the Arts and Crafts movement.

1 From The Plough, turn right along the lane beside the inn and walk through the village to a T-junction. Turn right towards Kelmscott Manor, pass the entrance and continue along the track to the River Thames. Go through the gate on your right to join the Thames Path. Walk beside the river for 1 1/2 miles and cross the second footbridge over the river. Follow the path around the field edge and cross a stile to reach Buscot Lock.

2 To view Buscot Weir, church and Old Parsonage (National Trust), cross the lock gates on your left and follow the path over the weir. Pass Lock Cottage and take the footpath right to visit the church and adjacent Old Parsonage. Return across the weir and lock, and keep ahead across the second lock to a stile. Turn left along the field edge and rejoin the Thames Path.

fact file

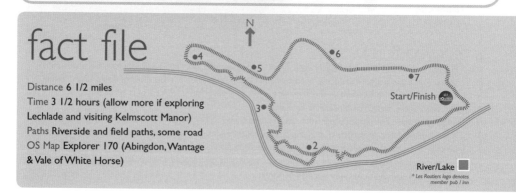

Distance **6 1/2 miles**
Time **3 1/2 hours (allow more if exploring Lechlade and visiting Kelmscott Manor)**
Paths **Riverside and field paths, some road**
OS Map **Explorer 170 (Abingdon, Wantage & Vale of White Horse)**

River/Lake ■
Les Routiers logo denotes member pub / inn

3 Continue along the meandering path to a further footbridge. Ignore the alternative Thames Path signed right across the footbridge. Shortly, pass beneath the A417 to reach St John's Lock. With excellent views of Lechlade Church, continue for a further 1/2 mile to Ha'penny Bridge and the A361. Leave the Thames Path and cross the bridge to enter Lechlade.

4 Turn right at the T-junction in the town centre, then bear off right to the church. Take the paved path through the churchyard (Shelley's Walk) to a lane. Cross and pass through two gates, then cross a meadow to a kissing gate. Follow the raised, tree-lined path ahead to a lane opposite a caravan park.

5 Take the lane ahead beside The Trout Inn. Follow the waymarked path left just before a house and stream. Skirt the house, then follow the path across fields close to the River Leech and pass behind a house to reach Mill Lane. Turn right, cross the river and pass Lechlade Mill. Continue along the narrow lane to a T-junction.

6 Turn right, then left following the footpath sign (Willow Walk) and bear diagonally left across pasture to a stile. Keep left along the field edge to a stile in the field corner and maintain this direction. Cross a footbridge and proceed across the field ahead on a worn path to a lane.

7

look out for

Kelmscott Manor The country home of William Morris – poet, craftsman and socialist – from 1871 until his death in 1896.
Buscot Lock On the banks of the Thames, close to the picturesque weir and lock at Buscot, stands the 18th-century Old Parsonage (National Trust; limited opening times) and St Mary's Church, noted for its stained glass by Morris & co.

Turn right and follow the road into Kelmscott. Pass the church and turn right, signed to The Plough Inn. For pub see entry 91

...for events

Winchcombe, Gloucestershire
To Belas Knap from The White Hart

Follow Windrush Way past magnificent Sudeley Castle and climb the Cotswold scarp for spectacular views across Gloucestershire to one of the great burial mounds of ancient Britain.

1 Turn left downhill from the pub car park. At Sudeley Country Cottages, take the arrowed path right (Windrush Way) through a kissing gate into parkland. Follow the path across pasture, crossing a track, soon to pass through a further gate in the field corner by woods. Turn left, cross the entrance drive to Sudeley Castle and go through a gate to the left of double gates, following the green-and-white marker of the Windrush Way.

2 Continue across parkland, with Sudeley Castle visible left, keeping left through a further gateway. Here, at the fork, bear half-right and keep to the marker posts on a defined grassy path, gently descending to cross a brook. Go through a swing gate, bear right across the river and turn left to a stile beside a gate.

3

Bear half-right uphill through pasture (right of a telegraph pole) to a stile. Keep ahead to another stile, walk beside woodland to a further stile and descend to a stile by a brook. Continue across a meadow to a track. Leave the Windrush Way and turn right along the 'road used as public path'. Soon reach a gate and New Meadow Farm.

4

Beyond the gate, take the waymarked path left through a green gate. Head uphill on a track between fields to a further gate. Continue uphill and turn right through double gates at woodland. Follow the path to a T-junction of tracks by Humblebee Cottages.

5

Turn left uphill along the Cotswold Way to a metalled lane. Turn right for 1/4 mile to reach a sign for Belas Knap. Climb the stile on your left, head uphill through trees to a kissing gate and follow the field edge left, soon to follow it right steeply uphill to a gate in the field corner affording superb views. Keep left to reach Belas Knap.

6

Retrace your steps back to the road and turn left. Where the road bends sharp right, take the arrowed path ahead up to a stone stile, signed Winchcombe. Head downhill across pasture, following marker posts to reach a stile. Turn right along a metalled track, passing the cricket pitch, to a gate and road.

7

Turn left, then, just beyond houses on your left, take the arrowed path right, through the first kissing gate. Follow the field-edge path to a gate and continue along the narrow path to another gate. Cross the pasture to a metal gate and turn left, crossing the river, then, at the village road, turn right back to the inn. For pub see entry 97

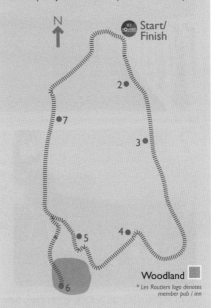

fact file

Distance **5 miles**
Time **3 hours**
Paths **Field paths, defined tracks, the Cotswold Way, quiet lanes**
OS Map **Explorer OL 45 (The Cotswolds)**

Start/Finish
Woodland
* Les Routiers logo denotes member pub / inn

look out for

Winchcombe has a considerable history. Visit the huge 'wool church' and its two interesting museums, the Folk Museum and the Railway Museum.
Sudeley Castle Worth visiting for its ruined banqueting hall and immaculate, ornate gardens.
Belas Knap Dates from around 2500BC – an impressive burial mound.

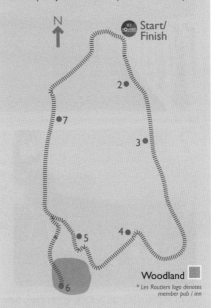

...for competitions

Hamble, Hampshire
Exploring the Hamble estuary from The Bugle

An easy walk that takes you along a delightful path beside the River Hamble to Bursledon, once famous for boat building, returning through pretty Old Bursledon before circuiting Hamble Common with its breezy shoreline path and quaint creeks.

1 From the quayside car park, take the passenger ferry across the estuary to Warsash (daily 9am-5pm). Turn left along the raised gravel path beside the estuary and mudflats. Cross a footbridge and continue to a gravelled parking area. During exceptionally high tides, the path may flood, so walk through the car park and rejoin it by the marina.

2 Follow the footpath markers through a boatyard and continue along the waterside path to a road. Continue between industrial buildings to the A27. Turn left, cross Bursledon Bridge, pass beneath the railway and turn left, signed to the station. Keep right at a fork with Station Road and shortly turn left into Church Road. At the sharp right bend by the church, keep ahead along a footpath that leads down to Station Road.

Turn right, then at a fork (triangle), bear right, then right again along the High Street into Old Bursledon. Pause at the viewpoint at Hacketts Marsh, then bear left at the phone box. Pass the Vine Inn and Salterns Lane into Kew Lane, then, at a right bend, bear off left along a footpath. Join a metalled lane beside the drive to the Coach House then, as the lane curves left, keep ahead beside a house called Woodlands, following the path downhill to a stream.

fact file

Distance **6 1/2 miles**
Time **3 hours**
Paths **Riverside, field and woodland paths, some stretches of road**
OS Map **Outdoor Leisure 22 New Forest**

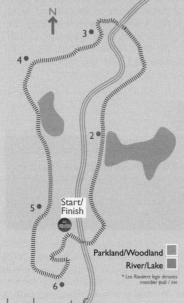

Parkland/Woodland
River/Lake

Les Routiers logo denotes member pub / inn

look out for

Just before high tide you may see up to 12 species of waders, including dunlin, redshank, lapwing and curlew, and wildfowl – shelduck, teal and Brent geese (in winter) – feeding on the rich mudflats as you stroll the riverside path.

It was from Hamble Common that Henry VIII watched in horror as his famous flagship, the 91-gun Mary Rose, sank with the loss of 700 men just off the nearby coast in 1545.

Head uphill through woodland (Mallards Moor). At a junction of paths on the woodland fringe, bear left with the bridleway, then, at a concrete road turn right, then left to join a fenced path between fields. Keep left at the road and, after a sharp left-hand bend, take a waymarked footpath on your right and follow this path behind houses for 1/2 mile. Proceed around modern housing to the end of a cul-de-sac and shortly reach Hamble Lane, opposite St Andrew's Church.

Cross the road, turn right and then left along Copse Lane. At the Hamble Common sign, take the footpath right into woodland. Keep to the main path close to the perimeter of an oil refinery and soon reach the shore. Keep to the shoreline path, disregarding the Solent Way sign left, and continue to the car park by a gun emplacement.

At the end of the car park, cross the access lane and go through the gate ahead. Follow the waymarked Strawberry Trail across Hamble Common and beside creeks, eventually reaching a gravel car park beside a green in Hamble village. Turn right at the road back to the quay.
For pub see entry 100

...for special offers

Kington, Herefordshire
Titley, The Stagg Inn and the Mortimer Trail

This glorious figure-of-eight walk takes the walker right to the heart of the Welsh Marches, a wonderfully quiet and unspoilt rural district, following the Mortimer Trail, one of its loveliest upland routes.

From the inn, turn left and follow the road to Titley Church. Turn left immediately beyond it and follow the Mortimer Trail beside farm outbuildings. Avoid a path on the left and head up through the fields, following the frequent trail waymarkers. When the path curves left in line with the field boundary, look for a gap in the hedgerow and take the Mortimer Trail across pastures to Green Lane Farm.

Pass to the right of the outbuildings and keep to the Mortimer Trail, following the track beside a large corrugated barn. Cross several stiles to reach the remains of an old byre. To return to Titley, go to point 6; to complete the full walk, keep ahead on the trail.

Skirt the pasture, keeping woodland on the left, and make for the field corner. Enter bluebell woods and follow the trail through the trees to a stile on the right. Cross a field and look for a stile in the top boundary. Join an enclosed path and follow it for some time to a stile. Cut through a pine forest and drop down some steps to reach a waymarker.

Turn sharp right here, leaving the trail, and descend steeply, bending to the left. Keep dropping, avoiding any turnings to the left and right, and eventually you reach a T-junction with a track. Turn right and walk along to a ford and some cottages. Turn right before the water, avoid a turning on the right and follow the cycle trail between trees and hedges to reach Little Brampton.

www.routiers.co.uk

5

Look for the path signposted to Titley (1 1/2 miles) and follow the clear waymarks. The path eventually makes for the foot of the wooded escarpment and a line of coniferous trees. Cross the fields and continue on a track. Go through a gate and pass some outbuildings and a house. Turn right at the lane and return to The Stagg. For pub see entry 111

Turn right at the footpath sign, following the track to a field. Keep ahead towards the wooded escarpment and head for a stile. Swing left and climb through the trees. This is a lengthy ascent. Cross the edge of a tree-ringed field to two stiles with a path in between and turn left along the field.

6

fact file

Distance **7 1/2 miles (or 4 miles for the first loop and 3 1/2 the second)**
Time **4 hours for the full walk**
Paths **Field, woodland paths, tracks, sections of the Mortimer Trail. The full route is quite an adventurous walk, particularly the second loop.**
OS Map **Explorer 201 (Knighton and Presteigne)**

look out for

The Mortimer Trail, 30 miles in length, running from Ludlow to Kington, takes walkers through a land of lush pastures, wooded valleys and rolling hills.
Titley Church Mainly a Victorian restoration. In the churchyard is the grave of Lazar Meszarios, a Hungarian general who became ill and died while visiting the area.

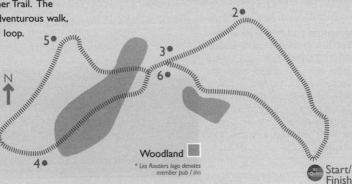

N ↑

Woodland ▪

*Les Routiers logo denotes member pub / inn

Start/ Finish

...for the latest news

Berkhamsted, Hertfordshire
The Alford Arms and the Ashridge Estate

A charming blend of peaceful commonland and glorious beech woodland forms the scenic backdrop of this very varied walk through the beautiful Ashridge Estate.

1 From the front of the pub, cross the road and take the path opposite, following it uphill through trees and bluebell woods. Keep to the wide path, cross a drive and continue alongside hedging. Enter woodland and bend right, keeping right after a few paces to pass by trees and private gardens.

2 Soon you reach the fairways of a golf club. Skirt the fairways, following the path through the trees to the road. Cross over, following the Hertfordshire Way across more fairways. Cut between trees and, further on, you will reach a waymarked crossroads.

3

Turn right, following the bridleway down into a dip at Frithsden Beeches and ascend the other side. Join a tarmac drive and when it bends right, keep ahead along the field edge and then down through the undergrowth to reach the road.

4

Cross over and take the path signposted to Little Gaddesden. Pass the entrance to a house called Rodinghead and then follow the path ahead between fences and across rolling parkland. Keep to the left and head down to a large dead tree and two beech trees. Cross the next stile to a track and veer left.

www.routiers.co.uk

5

Swing left after 120 yards and take the path up the slope to Ashridge House. Turn right at the corner of the building and follow the drive to a left bend. Turn right here by a National Trust bridleway sign and follow the track through the trees and across parkland. Enter woodland and, as the track loops dramatically to the left, look for a path running up the bank to an adventure playground. Cross it diagonally to the right corner and turn left at a path T-junction to reach the road.

6

Cross over to a field path and follow it down through a grassy valley. Cross a track and continue through the fields, passing a solitary tree, before reaching Nettleden. Join the road, pass a waymarked path to St Margaret's and turn right a few steps beyond it by Pightle Cottage. Follow the lane and, further up the slope, take the woodland path parallel to it on the left. Rejoin the lane and return to The Alford Arms. For pub see entry 118

fact file

Distance **6 3/4 miles**
Time **3 1/2 hours**
Paths **Common paths and bridleways, parkland paths and drives, field paths**
OS Map **Explorer 181 (Chiltern Hills North)**

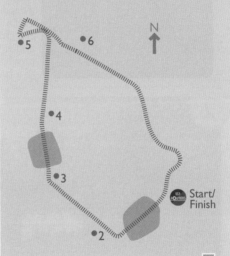

Woodland ▮
Les Routiers logo denotes member pub / inn

look out for

5,000 acres of Ashridge Estate is characterised by sprawling woodland, farmland and open downland, now in the care of the National Trust.
Ashridge House Its vastness takes the breath away. It was built in 1276 and restored by James Wyatt in 1808.

...for recipe ideas

Bodsham, Kent
North Downs ramble from the Timber Batts

Explore a hidden world of rolling hills, occasional dwellings and undiscovered green folds on this wonderfully quiet walk at the heart of Kent's North Downs.

From the front door of the pub, turn immediately right, passing a sign for Great Holt Farm. A footpath is signposted along the lane; there are farm outbuildings on the left. Just beyond them, climb over a stile on the left and go diagonally across the field, passing under telegraph wires. Go down the field slope to the corner of a wood, noting some farm buildings over to your right. Pass alongside fencing and head straight on across the field to a stile. Head diagonally across the next pasture to a stile and cross into the next field. After a few paces, you reach a further stile in the right-hand boundary. Cross it and turn left along the perimeter. At the next stile, cross over to a lane and turn right.

Follow the road, avoiding a bridleway on the left, and head for the buildings of Ipinge Farm. Keep to the lane beyond the farm, following it as it snakes and twists through the North Downs countryside. At length, it reaches a T-junction near Dean Farm. Turn left here, then sharp right after a few paces to follow a no-through road.

Pass a bungalow on the right, followed by a house on the left. Now the lane runs dead straight between hedgerows. Keep several dwellings and an ancient black-and-white timber-framed house on the left. On this stretch, the lane dwindles to a path. Begin a lengthy, unremitting climb through the trees, although the going is not especially steep. At the top of the slope, continue ahead on a track and follow it round to the right to reach a road on a bend.

www.routiers.co.uk

4

Go straight on, following it round to the right at the point where there is a track on the left. Pass through a tunnel of trees and look for a galvanised gate on the left. Once through it, veer left into an elongated field, following the path across it into woodland. Pass through the trees and down the hillside to a stile in the bottom boundary.

At the road, turn left and, at the next junction, follow the road round to the right for Bodsham, bearing right for the village when you reach the entrance to The Pottery. Follow the lane uphill and back to the pub.

For pub see entry 122

5

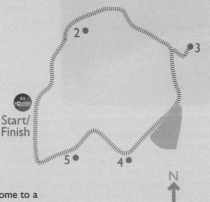

fact file

Distance **4 1/2 miles**
Time **2 hours**
Paths **Field paths and tracks, quiet country lanes with little or no traffic; moderate climbing**
OS Map **Explorer 138 (Dover, Folkstone & Hythe)**

look out for

Spong Wood is the scene of regular coppicing and home to a variety of rare plants, making it an important and ancient rural landmark. The sunken, oak-lined lane, which runs through the wood and forms part of the walk, was used by farmers to take livestock to market and to new pastures. Woodpeckers, warblers and sparrowhawk are familiar residents.

Start/Finish

2
3
5
4

N

Woodland
Les Routiers logo denotes member pub / inn

475

...for events

Clitheroe, Lancashire
The Freemasons Arms under Pendle's Spell

Forbidding Pendle Hill was the setting for the most notorious alleged acts of witchcraft in the early years of the 17th century. From the skirt of the hill, this easy walk meanders to the banks of the River Calder and the village of Whalley, with its ruined abbey.

1 Turn left from the pub, cross the lane and ascend Moor Lane. At the top, bear right into a stony field road. In 100 yards, take the stile on the right and head left to a ladder stile into woods. Keep straight ahead through stone gateposts to a stile into a field. Go ahead to decrepit sheepfolds; here drop right to a walled corner. Take the right-hand stile, then shortly, another. Turn right, aiming for the left of the woods below. Use the footbridge onto the golf course and turn right to reach a stile and nearby traffic lights.

2 Carefully cross into Accrington Road. In 300 yards, take the stile left just past the Whalley sign. Join the riverside path. Pass the weir and trace the rough lane to a village street. Turn right. In 50 yards, go left on to Abbey Mews and then wind through Cornmill Mews on a tarred path emerging beside the churchyard. Turn left to reach one of the Abbey's gatehouses. Explore!

Walk along The Sands, passing beneath the second gatehouse and the viaduct. Take the private road, passing under the bypass. Remain on this lane past the treatment works and ahead to the riverbank, then turn right. About 150 yards before the river bends, fork half-right up a scarred track and then half-left, a metal rail-fence soon on your right. Trace this track straight through a complex of gates and fences, then bend right with the rail-fence still on your right and an old orchard left. Remain on this track over a metal step stile. Continue to a road.

fact file

Distance **5 miles**
Time **2 1/2-3 hours**
Paths **Mostly field paths and lanes expect mud
and cattle**
OS Map **Explorer 287
(West Pennine Moors)**
NB **the route at Brook House Farm complex
(in Point 4) may change very slightly due
to building work.**

Woodland ▪
River/Lake ▪

** Les Routiers logo denotes
member pub / inn*

look out for

Pendle Hill Looms mysteriously above this walk.
It was on the slopes of this hill that Alice Nutter,
Demdike and other unfortunates were accused
of witchcraft by the local squire, Roger Nowell,
and ultimately convicted and hanged in Lancaster
Castle in 1612.
Whalley Abbey Founded by the Cistercian order
in 1296. Closed and looted in 1537 during the
reign of Henry VIII. Substantial remains survive in
a tranquil setting by the River Calder.
St Mary's Church Contains some exquisite
woodworking.

Cross and take the right-hand stile, walking
to the distant farm. Use the wooden gate
on to a concreted lane and go ahead to the
driveway. Turn left to Brook House Farm
(Whalley Cornmill). Bend left, then right (a
large green barn and horse yard on your
left), take the handgate and go ahead over a
bridge to a gate. Drift half-right to the field
edge, ignore the gate on your right and keep
ahead to a bridge and stile. Cross the railway
to another stile, then bend left up a wooded
strip. At the end, take the stile right and walk
the dirt field track through to a road.

Cross straight over into Whiteacre Lane.
Remain on this over the bypass. At the
junction, fork right to return to Wiswell
centre and the pub.
For pub see entry 129

...for competitions

Whitewell, Lancashire
Into Bowland from The Inn at Whitewell

Over the stepping stones from a famous inn for a circuit among the Forest of Bowland's little-known limestone scenery.

From the front of the inn, pass the church on the right and walk down into the car park. Go through the gateway and turn right towards the river. The riverbank path drops down to the left below the garden wall and leads to the stepping stones. Cross the River Hodder and follow the waymarkers on the opposite side to a gate at New Launds Farm.

Go through the gate and turn left through another gate on a steep track up the bank. The track peters out but the line is clear, with woods dropping down to the river on the left and open pastureland ahead and right. Continue up through the field to a gateway. Continue over the shoulder and bear slightly right before dropping down to a stile. Follow the fence on the right, then bear right, up to a gate and stile. Through these, turn left and join the track to Fair Oak. Descend through a gateway, cross a brook and walk up the ramp into a hamlet.

3 Bear left, then turn right opposite the barn, into a yard. Pass the cowshed on the left and locate a hand gate by the barn wall in the far corner. Follow the path to a stile into a field. Walk across the field, aiming to intercept the fence on the left-hand side at the far end. Cross a stile, then cut off the field corner to a stile leading to the road. Turn right and follow the road for 200 yards to a crossroads.

4 Go straight ahead, over the cattle grid. Follow the track over another cattle grid and then around a bend. It becomes surfaced and crosses yet another cattle grid, heading for sheds on the left. Go through a gateway by the buildings and continue, as the track swings left to descend to Dinkling Green Farm. Cross over a further cattle grid, then cross the bridge over the brook and bear left into the farmyard.

5

From a courtyard, turn right to a gate between a wooden shed and garden wall. Follow the snicket to a stile, then cross the field ahead, maintaining direction to a stile in the fence to the left of the gate. Cross the stile and bear half-right to another stile. Cross into the paddock and turn left towards the chicken sheds. Beyond these, cross the wooden bridge over the brook. Go through the gate and up a track into the farmyard.

6

fact file

Distance **5 1/2 miles**
Time **2 1/2 hours**
Paths **Field paths, farm tracks, quiet country lanes, stepping stones**
OS Map **Explorer OL41 (Forest of Bowland & Ribblesdale)**

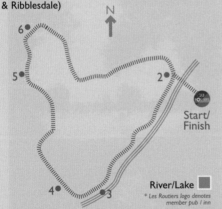

Start/Finish

River/Lake ■

* Les Routiers logo denotes member pub / inn

Go through the gate on the the other side, continue up the access track, bearing right at the fork. Follow the track over the saddle, then right, over the cattle grid and past Tunstall Ing. After a left turn, emerge at a minor road by a cattle grid. Turn left for 200 yards to a gate on the right. Go through and aim for the base of a round hillock. The contouring path leads round the foot of the hill to two gates. Take the left-hand gate and walk down the field with the fence on the right. At the bottom, take the right-hand gate to join the track that skirts the base of the escarpment. Through the next gate, turn right into New Launds Farm. Walk up through the yard, descend to a gate, then retrace your steps back to the stepping stones and return to The Inn.
For pub see entry 133

look out for

Forest of Bowland **Not a forest in the sense that it was wooded, but open moorland that was a hunting domain owned by the Duchy of Lancaster.**

...for special offers

479

Itteringham, Norfolk
Blickling Hall and the Bure Valley

This gentle ramble from The Walpole Arms explores the lush meadows in the peaceful Bure Valley and the splendid parkland that surrounds Blickling Hall, a magnificent Jacobean house and the focal point of the walk.

From The Walpole Arms pub car park, turn left, then right at the T-junction and cross the River Bure into Itteringham. Take the lane right (signed village stores) and turn immediately right along a track beside Manor Farm. Continue to a gate, bear slightly right to a stile and follow the field edge uphill. Bear right into the adjacent field and keep left along the field edge.

Follow the track past White House Farm and with good views of Wolterton Hall soon turn left along the metalled access lane. Pass a cottage on your left, then, at a sharp right bend, take the arrowed path ahead along a track.

Soon bear left following the yellow arrow along the left-hand field edge and cross the second stile right. Bear left across a meadow and walk alongside woodland to reach a footbridge across the River Bure. Bear slightly left across pasture (which can be wet or flooded if river high) to a footbridge and follow the path to a metalled lane.

www.routiers.co.uk

4

Turn right, then left in front of Moorgate Cottages, and follow the path left around the field edge. Continue to a junction with the Weaver's Way by a tree seat. Follow the track ahead across Blickling Park, with the lake on the left and the house soon visible ahead, to the main park gates.

Exit the park and follow the lane left to visit Blickling Hall. Retrace your steps to the park gates and take the track left across the park. Keep ahead at a fork and soon walk beside the Great Wood (Mausoleum), disregarding the estate walk markers.

5

Pass beside a gate and walk through trees to a metalled lane by a cottage. Turn left and keep to this quiet road through Itteringham Common back to The Walpole Arms. For pub see entry 161

6

fact file

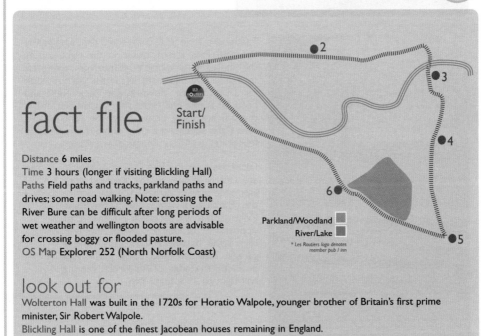

Start/Finish

Distance 6 miles
Time 3 hours (longer if visiting Blickling Hall)
Paths Field paths and tracks, parkland paths and drives; some road walking. Note: crossing the River Bure can be difficult after long periods of wet weather and wellington boots are advisable for crossing boggy or flooded pasture.
OS Map Explorer 252 (North Norfolk Coast)

Parkland/Woodland
River/Lake
* Les Routiers logo denotes member pub / inn

look out for

Wolterton Hall was built in the 1720s for Horatio Walpole, younger brother of Britain's first prime minister, Sir Robert Walpole.
Blickling Hall is one of the finest Jacobean houses remaining in England.

...for the latest news

Wadenhoe, Northamptonshire
Along the Nene Way from The King's Head

The village church seems to be the theme on this delightful walk, which begins by following the meandering River Nene between the settlements of Wadenhoe and Aldwincle. Several graceful spires can be seen from the viewpoint at the start, where a sundial depicts local parishes and their churches.

From the pub, turn left, go down to the entrance to the public car park, through a gate and straight ahead on the Lyveden Way for Wadenhoe church. Go uphill, pass St Michael and All Angels church and the sundial, walk through the parking area to a gate and then follow an avenue of hornbeams, planted in 1994 by the villagers of Wadenhoe in memory of their squire. Keep ahead to the junction and turn left.

Follow the road as it curves left, dropping gently downhill. Pass a farm track on the right and as the houses of Aldwincle edge into view, swing left to a stile. Aim diagonally left in the pasture, look for a line of trees down by the River Nene and head for a stile and Nene Way waymarker in the bottom boundary. Don't cross the stile; instead, turn right, keeping the river on your left. Cross a footbridge and pass alongside woodland.

From the path, the buildings of Aldwincle are clearly visible. Follow the field edge alongside private gardens and just before the church, turn right, following the Nene Way to the village green. At the road, opposite a turning to Lowick and Islip, turn right, passing Fullers Close and a garage. Turn left into Cross Lane and head for the edge of Aldwincle, veering half-right to a footpath sign.

www.routiers.co.uk

4

Cross a stile and follow the path down the field, keeping a line of small trees and a hedgerow on your right. Cross the next stile and continue along the perimeter of the pasture, passing various footbridges before reaching a junction with a track. The footpath continues ahead, but the route of the walk is to the right. Keep ahead when you reach a sign for the Lyveden Way and, at length, you reach double galvanised gates.

5

Continue ahead along the road for about 1/2 mile, then turn right, still following the Lyveden Way. Head down the field, pass through a kissing gate and cross the road to the turning for Wadenhoe – marked 'village only'. The church is seen over to the right across farmland. Follow the lane down to the war memorial, turn right, pass a phone box and make for Church Street. The King's Head is on the left-hand side as you approach the public car park at the start of the walk.
For pub see entry 167

fact file

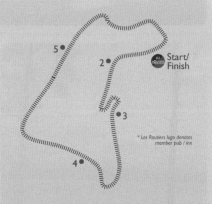

Distance **5 miles**
Time **2 hours**
Paths Field paths, tracks, quiet roads. Several sections can be very wet and muddy, so wear appropriate footwear
OS Map Explorer 224 (Corby, Kettering and Wellingborough)

* Les Routiers logo denotes member pub / inn

look out for

The walk follows part of the popular Nene Way and the Lyveden Way, the latter being a 9 1/2-mile walk through history, taking in Wadenhoe, Lyveden Manor and the visitor centre at Brigstock. Buy the booklet entitled *A Walk Around Wadenhoe*, available from the church for £1, and enjoy a fascinating stroll through the village.

...for recipe ideas

Kielder Water, Northumberland
To Kielder Water from The Pheasant Inn

Forest roads and bridle paths take this walk to clearings high in the forest, revealing airy views across the wild Northumbrian countryside. The return route follows peaceful lakeside paths beside Kielder Water.

1 From the inn, turn left along the main road and then right, signposted Falstone. Cross the River North Tyne, pass the Blackcock Inn then turn left, having passed under the railway bridge. In 100 yards, fork left on to the former railway line and remain on this, signed Reivers Cycle Route. At a junction, keep ahead to reach a cross-tracks above a farm. Turn right and ascend the track left of a house to pass through a wall.

2 In 50 yards, fork left off the track along a grassy forestry road. Gently climb towards the woods, the track eventually emerging from the trees to reveal some excellent views across the southern end of Kielder Water. The trees gather once again before parting to allow distant views north across Kielder Forest to the Cheviot Hills. Walk down to the wide forestry road.

3 Turn left and walk downhill for 800 yards to the second white post signed Wave Chamber, and a cycle-route waymarker. Fork right on to a sandy track though the trees, then turn right in 100 yards along a waymarked path, dropping to cross a marshy isthmus. Keep right at a fork, tracing the circular path out onto the Belling Peninsula, and savour superb views across the lake from rocky promontories.

www.routiers.co.uk

4 Remain on the path, marked by occasional orange waymarkers, to reach a white post signed Belvedere. Turn right along a gravelly path through trees, in 100 yards gaining a wider track, along which turn right. This narrows to a delightful path around rocky inlets and bays before reaching the remains of Gordon's Walls Castle. Just beyond this, the path leaves the shoreline at some rail fencing, soon reaching a wide forestry road. Turn right along this.

Remain on this roadway, passing behind the Hawkhope car park, sited at the north end of the reservoir dam close to the immense valve tower. Don't take the road to the dam; instead take the road signed 'Forestry Vehicles only'. At Hawkhope Farm, passed earlier in the walk, turn right at the cross-tracks, pass beside the farm and take the gate on the left, joining a gated road to Falstone. At the junction by the Blackcock Inn, turn right and retrace your outward steps back to The Pheasant Inn.

For pub see entry 171

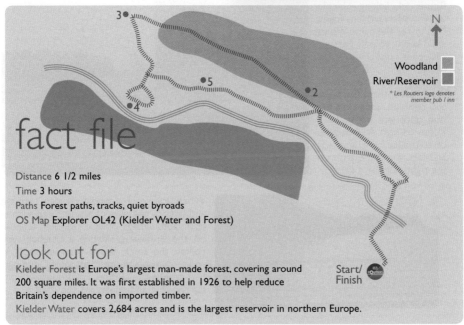

fact file

Distance **6 1/2 miles**
Time **3 hours**
Paths **Forest paths, tracks, quiet byroads**
OS Map **Explorer OL42 (Kielder Water and Forest)**

look out for

Kielder Forest is Europe's largest man-made forest, covering around 200 square miles. It was first established in 1926 to help reduce Britain's dependence on imported timber.
Kielder Water covers 2,684 acres and is the largest reservoir in northern Europe.

Woodland
River/Reservoir
Les Routiers logo denotes member pub / inn

Start/ Finish

485

...for events

Harby, Nottinghamshire
Doddington Hall from The Bottle & Glass

The flatlands of Lincolnshire dominate this attractive walk, which follows part of a popular cycle trail before making for one of the county's loveliest ancestral homes, Doddington Hall, with its colourful gardens and historic treasures.

1 Turn right out of the pub and follow the road for about 75 yards, veering right just before the T-junction to join a track running away from the houses of Harby. Swing sharp right on the edge of the village and then left. Keep to the clear path, following it as it weaves its way through open countryside. Look for some pylons ahead and make for a junction with a cycle trail just before them.

Turn right here and follow Route 64, linking Lincoln with Newark-on-Trent. Pass under the pylon cables and keep going. Farther on, pass under a road bridge, then cut between woodland and vegetation. Break cover from the trees and continue ahead on the trail until you come to a Route 64 sign. A path runs off to the left here. Ignore it and take the gated path on the right, skirting a field.

3 When you reach a bridleway sign, turn right and pass to the side of a lake. Keep silos and farm outbuildings over to the left. Continue on the bridleway, skirting a bluebell wood. Follow the track ahead between fields and soon you can see the rooftop of Doddington Hall against the skyline. The bridleway joins a tarmac lane and makes for the road.

4

Turn left, pass the church and keep ahead for a few paces to a post box. Turn right here for Home Farm. Follow the concrete track between outbuildings and houses. Look for a waymarker just beyond stables and swing right to join a footpath. Cross a field and a grassy avenue lined with broad-leaved limes. To the right is a striking view of Doddington Hall.

5

Keep ahead towards trees, following the waymarked grassy path to a stile at the corner of the wood. Keep right, skirting the field, then go through a gateway into the next pasture and cross it diagonally. Make for a pylon and a waymarker and turn left. The spire of Harby Church is visible now. Pass through a gate and go straight ahead across the field to the next gate. Continue ahead beside the ditch, keeping to the left of a paddock and turn right on reaching the recreation ground. Keep right at the road, walk straight ahead at the junction and back to the pub.

For pub see entry 177

fact file

Distance **6 1/2 miles**
Time **2 hours**
Paths **Tracks, cycleway, bridleways, field paths**
OS Map **Explorer 271 (Newark) and 272 (Lincoln)**

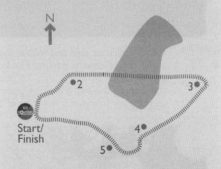

N

Start/ Finish

Woodland ◼

Les Routiers logo denotes member pub / inn

look out for

St Peter's Church The precise date of this Church at Doddington is not known, but the circular font dates back to the middle of the 13th century. The older parts of the church are constructed of rough Lincolnshire stone. **Doddington Hall** is a striking Elizabethan manor house built of mellowed brick. Inside is an impressive collection of china, tapestries and Stuart and Georgian furniture. It is open during the spring and summer months.

487

...for competitions

Henley-on-Thames, Oxfordshire
South Chiltern Hills from The Cherry Tree

A gently undulating ramble through the Chiltern Hills to Nuffield and the Ridgeway Path.

From the pub car park, turn right along the village street. Turn right just past the village hall, along a narrow path, with the exotic Maharajah's Well just a few steps further on the right. Descend to a metalled lane and turn left. This soon dwindles into a track. Continue beside a bluebell wood for 1/4 mile, then take the footpath right across a stile.

Climb a further stile and follow the left-hand field edge to a stile in the corner. Turn left along the bridleway, passing Oakingham House. Follow the drive out to a road. Cross straight over to join a 'right of way'. Pass the drive to Ridgeway Farmhouse and follow the lane to the entrance to Upper House Farm. Turn right along the field edge, keeping to the path towards a house, then right along the fence to a stile.

Cross the drive and follow the path around Ridgeway Farm. Enter a field and keep to the right-hand edge, soon to walk through a spinney, with super views west across South Oxfordshire. At a junction with the Ridgeway Path at Grim's Ditch, keep ahead and then along the edge of a field to reach a lane.

Turn right through Nuffield, passing the church, to reach a T-junction with Timbers Lane. Turn left, then immediately right along a footpath to the left of a house called Martyn's Close. At a gravel drive, bear right past Elderberry Cottage to join a bridleway.

5

Continue on the enclosed path and soon join a wider track. Keep right, ignore the stile on your right and follow the track left for Howberrywood Farm. Pass the farm, then, where the drive becomes metalled, keep right into woodland.

At a waymarker post, follow the yellow arrow right through the trees and along the woodland fringe to a stile. Keep right along the field edge and cross a stile by a gate and barn. Turn left along the track and bear left then right downhill past cottages to a metalled lane by a house called Squirrels.

6

Take the path ahead downhill through trees to a road, cross straight over and climb through woodland, keeping ahead at a crossing of paths. Shortly, bear right uphill to reach a road. Turn left and follow it back into Stoke Row. Turn right by the green for the pub. For pub see entry 183

7

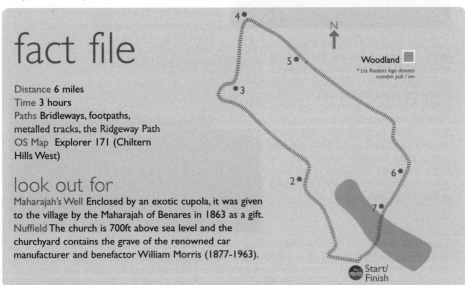

fact file

Distance 6 miles
Time 3 hours
Paths Bridleways, footpaths, metalled tracks, the Ridgeway Path
OS Map Explorer 171 (Chiltern Hills West)

look out for

Maharajah's Well Enclosed by an exotic cupola, it was given to the village by the Maharajah of Benares in 1863 as a gift.
Nuffield The church is 700ft above sea level and the churchyard contains the grave of the renowned car manufacturer and benefactor William Morris (1877-1963).

Woodland

* Les Routiers logo denotes member pub / inn

N

Start/ Finish

...for special offers

South Cadbury, Somerset
To Corton Denham from The Camelot

An up-and-down rural ramble taking in Cadbury Castle hill fort, wide views across Somerset and the sleepy village of Corton Denham, returning along the lofty Monarch's Way via the village of Sutton Montis

1 Turn right on leaving the pub, pass the church and look out for the access path to Cadbury Castle beside a house on the right. Climb and circuit the hill fort and return to the road. Turn right, pass the car park, then having passed a house and side road on the left, cross the stile on the left, signed Sigwells.

2 Cross the stile and footbridge ahead and continue along the left-hand field edge. Follow way markers right across a stile in the hedge and continue left along the field edge. Climb gradually, cross a stile by a gate and keep ahead along the field edge. At the end of the field turn right, soon to join a hedged track that leads to Whitcombe Farm. The track becomes metalled and leads to a road.

3 Turn left uphill and sharp left again at the next junction. Ascend for 1/4 mile to the top of the hill and turn right to gate, signed Corton Denham. Shortly, follow the fence left (summit trig point right), then left again at hill rim. With stunning views across Somerset and into Dorset, keep to the ridge path, cross a stile, then, as the path reaches a gate, slant half-right down the grass slope to a gate. Continue down to a gate and lane. Turn left, then left again at the village lane.

4 Leave the village and cross a stile on the right in 200 yards. Head down the field towards a farm to reach a gate and lane. Proceed ahead, soon to take Middle Ridge Lane (a track) ahead at a sharp left bend. Ascend this hedged track to a gate and the top of Corton Ridge. Turn right (Monarch's Way) and keep to this high-level bridleway, passing the bottom of an unmetalled lane (Ridge Lane) via gates.

www.routiers.co.uk

5

Beyond the second of two more gates, the paths starts to skirt round Parrock Hill. Gradually descend, soon to follow the main path left steeply down to a gate, and continue to the lane. Cross into the lane opposite and soon take the path (signed Sutton Montis) across double stiles on the left. Head across the field to a stile just to the right of a house and continue out to the lane.

6

Climb the stile opposite, cross an orchard, soon to exit a gate to reach the village lane. Turn right, pass the church and continue out of the village. In just over 1/4 mile, go through the waymarked gate on the right and keep to the path along the left-hand edge. Soon join a track and remain on this back into South Cadbury and the pub.

For pub see entry 194

fact file

Distance **6 1/2 miles**
Time **3 1/2 hours**
Paths **Field and downland paths, farm tracks and bridleways**
OS Map **Explorer 129 (Yeovil & Sherborne)**

look out for

Cadbury Castle is a spectacular fortified prehistoric encampment of 18 acres. It is one of the largest of its kind in Britain and is claimed, inevitably, as the one true Camelot, the royal court of the legendary King Arthur. In places, the surviving defensive banks rise to over 40ft from the external ditch.

From the summit of Corton Denham Beacon, on a clear day, you can look across Sparkford Vale to Glastonbury Tor and the Mendips beyond.

Start/Finish

● 6   ● 2

N

5 ●   3 ●

Les Routiers logo denotes member pub / inn

● 4

...for the latest news

Chichester, West Sussex
The Ship Inn and Chichester Harbour

Follow peaceful field paths to West Wittering and a short, optional extension to a sandy beach and East Head, with views to the Isle of Wight.

1 From the Ship, turn right along the lane back through the village (which can be busy). In 1/4 mile, turn right into the drive to Itchenor Park House and take the footpath immediately left to the side of the memorial hall. Follow the path along the field edge, across the footbridge in the corner and keep to the field edge.

2 Cross a track and continue through the centre of a field on a defined path. Soon reach the field edge and follow the path to a track. Turn right and remain on the track to Rookwood Road on a sharp bend. Cross straight over and walk along the pavement into West Wittering.

3 Pass shops and the memorial hall and cross over, noting the wall plaque to Sir Henry Royce. Turn right along Pound Road (signed to the Parish Church), pass the toilets and follow the lane left through the old village to the church.

fact file

Distance **6 3/4 miles**
Time **4 hours**
Paths **Field paths, tracks, village streets, beach, creekside paths**
OS Map **Explorer 120 (Chichester)**

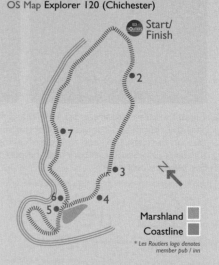

Marshland ■
Coastline ■

* Les Routiers logo denotes member pub / inn

look out for

West Itchenor A sleepy village with an attractive street leading down to Chichester Harbour. King Charles kept a yacht here in the 17th century. **West Wittering Parish Church** Dates from Norman and early-English periods and contains fine tombs and a remarkable old belfry staircase. **Chichester Harbour** At 3,000 acres, it forms the largest area of estuarine mudflats on the south coast, and is an ideal spot for watching waders and wildfowl.

4 Walk through the churchyard, pass the entrance and cross the stile ahead into a field. Cross the field to a gate and join a track. At a T-junction with a metalled track, turn right and follow this past big houses, with Snow Hill Marsh to your left, to a grassy area beside Chichester Harbour.

5

For the optional extension to the beach and East Head (sandy spit), bear left to join the footpath above the water (walk along the stony beach if the tide is out), and follow it to West Wittering beach. If the tide is out, you can walk around East Head (National Trust), which has super sea and harbour views. Return to the grassy area.

6 Follow the waymarked footpath that runs parallel with the water's edge. With good views and the opportunity to watch the wealth of birdlife, keep to this path, veering right before Ella Nore spit, and then head slightly inland by an impressive red-brick house, passing a further house called Tide's Reach.

7 The path continues to the right of the drive to Rednum Court soon to join the water's edge once again. Continue for 1 1/2 miles and cross a boatyard to join a fenced path leading to the quay at West Itchenor. Turn right up the lane back to the pub.

For pub see entry 220

...for recipe ideas

Leyburn, North Yorkshire
Uphill and down dale from The Sandpiper Inn

Walk in the footsteps of Victorian high society along the Leyburn Shawl promenade, an airy stroll rising gently above glorious Wensleydale, en route to pretty Preston, stately Bolton Hall and sublime Wensley herself, huddled around the Dales' best church.

1 Take Shawl Terrace, beside the Dalesman's Club in the top marketplace, Commercial Square. At the end, slip left into The Shawl, created as a promenade by townsfolk about 170 years ago to attract well-to-do visitors to take the air. Impressive views open out across Wensleydale; look back-left for Middleham Castle. Stay outside the playground and keep ahead at the gap, with the woods on your left. Remain beside these through several stiles to a final stile and gate 75 yards left of a barn and pylons. Enter the woods here.

2 The wide path snakes through beech and Scots pine woods clothing the steep limestone scar (edge). Keep to the upper path at old stone gateposts, remaining beside a wall. Take the stile near the end of the woods, walk 30 paces and take a stile left into the sloping field. Head half-right to a stile and then walk to the bottom-right corner to a stile and gateway. Keep the fence, then wall, on your left, ignore a field gate and continue to a rough lane beside the distant woods.

Cross slightly left into a woodland path, Keep left within a few yards, but at the next T-junction in 150 yards, turn sharp right following the blue waymarker, dropping to a culvert. On your right here, the ruined tunnel is a flue from Keld Head Lead Mine, once the largest in Wensleydale. Turn sharp left following the blue waymarker, along the well-walked path across several side streams to a gap stile into pasture. Go ahead to the far bottom corner where a gateway leads to a lane. Turn right to Preston-under-Scar.

4

At the foot of the green, go sharp left at the fingerposted footpath, down the driveway beside The Setts to a narrow path and gate into pasture. Head slightly left to a stile right of the small barn, then go ahead to a stile. Cross the railway and take the track opposite. Use the stile, but keep ahead to reach a road to the right of the house. Cross into the rough lane and follow this. At a T-junction, turn left to wind to and through Home Farm at Bolton Hall. Bend left with the concrete driveway to pass 150 yards below Bolton Hall. Walk through to Wensley village green.

5

Join the B6108 road beside the churchyard (signed for Middleham and Masham) and remain on this. Beyond the village, wide verges soon develop, making walking easier. In a mile, pass a small derelict barn on your right. In another 50 yards, look left for a narrow entrance to a hedged stony path. This is muddy underfoot for the first 300 yards before becoming a wider and firmer track. Follow it gently uphill past a barn, passing beneath the railway to gain a main road. Turn right to Leyburn and The Sandpiper Inn.

For pub see entry 250

fact file

look out for

Bolton Castle Started in 1379, for six months in 1568 this magnificent castle was prison to Mary, Queen of Scots.
Bolton Hall A stately pile in hundreds of acres of landscaped parkland beside the river Ure.
Holy Trinity Church in Wensley is oft-cited as the best in the Dales.

Distance **6 miles**
Time **3 hours**
Paths **Mostly field paths and byroads**
OS Map **Explorer OL30 (Yorkshire Dales, Northern & Central Areas)**

Start/
Finish

Parkland/Woodland
River/Lake

*Les Routiers logo denotes
member pub / inn*

...for events

Glencoe, Highland
Glencoe and The Clachaig Inn

A short forest walk reveals some surprising views of this great mountain valley.

1 From the front of the inn, turn left up the road towards Glencoe village. After 50 yards, turn left into a car-parking area. On the far side you will see a National Trust for Scotland (NTS) sign for An Torr. Walk through the parking area and continue up the forestry track to a gate in the deer fence. Go through the gate and continue along the forest track. After 110 yards, take the path ascending on the right, signposted An Torr.

2 Follow the narrow footpath as it climbs up through woods to the high point of An Torr. There are views behind you into Clachaig Gully. From the rocky outcrop, admire the vista across Achnacon towards Meall Mor. From the summit, retrace your steps back to the larger forestry track and turn right. Continue as it winds past an area of clear felled woodland and swings left down to a junction.

3 Turn right here, following the sign for Signal Rock. The track swings round to the left past another area of clear felled woodland. Ignore turnings to the left and right and continue up the muddy bank. Over the brow of a rise, continue to a gate in a deer fence and an NTS sign explaining access rights to Signal Rock.

4 Go through a deer gate and follow the track. It leads over a little shoulder and down some rocky steps. As it levels out in a clearing, ignore paths to the right and left and continue up the bank opposite with wood-and-earth steps cut into it.

5

At the top of the hill, Signal Rock comes into view. A short scramble leads up to the summit, or you can slip round on a path to the right of the rock and ascend by the series of steps on the far side. Now retrace your steps to the junction passed on your outward journey with signs to Signal Rock and The Clachaig Inn.

6

Bear right and carry on the good track down to the kissing gate in the deer fence. Descend to the river. The bridge here over the River Coe used to give access to the old visitor centre, before its site was levelled. Don't cross the bridge but turn left along the riverside path to some stepping stones. Cross over and turn left again, now following the tributary upstream with the fence on the right. Follow the little path as it crosses another tributary and eventually emerges on a back road to Glencoe village. Turn left to return to the inn.

For pub see entry 293

fact file

look out for

Glencoe provides walkers and climbers with a formidable range of mountains to clamber all over. The glen achieved its principal notoriety in 1692, when 38 members of the MacDonald clan were murdered here by government troops.

Signal Rock Believed to be the point from which the government troops gave the signal to move on the MacDonald clansmen.

Distance 1 1/2 miles
Time 1 hours
Paths Forest tracks and paths
OS Map Explorer 384 (Glencoe and Glen Etive)

Woodland
River/Lake

* Les Routiers logo denotes member pub / inn

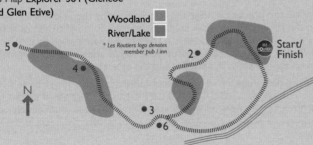

Start/Finish

...for competitions

Skenfrith, Monmouthshire
The Monnow Valley from The Bell

A delightful riverside walk with a longer option through the peaceful Monnow Valley and a final sharp ascent to the top of Coedanghred Hill for glorious views across Skenfrith and the upper Monnow Valley to the Black Mountains.

1 Cross the river bridge on leaving the pub and take the path right, signed 'Tregate Bridge 6.5km'. Follow the path beside the River Monnow and pass in front of Sand House. Walk through a copse to a stile and bear right around the field beside the river. Bear left in the corner and follow the arrowed path right into the adjacent field. Bear slightly left towards farm buildings and silos, cross a stile and continue up the slope to a gate.

2 Walk through Llanrothal farm and follow the access lane to cottages. Cross the stream, take the footpath right and soon follow the path left to reach St John the Baptist Church. Exit the churchyard via a stile and turn left around the field edge. Follow the river for nearly a mile to a stile and then turn right across Tregate Bridge.

3 Cross the stile on your right and bear diagonally left across the field towards a farm. Pass through a gate and continue behind the farm to a gate and poplar plantation.
Short walk:
Follow the path ahead and walk through the plantation, crossing a stream and eventually exiting the woodland on reaching the riverbank. Bear left across the field, soon to rejoin the riverbank, and keep beside the river through more woodland, soon to join the road by a house. Turn left steeply uphill, bearing right at the top (join long walk at point 8).

4 **Long walk:**
Turn left to a stile on the plantation edge and left again along the field edge to another stile. Bear right to the farm drive and walk uphill to the road. Turn right, then, as you begin to descend, cross the stile on the left and follow the narrow path beside fencing downhill towards a house. Pass in front of a garage, drop down steps and continue downhill – the path can be overgrown – to cross the stream and the stile ahead.

5 Keep ahead along the field edge, cross a stile and footbridge on your right and walk in front of a derelict cottage to a stile. Proceed across the field, ignore the stile on the boundary and turn left up the field edge to a stile. Climb the stile immediately to your right and bear half-left to pass to the right of a barn to a stile. Bear left and enter St Maughan's churchyard.

www.routiers.co.uk

fact file

Distance **5 or 7 miles**
Time **3 or 4 hours**
Paths **Riverside and field paths, tracks, some road**
OS Map **Explorer 189 (Hereford & Ross-on-Wye) & OL14 (Wye Valley & Forest of Dean)**

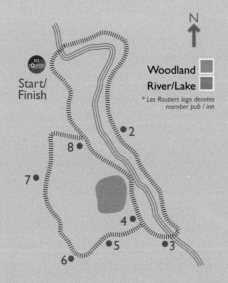

N

Start/ Finish

Woodland
River/Lake
Les Routiers logo denotes member pub / inn

look out for

Skenfrith Church Noted for its massive square tower.
Skenfrith Castle Built in the 13th century, it has a round keep, set within an imposing towered curtain wall.
St John the Baptist Church This church, in Llanrothal, dates from the late 13th century.

6 At the road, turn right, pass a farm, then, at a fork of drives, bear right towards Little Coxstone. Descend steeply, follow the hedged track to the left of the property uphill, then descend to a stream. Climb up the sunken path, which can be very wet. The path soon becomes a track leading to a metalled drive opposite a bungalow.

7 Turn right, pass to the left of the farmhouse, then, at a track, turn left downhill to a junction of paths. Bear right, then left and ascend beside woodland towards a house on the hill. Follow the field edge left, passing below White House to reach the drive. Turn right, then turn left at the T-junction at the top of a steep hill.

8 At a fork, keep left up the drive, pass to the left of the property and continue across the side of Coedanghred Hill. Soon, steeply ascend and pass beside a house to reach a stile on the summit. Descend steeply through fields to reach a lane. Turn left back to the inn.
For pub see entry 339

...for special offers

Just Off The Motorway

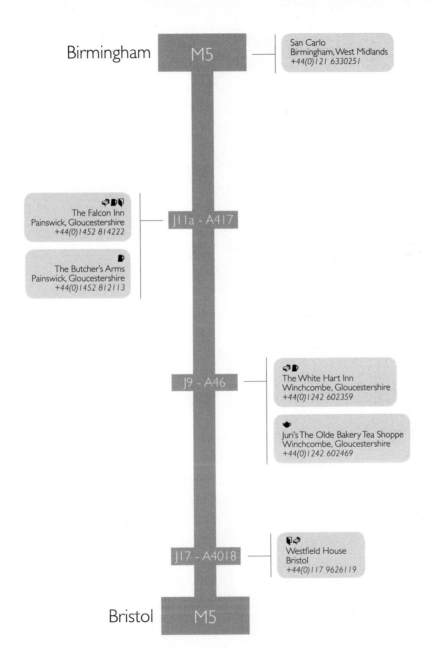

Birmingham — M5

San Carlo
Birmingham, West Midlands
+44(0)121 6330251

J11a – A417

The Falcon Inn
Painswick, Gloucestershire
+44(0)1452 814222

The Butcher's Arms
Painswick, Gloucestershire
+44(0)1452 812113

J9 – A46

The White Hart Inn
Winchcombe, Gloucestershire
+44(0)1242 602359

Juri's The Olde Bakery Tea Shoppe
Winchcombe, Gloucestershire
+44(0)1242 602469

J17 – A4018

Westfield House
Bristol
+44(0)117 9626119

Bristol — M5

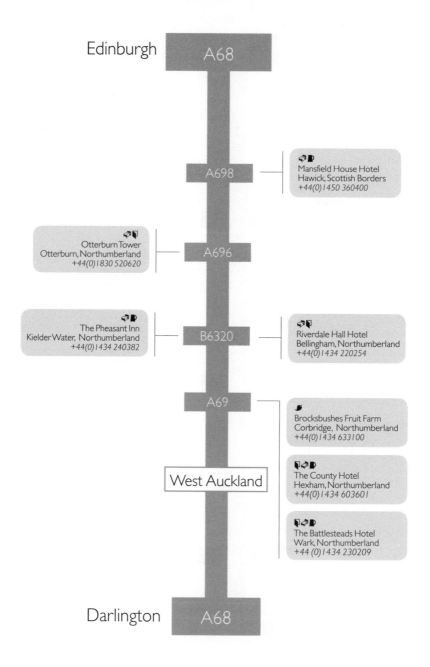

Edinburgh

A68

A698

Mansfield House Hotel
Hawick, Scottish Borders
+44(0)1450 360400

Otterburn Tower
Otterburn, Northumberland
+44(0)1830 520620

A696

The Pheasant Inn
Kielder Water, Northumberland
+44(0)1434 240382

B6320

Riverdale Hall Hotel
Bellingham, Northumberland
+44(0)1434 220254

A69

Brocksbushes Fruit Farm
Corbridge, Northumberland
+44(0)1434 633100

West Auckland

The County Hotel
Hexham, Northumberland
+44(0)1434 603601

The Battlesteads Hotel
Wark, Northumberland
+44 (0)1434 230209

Darlington

A68

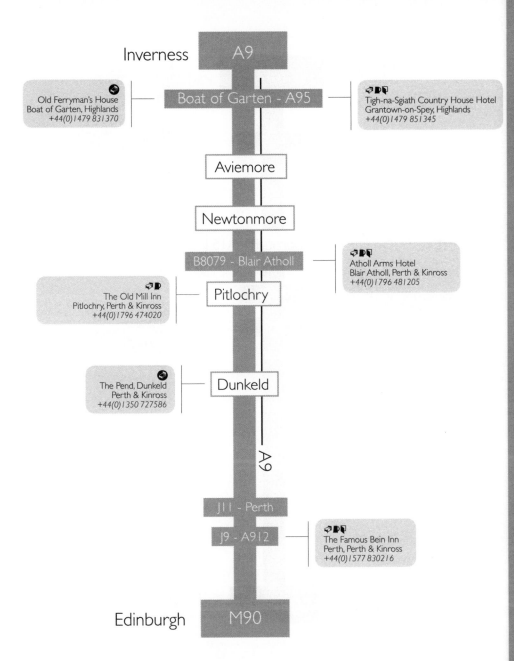

Inverness

A9

Old Ferryman's House
Boat of Garten, Highlands
+44(0)1479 831370

Boat of Garten - A95

Tigh-na-Sgiath Country House Hotel
Grantown-on-Spey, Highlands
+44(0)1479 851345

Aviemore

Newtonmore

B8079 - Blair Atholl

Atholl Arms Hotel
Blair Atholl, Perth & Kinross
+44(0)1796 481205

The Old Mill Inn
Pitlochry, Perth & Kinross
+44(0)1796 474020

Pitlochry

The Pend, Dunkeld
Perth & Kinross
+44(0)1350 727586

Dunkeld

A9

J11 - Perth

J9 - A912

The Famous Bein Inn
Perth, Perth & Kinross
+44(0)1577 830216

Edinburgh

M90

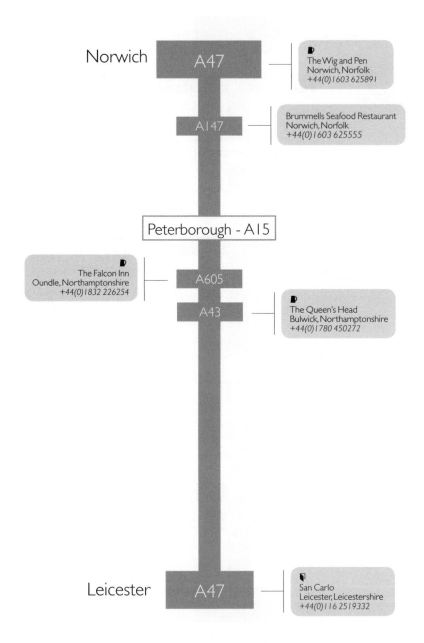

Norwich

A47

The Wig and Pen
Norwich, Norfolk
+44(0)1603 625891

A147

Brummells Seafood Restaurant
Norwich, Norfolk
+44(0)1603 625555

Peterborough - A15

The Falcon Inn
Oundle, Northamptonshire
+44(0)1832 226254

A605

A43

The Queen's Head
Bulwick, Northamptonshire
+44(0)1780 450272

Leicester

A47

San Carlo
Leicester, Leicestershire
+44(0)116 2519332

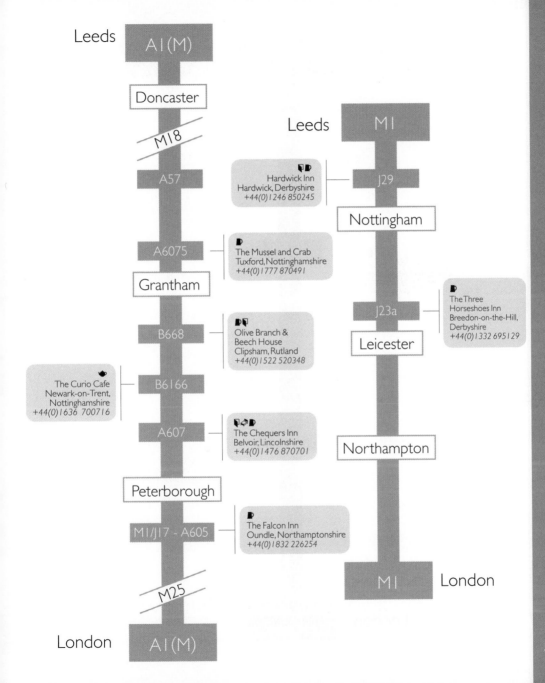

Leeds

A1(M)

Doncaster

M18

A57

Hardwick Inn
Hardwick, Derbyshire
+44(0)1246 850245

Leeds

M1

J29

Nottingham

A6075

The Mussel and Crab
Tuxford, Nottinghamshire
+44(0)1777 870491

Grantham

B668

Olive Branch &
Beech House
Clipsham, Rutland
+44(0)1522 520348

J23a

The Three
Horseshoes Inn
Breedon-on-the-Hill,
Derbyshire
+44(0)1332 695129

Leicester

The Curio Cafe
Newark-on-Trent,
Nottinghamshire
+44(0)1636 700716

B6166

A607

The Chequers Inn
Belvoir, Lincolnshire
+44(0)1476 870701

Northampton

Peterborough

M1/J17 - A605

The Falcon Inn
Oundle, Northamptonshire
+44(0)1832 226254

M25

London

A1(M)

M1

London

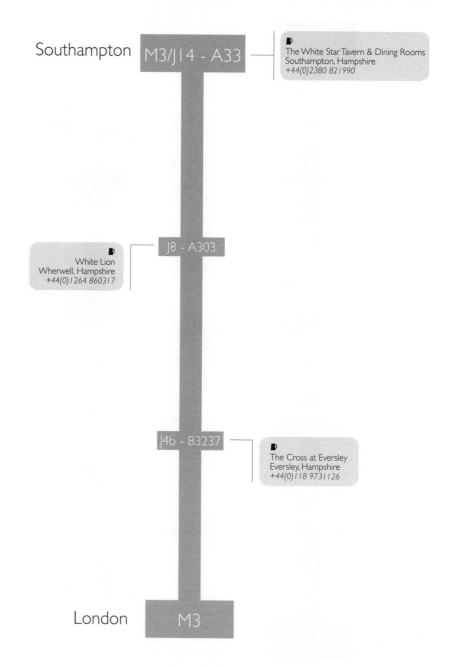

Southampton

M3/J14 - A33

The White Star Tavern & Dining Rooms
Southampton, Hampshire
+44(0)2380 821990

J8 - A303

White Lion
Wherwell, Hampshire
+44(0)1264 860317

J4b - B3237

The Cross at Eversley
Eversley, Hampshire
+44(0)118 9731126

London

M3

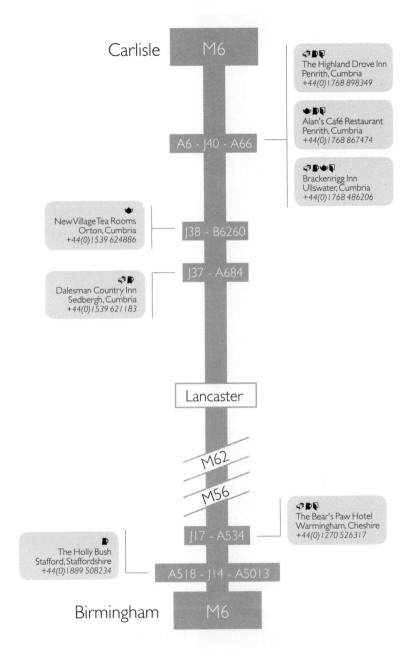

Carlisle

M6

The Highland Drove Inn
Penrith, Cumbria
+44(0)1768 898349

A6 - J40 - A66

Alan's Café Restaurant
Penrith, Cumbria
+44(0)1768 867474

Brackenrigg Inn
Ullswater, Cumbria
+44(0)1768 486206

New Village Tea Rooms
Orton, Cumbria
+44(0)1539 624886

J38 - B6260

J37 - A684

Dalesman Country Inn
Sedbergh, Cumbria
+44(0)1539 621183

Lancaster

M62

M56

The Bear's Paw Hotel
Warmingham, Cheshire
+44(0)1270 526317

J17 - A534

The Holly Bush
Stafford, Staffordshire
+44(0)1889 508234

A518 - J14 - A5013

Birmingham

M6

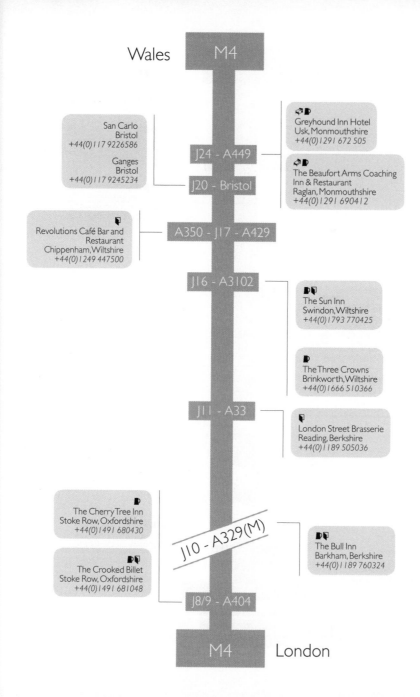

Wales

M4

San Carlo
Bristol
+44(0)117 9226586

Ganges
Bristol
+44(0)117 9245234

Greyhound Inn Hotel
Usk, Monmouthshire
+44(0)1291 672 505

The Beaufort Arms Coaching
Inn & Restaurant
Raglan, Monmouthshire
+44(0)1291 690412

J24 - A449

J20 - Bristol

Revolutions Café Bar and
Restaurant
Chippenham, Wiltshire
+44(0)1249 447500

A350 - J17 - A429

J16 - A3102

The Sun Inn
Swindon, Wiltshire
+44(0)1793 770425

The Three Crowns
Brinkworth, Wiltshire
+44(0)1666 510366

J11 - A33

London Street Brasserie
Reading, Berkshire
+44(0)1189 505036

The Cherry Tree Inn
Stoke Row, Oxfordshire
+44(0)1491 680430

J10 - A329(M)

The Bull Inn
Barkham, Berkshire
+44(0)1189 760324

The Crooked Billet
Stoke Row, Oxfordshire
+44(0)1491 681048

J8/9 - A404

M4   London

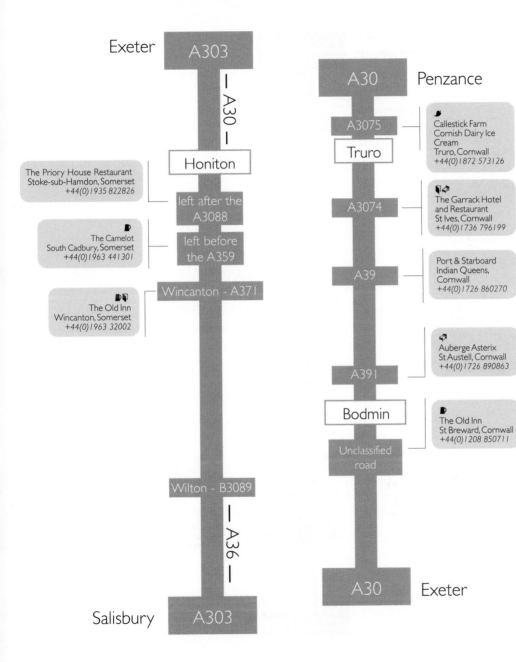

Exeter — A303

— A30 —

Honiton

The Priory House Restaurant
Stoke-sub-Hamdon, Somerset
+44(0)1935 822826

left after the A3088

The Camelot
South Cadbury, Somerset
+44(0)1963 441301

left before the A359

Wincanton - A371

The Old Inn
Wincanton, Somerset
+44(0)1963 32002

Wilton - B3089

— A36 —

Salisbury — A303

A30 — **Penzance**

A3075

Truro

Callestick Farm
Cornish Dairy Ice Cream
Truro, Cornwall
+44(0)1872 573126

A3074

The Garrack Hotel and Restaurant
St Ives, Cornwall
+44(0)1736 796199

A39

Port & Starboard
Indian Queens, Cornwall
+44(0)1726 860270

A391

Auberge Asterix
St Austell, Cornwall
+44(0)1726 890863

Bodmin

The Old Inn
St Breward, Cornwall
+44(0)1208 850711

Unclassified road

A30 — **Exeter**

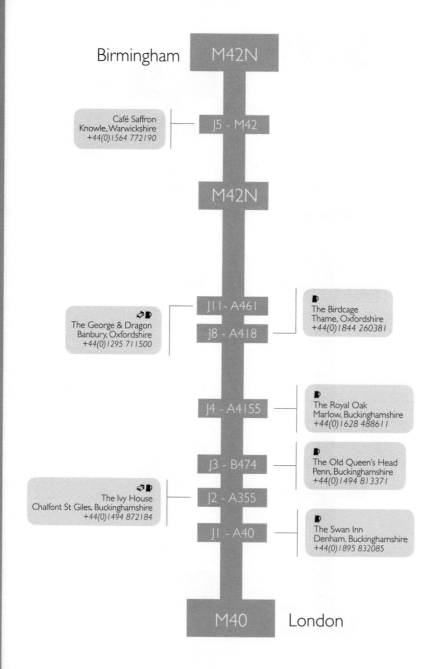

Birmingham

M42N

Café Saffron
Knowle, Warwickshire
+44(0)1564 772190

J5 - M42

M42N

J11 - A461

The Birdcage
Thame, Oxfordshire
+44(0)1844 260381

The George & Dragon
Banbury, Oxfordshire
+44(0)1295 711500

J8 - A418

J4 - A4155

The Royal Oak
Marlow, Buckinghamshire
+44(0)1628 488611

J3 - B474

The Old Queen's Head
Penn, Buckinghamshire
+44(0)1494 813371

The Ivy House
Chalfont St Giles, Buckinghamshire
+44(0)1494 872184

J2 - A355

J1 - A40

The Swan Inn
Denham, Buckinghamshire
+44(0)1895 832085

M40   London

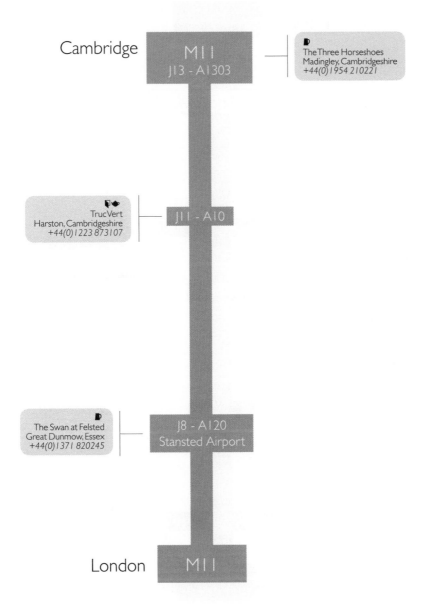

Cambridge

M11
J13 - A1303

The Three Horseshoes
Madingley, Cambridgeshire
+44(0)1954 210221

TrucVert
Harston, Cambridgeshire
+44(0)1223 873107

J11 - A10

The Swan at Felsted
Great Dunmow, Essex
+44(0)1371 820245

J8 - A120
Stansted Airport

London

M11

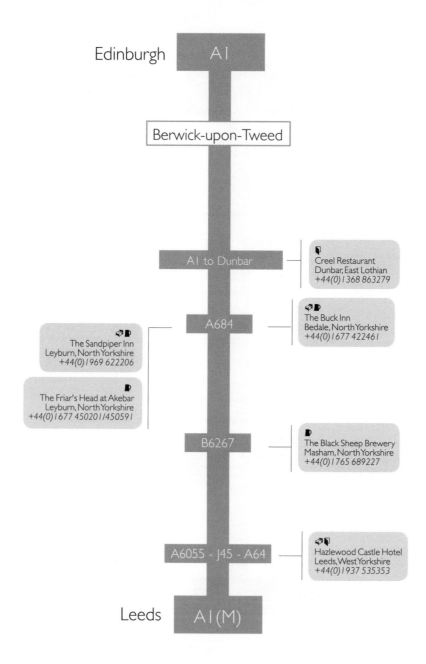

Edinburgh   A1

Berwick-upon-Tweed

A1 to Dunbar — Creel Restaurant
Dunbar, East Lothian
+44(0)1368 863279

A684 — The Buck Inn
Bedale, North Yorkshire
+44(0)1677 422461

The Sandpiper Inn
Leyburn, North Yorkshire
+44(0)1969 622206

The Friar's Head at Akebar
Leyburn, North Yorkshire
+44(0)1677 450201/450591

B6267 — The Black Sheep Brewery
Masham, North Yorkshire
+44(0)1765 689227

A6055 - J45 - A64 — Hazlewood Castle Hotel
Leeds, West Yorkshire
+44(0)1937 535353

Leeds   A1(M)

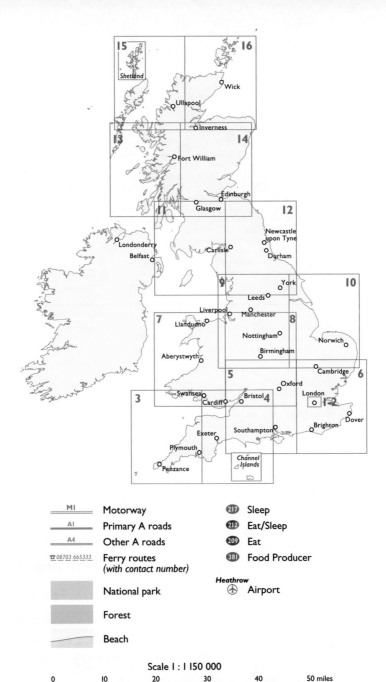

═══ M1 ═══	Motorway
── A1 ──	Primary A roads
── A4 ──	Other A roads
☎ 08703 665333	Ferry routes (with contact number)
	National park
	Forest
	Beach

(217)	Sleep
(212)	Eat/Sleep
(209)	Eat
(381)	Food Producer

Heathrow
⊕ Airport

Scale 1 : 1 150 000

0   10   20   30   40   50 miles

0   10   20   30   40   50   60   70 km

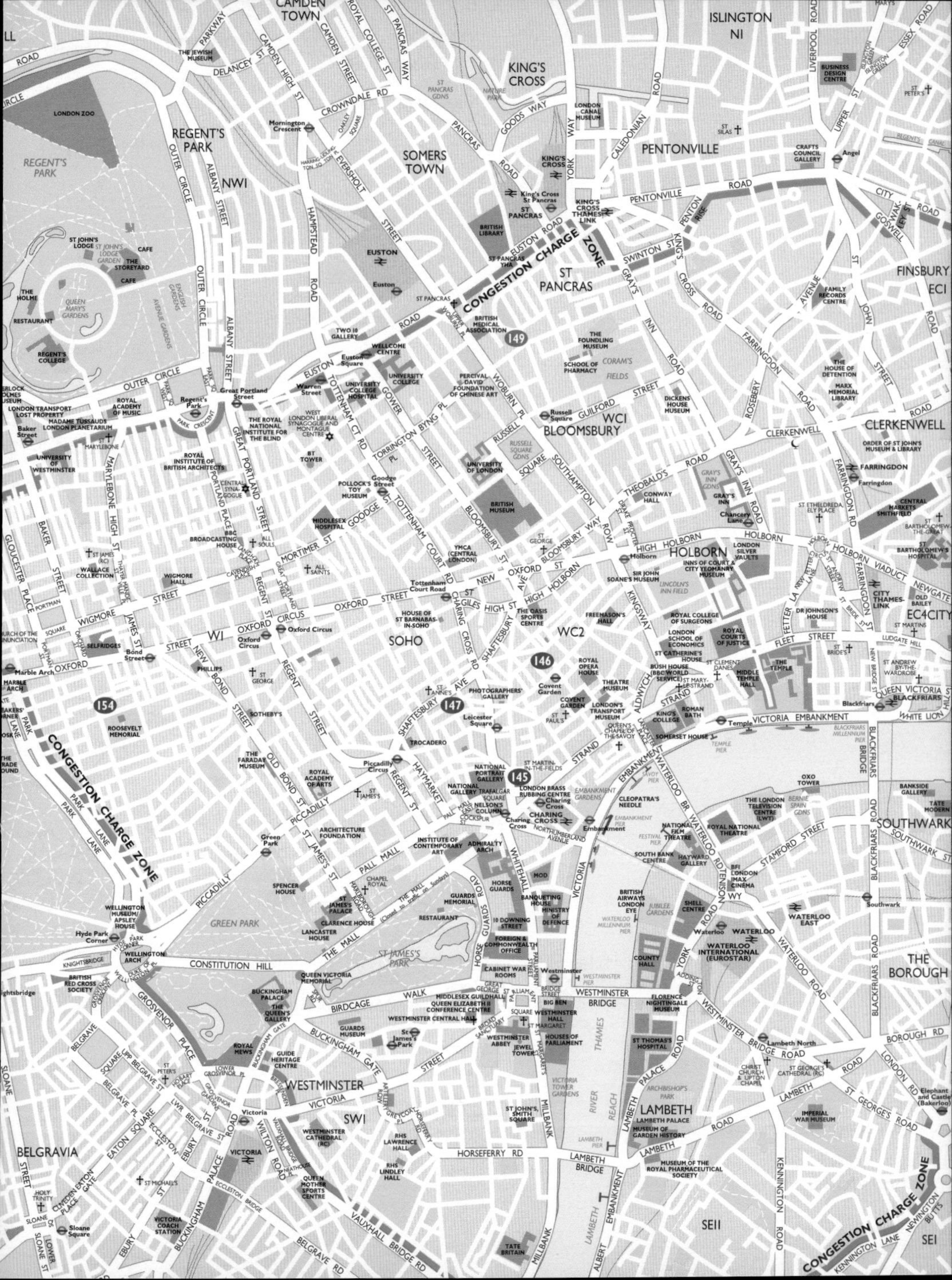

CAMDEN TOWN
ISLINGTON N1
KING'S CROSS
REGENT'S PARK
REGENT'S PARK
LONDON ZOO
SOMERS TOWN
NW1
PENTONVILLE
ST PANCRAS
CONGESTION CHARGE ZONE
FINSBURY EC1
CLERKENWELL
WC1
BLOOMSBURY
HOLBORN
EC4 CITY
SOHO
WC2
W1
SOUTHWARK
THE BOROUGH
WESTMINSTER
SW1
BELGRAVIA
LAMBETH
SE11
SE1
THE JEWISH MUSEUM
DELANCEY ST
CAMDEN HIGH ST
CAMDEN STREET
ROYAL COLLEGE ST
ST PANCRAS WAY
CROWNDALE RD
Mornington Crescent
ST PANCRAS GDNS
NATURE PARK
GOODS WAY
LONDON CANAL MUSEUM
CALEDONIAN ROAD
YORK WAY
BUSINESS DESIGN CENTRE
LIVERPOOL ROAD
ESSEX ROAD
ST PETER'S
ST SILAS
CRAFTS COUNCIL GALLERY
Angel
REGENT'S CANAL
KING'S CROSS
King's Cross St Pancras
ST PANCRAS
KING'S CROSS THAMES LINK
PENTONVILLE ROAD
CITY ROAD
GOSWELL
BRITISH LIBRARY
EUSTON ROAD
ST PANCRAS YHA
SWINTON ST
KING'S CROSS ROAD
GRAY'S INN ROAD
EUSTON
Euston
OUTER CIRCLE
ALBANY STREET
HAMPSTEAD ROAD
EVERSHOLT
ST JOHN'S LODGE
CAFE
THE STOREYARD
THE HOLME
QUEEN MARY'S GARDENS
RESTAURANT
REGENT'S COLLEGE
ENGLISH GARDENS
AVENUE GARDENS
TWO 10 GALLERY
WELLCOME CENTRE
Euston Square
BRITISH MEDICAL ASSOCIATION
149
THE FOUNDLING MUSEUM
SCHOOL OF PHARMACY
CORAM'S FIELDS
FAMILY RECORDS CENTRE
FARRINGDON ROAD
THE HOUSE OF DETENTION
MARX MEMORIAL LIBRARY
ROSEBERY AVENUE
ST JOHN STREET
Warren Street
UNIVERSITY COLLEGE
UNIVERSITY COLLEGE HOSPITAL
PERCIVAL DAVID FOUNDATION OF CHINESE ART
Great Portland Street
Regent's Park
ROYAL ACADEMY OF MUSIC
LONDON TRANSPORT LOST PROPERTY
MADAME TUSSAUDS LONDON PLANETARIUM
Baker Street
ST MARYLEBONE
UNIVERSITY OF WESTMINSTER
THE ROYAL NATIONAL INSTITUTE FOR THE BLIND
WEST LONDON LIBERAL SYNAGOGUE AND MONTAGUE CENTRE
Russell Square
GUILFORD STREET
DICKENS HOUSE MUSEUM
CLERKENWELL ROAD
ORDER OF ST JOHN'S MUSEUM & LIBRARY
FARRINGDON
Farringdon
ROYAL INSTITUTE OF BRITISH ARCHITECTS
BT TOWER
UNIVERSITY OF LONDON
RUSSELL SQUARE GDNS
THEOBALD'S ROAD
GRAY'S INN GDNS
GRAY'S INN
CONWAY HALL
Chancery Lane
ST ETHELDREDA, ELY PLACE
CENTRAL MARKETS SMITHFIELD
ST BARTHOLOMEW-THE-GREAT
ST BARTHOLOMEW'S HOSPITAL
CENTRAL SYNAGOGUE
POLLOCK'S TOY MUSEUM
Goodge Street
BRITISH MUSEUM
MIDDLESEX HOSPITAL
BBC BROADCASTING HOUSE
ALL SOULS
ST JAMES (RC)
WALLACE COLLECTION
YMCA (CENTRAL LONDON)
ST GEORGE
Holborn
HIGH HOLBORN
LONDON SILVER VAULTS
INNS OF COURT & CITY YEOMANRY MUSEUM
HOLBORN VIADUCT
SIR JOHN SOANE'S MUSEUM
LINCOLN'S INN FIELD
CITY THAMESLINK
OLD BAILEY
NEWGATE
WIGMORE HALL
ALL SAINTS
Tottenham Court Road
NEW OXFORD ST
DR JOHNSON'S HOUSE
ST BRIDE ST
ST MARTINS
WIGMORE STREET
OXFORD STREET
HOUSE OF ST BARNABAS-IN-SOHO
THE OASIS SPORTS CENTRE
FREEMASON'S HALL
ROYAL COLLEGE OF SURGEONS
LONDON SCHOOL OF ECONOMICS
ROYAL COURTS OF JUSTICE
FLEET STREET
LUDGATE HILL
SELFRIDGES
Oxford Circus
Bond Street
Marble Arch
146
ROYAL OPERA HOUSE
ST CATHERINE'S HOUSE
BUSH HOUSE (BBC WORLD SERVICE)
ST CLEMENT DANES
THE TEMPLE
MIDDLE TEMPLE HALL
ST BRIDE'S
ST ANDREW BY-THE-WARDROBE
QUEEN VICTORIA ST
BLACKFRIARS
Blackfriars
PHILLIPS
ST GEORGE
ST ANNE'S
PHOTOGRAPHERS' GALLERY
Covent Garden
THEATRE MUSEUM
ST MARY-LE-STRAND
154
SOTHEBY'S
147
COVENT GARDEN
LONDON'S TRANSPORT MUSEUM
ST PAUL'S
KING'S COLLEGE
ROMAN BATH
Temple
VICTORIA EMBANKMENT
ROOSEVELT MEMORIAL
Leicester Square
QUEEN'S CHAPEL OF THE SAVOY
SOMERSET HOUSE
TEMPLE PIER
BLACKFRIARS MILLENNIUM PIER
BLACKFRIARS BRIDGE
TROCADERO
THE FARADAY MUSEUM
Piccadilly Circus
NATIONAL PORTRAIT GALLERY
ST MARTIN-IN-THE-FIELDS
145
SAVOY PIER
OXO TOWER
ROYAL ACADEMY OF ARTS
ST JAMES'S
NATIONAL GALLERY
TRAFALGAR SQUARE
LONDON BRASS RUBBING CENTRE
Charing Cross
EMBANKMENT GARDENS
CLEOPATRA'S NEEDLE
THE LONDON TELEVISION CENTRE (LWT)
BERNIE SPAIN GDNS
BANKSIDE GALLERY
TATE MODERN
NELSON'S COLUMN
CHARING CROSS
Embankment
EMBANKMENT PIER
NATIONAL FILM THEATRE
ROYAL NATIONAL THEATRE
STAMFORD STREET
SOUTHWARK STREET
Green Park
ARCHITECTURE FOUNDATION
INSTITUTE OF CONTEMPORARY ART
ADMIRALTY ARCH
NORTHUMBERLAND AVENUE
FESTIVAL PIER
SOUTH BANK CENTRE
HAYWARD GALLERY
BFI LONDON IMAX CINEMA
PALL MALL
CHAPEL ROYAL
HORSE GUARDS
MOD
SPENCER HOUSE
GUARDS MEMORIAL
BANQUETING HOUSE
BRITISH AIRWAYS LONDON EYE
JUBILEE GARDENS
SHELL CENTRE
Southwark
WATERLOO EAST
WELLINGTON MUSEUM/APSLEY HOUSE
ST JAMES'S PALACE
RESTAURANT
10 DOWNING STREET
MINISTRY OF DEFENCE
WATERLOO MILLENNIUM PIER
Waterloo
WATERLOO
WATERLOO INTERNATIONAL (EUROSTAR)
GREEN PARK
Hyde Park Corner
CLARENCE HOUSE
LANCASTER HOUSE
ST JAMES'S PARK
FOREIGN & COMMONWEALTH OFFICE
WELLINGTON ARCH
THE MALL
COUNTY HALL
CONSTITUTION HILL
CABINET WAR ROOMS
Westminster
WESTMINSTER PIER
WESTMINSTER BRIDGE
BRITISH RED CROSS SOCIETY
QUEEN VICTORIA MEMORIAL
BUCKINGHAM PALACE
THE QUEEN'S GALLERY
BIRDCAGE WALK
MIDDLESEX GUILDHALL
QUEEN ELIZABETH II CONFERENCE CENTRE
BIG BEN
FLORENCE NIGHTINGALE MUSEUM
WESTMINSTER CENTRAL HALL
WESTMINSTER HALL
GUARDS MUSEUM
St James's Park
WESTMINSTER ABBEY
JEWEL TOWER
HOUSES OF PARLIAMENT
THAMES
Lambeth North
WESTMINSTER BRIDGE ROAD
BOROUGH RD
ROYAL MEWS
BUCKINGHAM GATE
GUIDE HERITAGE CENTRE
ST THOMAS'S HOSPITAL
CHRIST CHURCH & UPTON CHAPEL
ST GEORGE'S CATHEDRAL (RC)
GROSVENOR PLACE
VICTORIA TOWER GARDENS
RIVER REACH
ARCHBISHOP'S PARK
IMPERIAL WAR MUSEUM
Elephant and Castle (Bakerloo)
Victoria
VICTORIA STREET
ST JOHN'S SMITH SQUARE
LAMBETH PALACE
MUSEUM OF GARDEN HISTORY
WESTMINSTER CATHEDRAL (RC)
RHS LAWRENCE HALL
LAMBETH PIER
VICTORIA
HORSEFERRY RD
LAMBETH BRIDGE
MUSEUM OF THE ROYAL PHARMACEUTICAL SOCIETY
RHS LINDLEY HALL
ST MICHAEL'S
QUEEN MOTHER SPORTS CENTRE
HOLY TRINITY
VICTORIA COACH STATION
Sloane Square
TATE BRITAIN
MILLBANK
ALBERT EMBANKMENT
KENNINGTON ROAD
KENNINGTON LANE
NEWINGTON BUTTS
VAUXHALL BRIDGE RD
BELGRAVE RD
EATON SQUARE
ECCLESTON ST
EBURY ST
BUCKINGHAM PALACE ROAD
SLOANE STREET
PARK LANE
PICCADILLY

Coast

Milford Haven ○ ○ Saundersfoot   Kidwelly ○   Llanelli ○

Pembroke Dock ○   ○ Tenby

Linney Head   Caldey   Carmarthen   Swans
                Island   Bay   SWA

                        Worms Head ○   ○ Port Eynon

to Cork ☎ 01792 456116

C e l t i c   S e a   B r i s t o

Lundy ⟨   ☎ 01271 863636   Ilfracombe
                                    68   Combe
                                        Martin

                            Braunton ○
                            Barnstaple ○
                        Northam   64   Bideford

                Clovelly ○

                    Great Torrington ○

            Bude ○   A3072   Holsworthy ○

                            Okehampton ○

                                Tamar

                        Launceston ○
            Port Gaverne   A39   A395
                    33   St Breward ○   D
            Padstow ○   Wadebridge ○   *Colliford*   Tavistoc
                37   *Reservoir*

        Newquay   Bodmin ○   A38   Liskeard ○
    Newquay ○ ⊕   *CORNWALL*   29   *Plymouth*
    Kelsey Head   28   Roche ○   Lostwithiel ○   ⊕
            32   35   31   Saltash ○   73
            Indian   34   Tregrehan Mills   Plymouth ○
            Queens   St Austell ○   Looe ○   Yealmpton
            349   36   Polperro ○

                Truro ○
        St Ives ○   Redruth ○
    Treen   Camborne ○   40   Tolverne
        38   39   St Mawes ○
    St Just ○   Falmouth ○
        Penzance ○   Helston ○   *Falmouth Bay*
Land's End ○ Sennen   A394

**ISLES OF
SCILLY**
Tresco
    St Martin's   Lizard ○   30
    St Mary's   ☎ 08457 105555   Lizard Point
Isles of Scilly

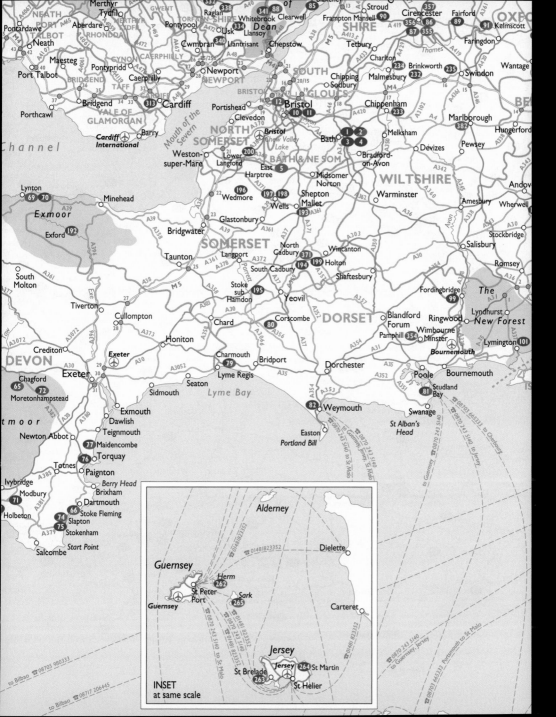

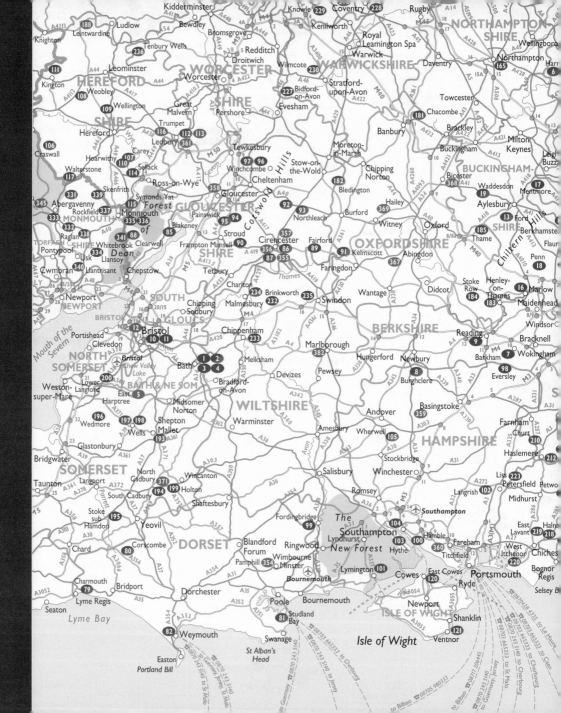

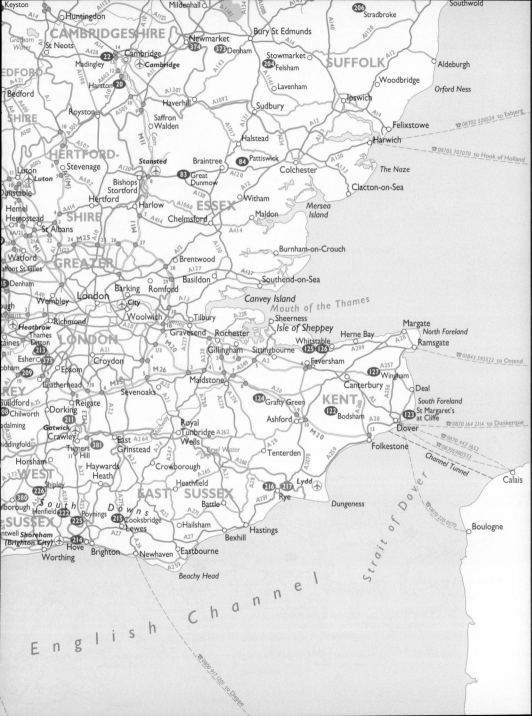

4

ISLE OF ANGLESEY

Amlwch

Great Ormes Head

Prestatyn

325 Thurstas

to Dublin ☎ 08705 707070
to Dublin ☎ 08705 171717
to Dun Laoghaire ☎ 08705 707070

Holyhead

Anglesey

Llandudno 323
Conwy
Colwyn Bay

Rhyl

Holywell
A55

A55

Holy Island

Bangor

Tyn-y-Groes 322

St George

324 St Asaph

326 Denbigh

FLINT SHIRE

Mold

Caernarfon

Llanrwst

CONWY

Llyn Brenig

Ruthin

DENBIGH

Caernarfon Bay

A4086

Capel Curig 321

319 320 Betws-y-coed

A5

SHIRE

A499

Beddgelert A498

470 Blaenau Ffestiniog

Llangollen

Nefyn

Criccieth

A487 Porthmadog

Llyn Trawsfynydd

A4212

Llyn Celyn

Bala
Llyn Tegid

Llangollen

Pwllheli

GWYNEDD

Snowdonia

Lake Vyrnwy

Llanfyllin

Abersoch

Llanbedr

A494

A470

Llanfyllin

Bardsey Island

328 329
Barmouth 330 Dolgellau

A493

Dinas Mawddwy
A458

Welshpo

Cardigan Bay

327
Aberdyfi

Machynlleth 347

POWYS

A489

Newtow

Talybont

A487

Cambrian Mountains

Aberystwyth 318

A44

Llanidloes

Llangurig

A4120

Devil's Bridge

A470

Rhayader

A44

A488

CEREDIGION

Aberaeron

New Quay 317

Tregaron

Llyn Brianne Reservoir

Builth Wells

Llandrindod Wells

A483

Cardigan

A484

Newcastle Emlyn

A475

A485

Lampeter

Teifi

A483

Tywi

Llandovery

Beulah
Llanwrtyd Wells

Felin Fach 344

Strumble Head

Fishguard

342 Trefin

PEMBROKESHIRE

Brechfa 314

Llanwrda

Brecon

St David's Head

343

Wolfscastle

A478

CARMARTHENSHIRE

Carmarthen

Llandeilo

Brecon Beacons

St David's

A487

316 Llanboidy

315

A483

Crickhow

Ramsey Island

A40

Whitland

Llanarthne

Pembrokeshire Coast

Haverfordwest

A477

St Clears

A48 Ammanford

A476

NEATH PORT TALBOT

Merthyr Tydfil

Aberdare

RHONDDA

A4076

Kidwelly

A484

48

Pontardawe

47 45

Milford Haven

Saundersfoot

Llanelli

43 42

Neath

Maesteg

Pontypridd

Caerphilly

Pembroke Dock

Tenby

A4118

Swansea

40

Linney Head

Caldey Island

Carmarthen Bay

SWANSEA

Port Talbot

BRIDGEND

TAFF

313

Worms Head

Port Eynon

37

Porthcawl

Bridgend

VALE OF GLAMORGAN

Card

to Rosslare ☎ 08705 707070

to Rosslare ☎ 08705 171717

to Cork ☎ 01792 456116

Filey 244

Wold Newton 239

Flamborough Head

237 238 Bridlington

A165

A164

Driffield

T RIDING
ORKSHIRE
arket eighton

Bridlington Bay

240 Skipsea

Hornsea

A165

A1035

Beverley

ton-upon-Humber

Kingston upon Hull

A1033

Withernsea

ORTH
OLNSHIRE

Scunthorpe

M180

Humberside

NE
LINCOLNSHIRE

Spurn Head

A180

Grimsby

Cleethorpes

Mouth of the Humber

☎ 08705 980333 to Rotterdam

A15

A46

Market Rasen

A631

A157

A153

A16

Louth

Mablethorpe

A52

Harby

7

Lincoln

Horncastle

Witham

A158

A1028

Partney

A158

Skegness

A52

139 Thorpe on the Hill

140 Nocton

A155

A16

LINCOLNSHIRE

☎ 08705 980333 to Zeebrugge

A153

Sleaford

A1121

Cley next the Sea

158

160

Cromer

141 Aswarby

A52

Boston

Hunstanton

Brancaster Staithe

A148

364 North Walsham

Grantham

Belvoir

The Wash

A149

Fakenham

Itteringham

161

A140

A151

A15

Holbeach

A148

A1065

Wensum

Aylsham

A149

159 Catfield

186

Clipsham

akham

A606

A16

Bourne

A151

Spalding

A17

A1101

A10

Kings Lynn

A1075

East Dereham

A140

Norwich

162 163

The Broads

Great Yarmouth

A47

Stamford

and Water

A47

Wisbech

A1122

Swaffham

A11

Norwich

A146

Lowestoft

ppingham
Bulwick

164

Fotheringhay

Peterborough

17

A605

16

March

A1101

Great Ouse

Downham Market

A134

Wymondham

A11

NORFOLK

Bungay

203 Barnby

Corby

166

Oundle

Chatteris

A142

Nene

Little Ouse

Thetford Forest Park

Thetford

A1066

Diss

Waveney

A144

Halesworth

205

167 Wadenhoe

A1(M)

Ely

A11

A134

A1088

A143

206 Stradbroke

A140

Southwold

Kettering

21 Keyston

A14

Mildenhall

A1101

A120

CAMBRIDGESHIRE

Huntingdon

A10

A123

Newmarket

Bury St Edmunds

Stowmarket

Wellingborough

Grafham Water

St Neots

14

A428

Cambridge

374

373 Denham

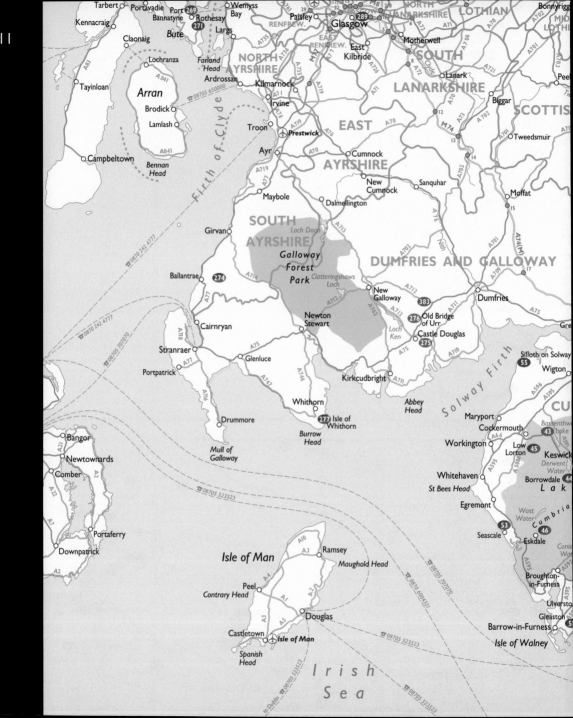

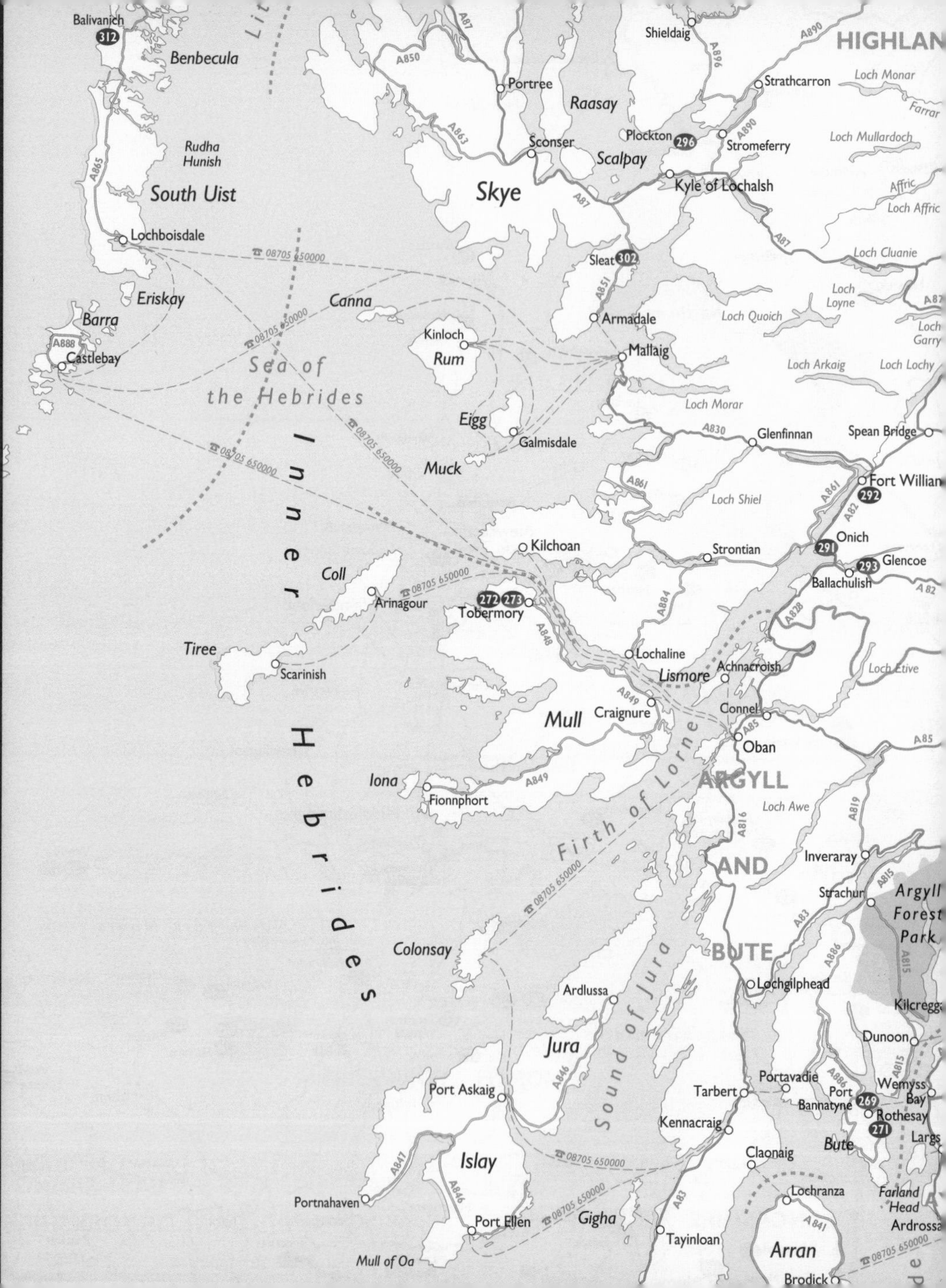

HIGHLAN
Balivanich
312
Benbecula
South Uist
Rudha Hunish
Lochboisdale
Eriskay
Barra
Castlebay
A888
A865
Canna
Kinloch
Rum
Sea of the Hebrides
Eigg
Galmisdale
Muck
Inner Hebrides
Skye
Portree
Raasay
Sconser
Scalpay
Plockton
296
Stromeferry
Strathcarron
Shieldaig
Kyle of Lochalsh
Sleat
302
Armadale
Mallaig
Loch Monar
Farrar
Loch Mullardoch
Affric
Loch Affric
Loch Cluanie
Loch Loyne
Loch Quoich
Loch Garry
Loch Arkaig
Loch Lochy
Loch Morar
Glenfinnan
Spean Bridge
Fort William
292
Loch Shiel
Onich
291
Glencoe
293
Ballachulish
Strontian
Kilchoan
Coll
Arinagour
272
273
Tobermory
Tiree
Scarinish
Lochaline
Lismore
Achnacroish
Loch Etive
Mull
Craignure
Connel
Oban
Iona
Fionnphort
Firth of Lorne
ARGYLL AND BUTE
Loch Awe
Inveraray
Strachur
Argyll Forest Park
Colonsay
Lochgilphead
Kilcregga
Ardlussa
Jura
Sound of Jura
Dunoon
Portavadie
Wemyss Bay
Port Bannatyne
269
Rothesay
271
Tarbert
Kennacraig
Port Askaig
Islay
Claonaig
Bute
Largs
Lochranza
Farland Head
Ardrossan
Portnahaven
Port Ellen
Gigha
Tayinloan
Arran
Brodick
Mull of Oa
08705 650000
A87
A850
A863
A890
A896
A851
A830
A861
A82
A828
A884
A848
A849
A85
A816
A819
A815
A83
A886
A846
A847
A841

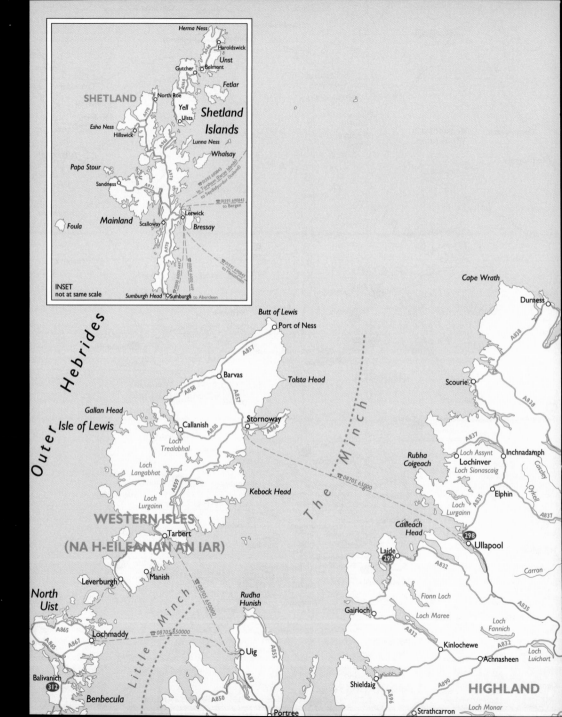

15

INSET
not at same scale

SHETLAND

Herma Ness
Haroldswick
Unst
Gutcher • Belmont
North Roe
Fetlar
Yell
Ulsta
Shetland
Islands
Esha Ness
Hillswick
Lunna Ness
Whalsay
Papa Stour
Sandness
☎ 01595 690841
to Torshavn (Faroe Islands)
to Seyðisfjörður (Iceland)
☎ 01595 690845
to Bergen
Mainland
Scalloway
Lerwick
Bressay
Foula
A970
☎ 0800 3000 111
to Hanstholm
☎ 01595 690041
to Hanstholm
Sumburgh Head • Sumburgh to Aberdeen

Cape Wrath
Durness
A838

Butt of Lewis
Port of Ness

A857
Barvas
Tolsta Head
A857
Scourie
A838

Gallan Head
Outer Isle of Lewis
A858
Callanish
A858
Stornoway
A866
Loch
Trealabhal
The Minch
Rubha
Coigeach
Loch Assynt
Inchnadamph
Lochinver
Loch Sionascaig
A837
Cassley
Loch
Langabhat
A859
Kebock Head
☎ 08705 65000
Loch
Lurgainn
Elphin
A835
A837
Loch
Lurgainn
WESTERN ISLES
(NA H-EILEANAN AN IAR)
Tarbert
Cailleach
Head
298
Ullapool
Leverburgh
Manish
The Little Minch
Laide
295
A832
Carron
North
Uist
Rudha
Hunish
Fionn Loch
A835
Balivanich
312
A865
A867
Lochmaddy
☎ 08705 650000
Gairloch
Loch Maree
Loch
Fannich
Benbecula
A850
Uig
A855
A87
Shieldaig
Kinlochewe
A832
Achnasheen
Loch
Luichart
A835
HIGHLAND
A890
Strathcarron
Loch Monar
Portree
A896

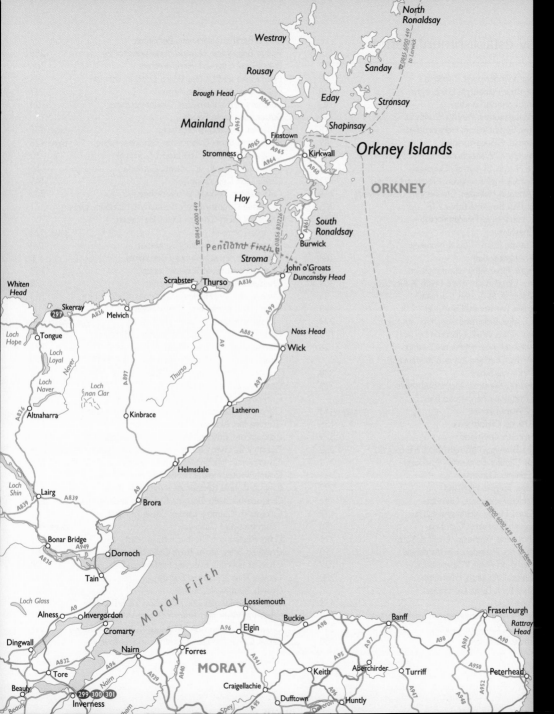

North Ronaldsay

Westray

Rousay

Sanday

Brough Head

Eday

Stronsay

Mainland

Shapinsay

Finstown

Orkney Islands

Stromness

Kirkwall

A964

A965

A965

A967

A966

A960

ORKNEY

Hoy

A961

South Ronaldsay

Burwick

0845 6000 449 to Lerwick

☎ 0845 6000 449

☎ 01856 831226

Pentland Firth

Stroma

John o'Groats

Duncansby Head

Scrabster

Thurso

A836

A99

Whiten Head

Skerray

297

A836

Melvich

Noss Head

Tongue

A9

A882

Wick

Loch Hope

Loch Loyal

Naver

Thurso

A897

Loch Naver

Loch nan Clar

A9

A99

A836

Altnaharra

Kinbrace

Latheron

Helmsdale

Loch Shin

Lairg

A839

A9

Brora

A839

Bonar Bridge

A949

Dornoch

A836

Tain

Moray Firth

☎ 0800 6000 449 to Aberdeen

Loch Glass

Lossiemouth

Fraserburgh

Alness

Invergordon

Buckie

Banff

Rattray Head

Dingwall

Cromarty

A96

Elgin

A98

A97

A98

A881

A90

Nairn

Forres

MORAY

A941

A95

Aberchirder

Turriff

A950

Peterhead

Beauly

A832

Tore

A96

Nairn

A939

A940

Keith

A96

A947

A952

299 300 301

Inverness

Craigellachie

Dufftown

Deveron

Huntly

Spey

A95

Loch Loyal

A835

A-Z by establishment name

A-Z by listing town

Quick-reference guide

Best Pubs with Summer Gardens

Fish & Seafood

Best Views

Waterside Locations

Game

Private Dining Facilities

Afternoon Tea

Breakfast or Brunch

Value for Money Food

To the Editor, Les Routiers Guide 2008
Report Form

☐ From my personal experience, I believe the following establishment should be a member of Les Routiers

☐ From my personal experience, I believe the following establishment should not be a member of Les Routiers

Establishment PLEASE PRINT IN BLOCK CAPITALS
....

Address ....

....

I had ☐ lunch ☐ dinner ☐ stayed there on (date) ....

Details ....

....

....

....

....

....

Reports received up to the end of July 2007 will be used in the research of the 2008 edition

☐ I am not connected in any way with the management or proprietors

Name ....

Address ....

....

As a result of your sending Les Routiers this report form, we may send you information on Les Routiers in the future.
If you would prefer not to receive such information, please tick this box ☐

To send your report...
Fax: Complete this form and fax it to 01372 466062
Post: Complete this form and mail it to
The Editor, Les Routiers, Oak House, 39-41 The Parade, Claygate, Surrey KT10 0PD
Email: info@routiers.co.uk

I believe the following establishment should be a Les Routiers award winner

Establishment

....

Address

....

....

I had ☐ lunch ☐ dinner ☐ stayed there on (date)

....

Details

....

....

....

....

....

....

I would like to recommend the establishment for the following award:

☐ Local food supporter

☐ Hotel of the year

☐ Restaurant of the year

☐ Bed and breakfast of the year

☐ Café of the year

☐ Wine list of the year

☐ Inn of the year

☐ Dining pub of the year

☐ Real-ale pub of the year

☐ Hospitality and service award